Rhythmic Activity
in
Animal Physiology
and
Behaviour

THEORETICAL AND EXPERIMENTAL BIOLOGY

An International Series of Monographs

CONSULTING EDITOR

J. F. Danielli

State University of New York at Buffalo, Buffalo, New York, U.S.A.

Volume 1   J. L. CLOUDSLEY-THOMPSON, Rhythmic Activity in Animal Physiology and Behaviour. 1961

Volume 2   W. P. ROGERS, The Nature of Parasitism: The Relationship of Some Metazoan Parasites to Their Hosts. 1962

Volume 3   C. B. WILLIAMS, Patterns in the Balance of Nature. 1964

Flashlight photograph taken at night in Tunisia showing two toads, *Bufo mauritanicus* Schl. at the entrance to their hole. During the day they were out of sight, at the bottom of the hole four feet underground. (After Cloudsley-Thompson, 1956c)

Rhythmic Activity in Animal Physiology and Behaviour

Professor of Zoology, University of Khartoum

1961

NEW YORK and LONDON

To my friend and former Professor, J. F. Danielli, F.R.S., without whose encouragement and help this book would never have been completed.

Acknowledgments

This book has gained much from conversations I have had with many colleagues and friends working in the field of biological rhythm. I would like to mention especially Sir Nigel Ball, Professor Frank A. Brown, Jr. and Dr G. Edgar Folk, Jr. with whom many pleasant hours have been spent discussing various aspects of the problem. My thanks are also due to Mrs C. A. Morrison and Miss Dilys Gwyn Thomas for typing the manuscript.

London, *June* 1961

Contents

Acknowledgments   vi

Introduction   1

1   Methods of Investigation   11

2   Periodicity from Cells to Communities   24

3   Diurnal Rhythms and Animal Ecology: a Review   38

4   Lunar and Tidal Rhythms   81

5   Seasonal and Reproductive Rhythms   94

6   Biological 'Clocks' in Crustacea and the Influence of Exogenous Factors   108

7   Further Evidence for the Existence of Environment-Independent Chronometers in Animals   119

8   Activity Rhythms in Mammals and the Search for their Control Centre   140

9   Some Aspects of the Physiological Mechanisms of Rhythmic Activity   157

10   The Physiological Effects of Temperature on Rhythmic Phenomena   172

11   Consideration of Special Themes   186

Appendix   199

Bibliography   203

Author Index   225

Subject Index   230

Introduction

RHYTHMICITY is characteristic of nature. Summer follows winter, new moon follows old, day follows night. "So do flux and reflux—the rhythm of change—alternate and persist in everything under the sky," wrote Thomas Hardy. The universe is not static: every component from an electron to a galaxy is continually moving and such movement cannot proceed for ever in the same direction. Sooner or later it must complete a circle, or stop and return in the opposite direction. In either case, a continuously repeated rhythm, cycle or periodicity ensues, often resulting in a balance of centrifugal and centripetal forces. This applies equally to biological as to mechanical systems. Indeed, since the former are based essentially upon physico-chemical processes, such as biochemical reaction systems or electrical nerve impulses, the situation could not be otherwise.

In the field of morphogenesis, the main scientific problem lies in understanding the unification of great numbers of individual cells into a functional whole. Similarly, in the study of biological rhythms and periodicities, some of the fundamental problems lie in the manner of co-ordination of innumerable small rhythmic physiological cycles within the body of a single animal, and of the activities of numerous individuals within a single population.

Owing to the vast size of the subject which, indeed, involves one of the more fundamental aspects of nature, several encyclopaedic volumes would be required to cover even those aspects which bear upon the behaviour of animals, if all the relevant literature were to be reviewed. My method is shorter: I have attempted to sort out what seem to me to be the more important aspects of the subject and to illustrate them with a few selected examples.

Many problems are as yet unsolved, or rather unexplained. Others have been created unnecessarily by what would appear to be 'red herrings'. To take a very simple example, several workers have established statistical correlations and then quite unjustifiably assumed a causal relationship between them. Thus the increasing death rate from cancer can doubtless be correlated mathematically with increased tobacco consumption, the use of aircraft and diesel engined buses, the patronization of television and cinemas, football matches and race courses, with sunbathing or broadcasting. The difficulty of course lies in determining which, if any, of these factors is the actual cause of the disease. Similarly, in the northern temperate zone of the Continental United States, there is a correlation, significant at the 5 per cent level, between the number of letters in the name of a month and its average rainfall (Sargent, 1955). The winter months tend to have longer names than the summer, but no one would seriously suggest either that the name of the month influences its rainfall, or that rainfall has influenced the choice of names!

This criticism is especially applicable to most of the work that has been carried out on the medical aspect of biological rhythm, probably on account of the difficulty of carrying out suitably controlled experiments on human material. At the same time, even where a causal relationship has been established experimentally, there may be several intermediate interactions because cause and effect are still by no means clearly understood. On the other hand, if there is a statistical correlation between time series over a sufficiently long period it must be assumed that there is some connection between them.

DEFINITION OF TERMS

The terms 'rhythm', 'cycle' and 'periodicity' have, in the past, been applied somewhat indiscriminately to various recurring phenomena and events. Kleitman (1949) has attempted to bring order from chaos by restricting 'rhythm' to *regularly* recurring quantitative changes in some variable biological process, whether it takes place in a cell, tissue, organ, organism or population. He applies the term 'cycle' to repetitive series of events or to successive changes of state, either qualitative or quantitative in nature, but with the distinctive feature that the sequence of occurrence rather than of duration tends to be constant.

Since cyclic events naturally tend to become regular in time under unvarying conditions, there does not appear to be any fundamental distinction between the two types and Kleitman's suggestion cannot therefore be adopted. In general, it seems that periodicities of short phase duration, such as those of the heart-beat, the emptying of contractile vacuoles and so on, taking place in cells, organs or tissues, are commonly spoken of as 'cycles', as also are reproductive periodicities; while 24-hour lunar and tidal periodicities are conventionally called 'rhythms'. There is no more to it than this.

Szymanski (1914) introduced the term 'polyphasic' to designate animals which show several periods of activity in 24 hours, as contrasted with 'monophasic' animals with only one period. Thus, blowflies, *Calliphora* spp., are diurnal and monophasic; crayfish, in general, are nocturnal and monophasic; while earthworms are nocturnal and polyphasic, showing about four rest and activity periods in the 24-hour cycle.

Although these terms have been generally adopted, Kleitman (1949) suggests that they should be discarded as each period comprises a phase of rest as well as an active period. Appropriate terms, according to Kleitman, would be 'polycyclic' and 'diurnally rhythmic' or 'periodic'.

Rhythms that are so directly dependent upon environmental changes that they at once become arhythmic when the external conditions are made uniform, are referred to by Kleitman (1949) as 'causal, synchronous, associated or coupled periodicities', but there seems to be no valid justification for not applying the term 'rhythm' to such phenomena.

According to Kleitman (1949): "Two conditions are necessary to make such a recurring stage into a rhythm: (a) it must be extrinsic in origin, depending upon a regular change in the environment, such as light or temperature, usually associated with terrestrial or cosmic periodicity, developing in each biological system *de novo*; and (b) when fully established, it must persist for some time, even when the environmental changes are absent. Except that the regulating system need not be nervous, a rhythm may be likened to a conditioned response, which is also individually acquired and depends on an extrinsic reinforcement for its establishment, yet will persist for a shorter or longer period of time in the absence of such reinforcement. This is the sense in which Welsh (1938) used the term in his review of diurnal rhythms." The necessity for an extrinsic origin to apparently environment-independent rhythms is by no means certain, however, as I have pointed out below, unless Kleitman is speaking from an evolutionary view point.

Park (1940, 1941a) subdivides rhythmic phenomena into two main categories; 'exogenous' rhythms which are a direct response to physical changes in the environment and do not persist when conditions are kept constant; and 'endogenous' rhythms which continue, at any rate for a time, under constant conditions. He suggests that the majority of species in their natural environment appear to show a combination of both types, and such rhythms he designates 'composite'. He further subdivides 'endogenous' rhythms into 'inherent' (i.e. genetical) and 'habitual' ones, but Calhoun (1944) considers all diurnal 'endogenous' rhythms to be of the latter category because, he claims, "the genetical determination 24-hour periodicity has in no case been demonstrated".

'Endogenous' rhythms are frequently correlated with environmental changes although they are not necessarily a direct response to them. Thus if the cockroaches *Blatta orientalis* and *Periplaneta americana* are subjected to alternating 12-hour periods of light and darkness, their activity is largely confined to the latter although locomotion may actually begin shortly before the light is extinguished. This activity rhythm persists for some days in continuous light or darkness, but

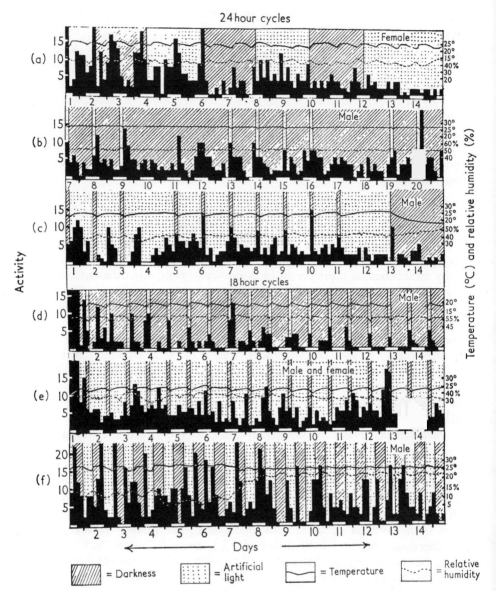

FIG. 1. Locomotory activity in the cockroach, *Periplaneta americana*. Ordinates: activity on the left, temperature and relative humidity on the right. Abscissa: time in days. The black strips represent 12-hour periods from 18.00 to 06.00 hrs.

A   Absence of effect on activity of alternating 48-hour periods of light and darkness; 18-hour cycle of temperature fluctuation.

B   Effect of 3 hours of light alternating with 21 hours of darkness.

C   Effect of 3 hours of darkness alternating with 21 hours of light.

D   Effect of 3 hours of light alternating with 15 hours of darkness.

E   Effect of 3 hours of darkness alternating with 15 hours of light.

F   Effect of 9 hours of light alternating with 9 hours of darkness.

(After Cloudsley-Thompson, 1953d)

eventually becomes more evenly spread over the whole day (Gunn, 1940; Mellanby, 1940). If the periods of light and dark are now doubled, the 24-hour rhythm of activity and rest is still maintained, but the insects show an outburst of locomotory activity either when the light is switched on, or when it is extinguished (Cloudsley-Thompson, 1953b). We have therefore the concept of an innate 'endogenous' rhythm synchronized by changes in environmental factors such as light, temperature and humidity. As the rhythm is not a direct response to these however, such factors have been referred to as 'synchronizers' (Halberg, 1953) or 'clues' (Cloudsley-Thompson, 1952b, 1953a), terms which appear to correspond with the German '*Zeitgeber*' (Aschoff, 1954) and their importance lies in keeping the rhythm in phase with the environment.

The terms 'synchronizer' and 'clue' as they have been defined, are not quite synonymous, for the function of 'clues' lies in the maintenance of rhythms as well as in keeping them in phase with the environment. In his mammalian work, Halberg finds it desirable to use 'synchronizer' in the restricted sense, whereas in work on terrestrial arthropods, the writer finds the inclusive term more useful in instances where a dual effect is exerted by an environmental factor on a rhythm. (*See* Halberg, 1959 and also p. 177).

Under natural conditions there are probably several 'clues' active at the same time as we shall see, of which one is generally the ruling factor of an animal's periodicity. However, there can be competition between different 'clues' and changes in the sensitivity and physiological state of an animal may engender considerable changes in the relationship of the various factors involved.

Harker (1958a) whilst agreeing that the evidence for the inheritance of rhythms is accumulating, claims that it is still inconclusive. She adds: "It will be remembered that rats, and the larvae of some insects, bred in darkness show a rhythm, and that *Drosophila* could be bred for many generations in continuous darkness and it still showed a rhythm. These results could be countered by the fact that there might still be other environmental factors which were not kept constant; but on the other hand, animals raised in light-dark cycles of other than 24-hours not only do not follow these cycles but they revert to a 24-hour one."

Again, Brown and his co-workers (1954–9) believe that some extraneous force such as cosmic ray showers, barometric pressure, conductivity or ionization of the atmosphere or changes in the earth's geomagnetic field may always be involved as synchronizers. On the other hand, Pittendrigh and Bruce (1957) take the opposite point of view. They claim that there is no evidence that either typical or atypical natural periods can be learned, and suggest that the frequencies of all biological clock systems are inherited.

The subject will be discussed in more detail in a later chapter, especially in relation to the emergence rhythm of *Drosophila* flies from their pupae and the colour change in marine crustaceans, to which certain 'endogenous' rhythms in plants and fungi afford a close parallel.

Table I (prepared in collaboration with Dr. G. E. Folk) presents examples of the different types of rhythm and an attempt to illustrate some of the synonomy of the names applied to them. The term 'composite' has not been included because a 'composite' rhythm as defined by Park differs from an 'endogenous' rhythm only in that it becomes instantaneously synchronized with new environmental factors—that is, apparently like an 'exogonous' rhythm, it will persist for a while in unvarying environmental conditions. Since the rapidity of synchronization may depend upon the *intensity* of the environmental 'clues' (Johnson, M. S. 1939) there can be no clear distinction between 'composite' and 'endogenous'.

It is important that any terminology adopted should be not only unambiguous, but that it should not commit its user to any particular theory. For this reason, terms such as 'causal, synchronous, associated or coupled periodicities', 'habitual', 'inherent', or 'endogenous self-sustaining oscillations' are unsuitable; while 'extrinsic', 'exogenous' and 'endogenous' are open to the objection that they need careful definition.

Perhaps the most satisfactory classification yet proposed is that of Stephens (1957) who points out that neither the frequency of rhythmic phenomena nor the habitats and systematic positions of organisms provide suitable criteria for distinguishing various types of periodicity. Frequency is complicated by the fact that many of the persistent rhythms which have been described have two or more frequency components. "Of course this fact does not militate against distinguishing between the diurnal and lunar components of an oxygen consumption rhythm if it is convenient to do so, but in these cases there does not seem to be much evidence to support separations of the mechanism of one from the other. Considering the occurrence of such complex rhythms, it would appear that frequency should not be considered a basic differentiating characteristic in itself. To extend our analogy of taxonomic treatment of the subject, frequency might have specific or generic status, but should not define a class."

On the other hand if phenomena as diverse as heart rates, annual breeding cycles and long-term population cycles are considered, a very fundamental distinction becomes apparent. "This is the distinction between 'private time' or 'physiological time', and 'astronomical time' or 'cosmic time'. Heart rate is clearly a private phenomenon dependent on the size of the animal, surface:volume ratio, circulatory efficiency, and a host of other such physiological features of the individual; it is

Vocabulary of Periodicity
Various Terminology for the Three Types

	Type A	Type B	Type C
Examples of Invertebrate Rhythms	Planktonic animals show a vertical migration dependent on responses to changing light intensity. The response does not persist in a constant environment. (Harris and Wolf 1955)	The cockroach, scorpion and spider will take on an 18-hr. rhythm. The spider was tested for persistence, showing 3 cycles in darkness, then it reverted to the 24-hr. rhythm. (Cloudsley-Thompson 1953d, 1956c, 1957a) Five other examples given by Pittendrigh and Bruce 1957)	Melanophore rhythm of fiddler crab, emergence of *Drosophila*, and activity of millipede all show stable 24-hr. frequency. (Stephens 1957a, Pittendrigh 1957, Cloudsley-Thompson 1951b)
Examples of Mammalian Rhythms	A South African rodent (*Pedetes*) is strictly nocturnal, except when light is dim on cloudy days. (Roosevelt 1910 quoted by Allee *et al.* 1949). The emergence of badgers from their setts is closely correlated with the time of sunset and is inhibited by moonlight (Neal 1948)	The white rat has been induced to take on a 16-hr. rhythm. Persistence not tested. (Browman 1952)	The laboratory rat and the laboratory mouse seem to show genetically determined stable 24-hr. rhythms. (Aschoff 1954 and Folk 1957) Some insectivores and some wild mice have inherent rhythms varying from $2\frac{1}{2}$ to 8 hrs. uninfluenced by light/darkness cycle. (Crowcroft 1954)

Authors	Terms used to describe the above		
Welsh 1938	Extrinsic rhythms	—	Persistent rhythms
Park 1949a	Exogenous rhythms	Habitual endogenous rhythms (in part)	Inherent (genetical) endogenous rhythms
Kleitman 1949	Causal, synchronous, associated or coupled periodicities	—	Persistent rhythms
Stephens 1957	Environment-dependent frequencies	Environment-induced frequencies	Environment-independent frequencies[†]
Pittendrigh 1958	Field rhythms	Impressed rhythms or entrained oscillations	Overt persistent rhythms or endogenous self-sustaining oscillations
Harker 1958a	Exogenous rhythms	—	Persistent or endogenous rhythms

[†]The mammalian rhythms with a frequency of $2\frac{1}{2}$ to 8 hrs. given in the example would be referred to by Stephens as physiological rather than cosmic rhythms.

Note. Type B *may* also include the 24-hour rhythm induced in a cockroach which has previously lost its periodicity in unvarying conditions: this type of rhythm is common among insects; but only when an unnatural frequency shows persistence can one be sure that the periodicity has been learned. Type C rhythms can be recognised by the fact that they cannot be converted to cycles of other than 24 hours.

then a biological rhythm on a physiological time scale and bears no particular relation to astronomical time. This is not to say that there might not be a diurnal rhythm of heart rate but it merely denies that the rate itself marks 'cosmic time'. On the other hand, seasonal breeding cycles, lunar cycles, and diurnal rhythms are significant and distinctive precisely because they are independent of just those factors which control the scale of physiological time. They are adaptively significant, as has been often pointed out, precisely because they keep cosmic time and are not modified by the usual physiological variables." Having established this primary division, Stephens (1957) then proceeds to subdivide 'cosmic' rhythms into 'environment-dependent', 'environment-induced' and 'environment-independent frequencies'. The first of these types is apparently synonymous with 'exogenous' or 'extrinsic' rhythms; the second with 'habitual' or 'learned'; the third, which perhaps represents "the final step in attaining independence of physiological time is the development of a clock mechanism with a very stable and possibly genetically determined 24-hour frequency."

Thus 'environment-independent' appears to be synonymous with 'endogenous'. Whether these distinctions are, in fact, valid, will be seen later. In any case, the use of the term 'frequency' as a synonym for 'rhythm' or 'periodicity' is objectionable and the word should be restricted to describe the rate or time of a single 'oscillation' or 'period' of a rhythm.

Recurring phenomena which take place at roughly 24-hour intervals are usually called 'diurnal', '24-hour' or 'circadian' rhythms. The word 'diurnal' may be ambiguous, since it is also used for activity that takes place during the day as opposed to 'nocturnal' activity. For this reason, Calhoun (1944) and others have used the term 'diel' originally proposed by Carpenter (1934) to designate periodic phenomena occurring on a 24-hour frequency. I have not adopted the word 'diel', however, because I have tried to avoid unnecessary terminology and it is quite possible by careful expression to avoid ambiguity without loss of clarity. Furthermore, the term '24-hour rhythm' is itself not entirely satisfactory, as the rhythms to which it refers may not be precise in their 24-hour repetitions. Indeed, 'circadian' (about a day), proposed by Halberg (1959) is clearly the most precise of these terms, but 'diurnal' has the advantage of long usage.

Within recent years, endogenous rhythms have tended to be regarded as manifestations of biological 'clocks' or 'chronometers'—processes measuring absolute time—an approach which has proved most stimulating. As a result of observations on the rate of cicatrization of wounds and growth of tissue cultured *in vitro*, Noüy had concluded as early as 1935 that there were two kinds of time, one corresponding to the classical notion of siderial or physical time flowing, without beginning or end, in a continuous, uniform stream; the other, physiological time, persisting only as long as the life of the organism and not affecting it in the same way at the beginning or end of that life. More recently, Gooddy (1959) has called these two 'government time' and 'personal time'.

A problem arises, therefore, in understanding what is meant by a 'clock'. Presumably it must be regarded as an instrument for measuring time through the interaction of two systems affecting one another by mutual negative feed-back.

To summarise. The terms 'rhythm', 'cycle' and 'periodicity' are here regarded as synonymous when applied to biological phenomena, their use being dictated by linguistic convention alone. Rhythms having a 'period' or 'frequency' of approximately 24 hours are called '24-hour', 'circadian' or 'diurnal rhythms', while by 'diurnal activity' is meant activity taking place during the hours of daylight ('day-active') as opposed to 'nocturnal' ('night-active'). 'Physiological rhythms' such as those of the heart, contractile vacuole, or mitotic cycle, are contrasted with 'exogenous' or 'environment-dependent', and 'persistent' or 'endogenous' rhythms. Because one rhythmic activity in an organism can be assigned to a particular category, it does not necessarily imply that all the rhythmical activities of that organism are of the same type. Furthermore, the distinction breaks down in practice. For not only are unequivocal examples of 'exogenous' rhythms extremely rare, but they probably represent 'endogenous' rhythms which rapidly get out of phase with the rhythm of the environment.

THEORIES OF RHYTHM CAUSATION

Three theories as to the origin of 24-hour rhythms have been proposed. According to the first of these, the organism responds entirely to periodic factors in the environment and there is no such thing as an endogenous rhythm. Such factors have been referred to as 'residual periodic variables' since they are claimed to operate after the experimental elimination of such obvious influences as light intensity and temperature changes etc.

They are believed to include cosmic ray showers, magnetic lines of flux, air pressure, ionisation and humidity.

According to the second theory, animals and plants are arhythmic when they first develop from the zygote, but they soon 'learn' a 24-hour rhythm from the environment or from their parents and this 'imprinted' rhythm is reinforced as development proceeds.

The third theory, to which the majority of workers in the field of rhythms now subscribe, assumes the presence of an inherited 24-hour 'clock'. Considerable evidence is afforded for this view from the fact that certain periodicities may be accelerated or retarded under 'constant' laboratory conditions. It is argued that if subtle environmental 'residual periodic variables' were responsible for the rhythm of the organism, they would surely have acted as 'clues' and set up an *exact* 24-hour periodicity. But this is not conclusive as we shall see.

These theories are discussed in detail later, the first especially in Chapter 6, the second in Chapter 9. The implications of the third are manifest throughout.

CHAPTER 1

Methods of Investigation

A NUMBER of ordinary physiological techniques, such as measurement of the rate of oxygen consumption and of carbon dioxide output, have been carried out over periods of 24 hours or more to provide data on diurnal periodicity. In the following paragraphs an account is given of various traps that automatically segregate their catch at various intervals of time, and mention is made of some of the methods that have been used satisfactorily to record locomotory and other activities of individuals or of groups of animals.

Godfrey (1954) employed a portable Geiger-Müller counter unit to trace the movements of field voles, *Microtus agrestis*. Brass tubes containing 5 to 10 mg. Cobalt-60 as a source of γ-radiation were soldered to monel metal rings which were fitted to the legs of the voles with special pliers. Voles bearing these rings could be detected at a distance of 8 to 10 ft. from the observer, though in order to determine their positions accurately it was necessary to approach to within 2 to 4 ft.

Southern, Watson and Chitty (1946) have overcome the difficulty of watching the activities of nocturnal vertebrates such as brown rats, *Rattus norvegicus*, by means of an infra-red radiation transmitter coupled with a special infra-red sensitive telescope mounted and aligned as a single unit. When photographs are required, a flood light is switched on to provide illumination.

Nielsen (1957) has employed electronic flash photographs to record the movements of mosquitoes. By using the displacement of one individual between two successive pictures as a unit, he has been able to obtain detailed quantitative measurement of activity. By this method it is possible also to record the movements of several individuals simultaneously under identical conditions. Perhaps its greatest value, however, lies in the fact that it enables him to see what the insects are actually doing, thus facilitating the analysis of their behaviour. Mosquitoes do not appear to be disturbed by the discharge of the electronic flash, although the firing of ordinary flash bulbs will always cause them to disperse and fly away.

In order to estimate the attack of biting insects such as mosquitoes on

11

man, the people who act as bait may perform the work of catching the insects, as occurs in 24-hour catch systems with human catchers (Haddow, 1954 etc.). In the case of other animals, however, a difficulty arises. If men are used for catching the mosquitoes, etc. alighting on the bait, there is a doubt as to whether the insects are attracted primarily to the animal, or to the man. Alternatively, some insects biting the man might be expected to bite the animal if it were alone.

In order to resolve this difficulty Lumsden (1958) has designed a trap which samples at regular intervals the flying insects in the vicinity of animal bait which is as nearly as possible freely exposed.

A fan is mounted on an iron framework above a platform of hardboard, in the centre of which the bait is tethered. The trap is quite open around the platform for a height of 15 cm., above which a conical space is partially enclosed by truncated sectional pieces of transparent cellulose acetate sheet, between the edges of which are spaces about a centimetre wide. The bait is thus visible from all directions except from directly overhead and the access of insects is practically unimpaired. Above the fan, a metal cylinder carries a wire gauze chamber which leads laterally to a small chamber fitted with a collecting bottle containing potassium cyanide or pyrethrum.

The switching of the fan motor is performed by a hotwire vacuum switch using as a control an ordinary alarm clock, the minute hand of which trails a piece of hair-spring over a surface of aluminium foil, out of which are cut sectorial pieces to correspond with the desired "off" periods.

A suction trap for small airborne insects which automatically segregates the catch into successive hourly samples, has been described by C. G. Johnson (1950). The trap is composed of an electric fan, a copper gauze cone and a collecting tube. It is mounted so that its opening faces upwards and the fan revolves in a horizontal plane: wind blowing across the top therefore, does not directly enter the opening. Air is sucked in, together with insects, which are blown down the cone into the collecting tube at the pointed, lower end. This collecting tube is of copper gauze which not only allows rain water to run away, but is essential for the proper working of the segregating mechanism which is composed of a pile of metal discs supported beneath the fan motor by a pivoted release mechanism. At each hour, a time-switch allows a current to pass through the transformer to a solenoid which, becoming a magnet, pulls the release across and allows a disc to drop down a central rod which guides it to its resting place in the gauze collecting tube. After a disc drops, the one above falls into its place on the release, ready to drop after another hour has passed. The time-switch then, after a few seconds, turns off the current.

Various improvements in the design of this trap have been suggested by Taylor (1951) and the development of large suction traps for airborne insects is discussed by C. G. Johnson and Taylor (1955). These can be used in more exposed situations where insect densities are very low, or high in the air where winds are strong.

In order to investigate diurnal activity in terrestrial invertebrates, G. Williams (1958) has devised pitfall traps in which a mechanism is incorporated to separate the catch into six periods of activity during the day. The pitfall consists of a large can sunk into the ground with its mouth flush with the surface. The rim is bent inwards so that there is no opportunity for an animal to recover its balance and escape. A 'perspex' cover supported around the periphery of the trap by six pins prevents rain and débris from falling in. Suspended from this is a metal disc, smaller in diameter than the mouth of the trap and level with its rim. This disc prevents leaves and other material from being blown in horizontally and blocking the mouth of the funnel below. This funnel leads into a pot containing dilute glycerine so that animals falling in can neither escape nor eat each other. Sorting the catch into different periods is achieved by changing the pot at regular intervals. Movement of the pots is achieved by a gramophone motor and the time of change is controlled by a time-switch. An experiment to determine the bias of the trap showed that of 17 groups into which the catch was classified, underestimates were made only in the case of Oribatid mites and parasitic Hymenoptera.

Of the various techniques that have been used to study animal activity in the field, the most practical for small mammals in particular is also a periodic trapping census, since these animals are impossible to keep under direct observation and, in fact, are seldom seen except when trapped. A trapping census, however, gives only an index of average activity at best and itself alters the normal actions of the animals in their environments. For this reason, it is usually necessary to bring animals into the laboratory for further study.

The mammalian activity recorder described by Hemmingsen and Krarup (1937) is an apparatus of considerable precision. It consists of an upright plywood partition for support, attached to which, on opposite sides, are a living cage and a revolving cage. These are in communication via an opening cut through the partition. A gearing mechanism transfers movements of the revolving cage, in which the test animal exercises itself, to a lever writing on a waxed-paper record. Any activity in the living cage is also recorded by means of an adjustable recording stylus attached to the free-swinging spring-suspended end. Consequently, activity of the experimental animal is recorded either while moving in the revolving cage or while eating, drinking etc. in the living cage. Modifications of this apparatus have been described by Park and Woods (1940).

Park (1937) has constructed an aktograph on auditory principles: the faint sound that any animal makes in moving is made audible by four stages of amplification. The apparatus includes a loud-speaker which can be switched in and out of circuit at will, a visual indicator in the form of a small bulb that lights momentarily with each movement of the experimental animal, and a relay pen that makes a continuous record of activity or other sounds upon a strip of waxed record paper carried on a revolving drum. One drawback of this type of equipment is the difficulty of excluding sounds of extraneous origin—a completely sound-proof cabinet is necessary.

More recently, Backlund and Ekerood (1950) have described an apparatus based on the capacitance method for use as a field aktograph. This is composed of a receiver, an oscillator and an amplifier, and it is sensitive even to the cleaning movements of a fly. The receiver is composed of parallel insulated copper wires: any object near to these influences the capacity of the condenser and, as the wires are placed in a zig-zag pattern, any movement of an animal near the bottom plate of the receiver must be at an angle to some part of the wires. Various other electro-acoustic techniques and their applications to the study of animal behaviour in general, have been described by Busnel (1958).

Haskell (1954) gives an account of an automatic recording maze for insect behaviour studies that can be used in a number of problems and with different animals. The maze is constructed of sheet copper bent to form a channel of $1\frac{1}{2}$ in. square cross-section and is closed at the top by sections of thin window glass. It is fixed to a sheet of aluminium whose high thermal conductivity gives rapid equalization of temperature even when heating is somewhat unevenly distributed. Activity in the maze is monitored by a cold cathode counter unit which feeds the information to a printer via a printer relay unit. The temperature and illumination of the maze can be pre-set by means of a cycling unit, and information about these changes is also fed to the printer for recording.

The first person to use aktograph apparatus for zoological research was Stewart (1898), who analysed the daily activity of rats and squirrels. The experimental animal was placed in a cylindrical cage 18 in. long and 20 in. in diameter, of fine wire netting soldered to a frame of stout wire revolving freely on a steel rod supported by a wooden frame. At one end was a hinged door and a light wooden nest-box hung from the axle. At the opposite end was an eccentric wheel which, with each revolution of the cage in either direction, pushed aside an upright lever attached to the wooden frame and in so doing pulled a wire connected to a lever writing on a smoked drum.

An activity cage and recorder for domestic fowl have been described by Ratner and Ringer (1959). Movement of an animal within tips the cage via a three point suspension system, so that it comes to rest on two out of eight available pins and the central supporting cone, depressing one of eight micro-switches mounted on the base of the cage. Two magnetic counters, activated by the micro-switches, serve as recorders.

In animal experiments, it is sometimes desirable to have an accurate indication of the time of onset of a burst of activity. This is achieved by a multiple point recorder, designed by Shipton, Emde and Folk (1959), which simplifies the assessment of data gathered from photoelectric aktographs registering total locomotor movements. The information is presented automatically in two forms: a curve of total activity over a 24-hour period, and a bar graph of the activity in each 30 minute time interval. A particular advantage lies in the fact that the recording pens are stationary, making it possible to plot the outputs from several activity counters across the whole width of the recording paper.

The problem of tracking the distances travelled by larger animals such as cattle and sheep, has exercised the minds of several workers who have produced plotting techniques, radio control and infra-red devices, none of which has been very successful. A simple cattle rangemeter consisting of a wheel harnessed by a single shaft has been described by Cresswell (1959). The wheel is maintained in an upright position by means of balancing spring steel tines, and the distance travelled is recorded by a cyclometer.

Guyselman (1957) has recorded the locomotory activity of crayfish using circular chambers constructed of $\frac{1}{16}$ inch vinyl acetate sheeting. Each chamber consists of two 12-inch circular discs cemented to and separated by a rim 3 inches wide. Two strips of plastic screen $\frac{3}{4}$ inch wide are cemented to the inner surface of the rim to provide traction for the animals. Two 3-inch 'perspex' wheels, separated from the discs by spacers are cemented to a plexiglas shaft as an axle. To provide for the entry and exit of water, twenty-four $\frac{3}{8}$-inch holes are cut in the peripheral area of each disc. Animals are placed in the chamber through a 2-inch circular opening, covered by a movable disc. The assembled chamber rotates about its axis and is supported by two nylon cables from the wheels of a chamber-suspension unit. This unit is composed of 'perspex' wheels identical with those on the activity chamber, so that each turn of the activity chamber causes one turn of the chamber suspension unit above it. The two wheels of the latter are connected by a shaft, the centre of which holds a commutator assembly consisting of a circular brass disc with notches milled in its circumference. As the commutator revolves, electrical connections are made and broken in the relay system of the recording apparatus.

Ghidini (1948) has also used the same principle of a revolving chamber with electrical connections to the recording apparatus, and Pavan

(1952a, b) describes a multiple aktograph with eight revolving chambers constructed of transparent 'perspex'. Each of these bears on its periphery a number of small metal bridges which, as the chamber revolves, make electrical contacts between two little cups of mercury below. Batteries connected in series with electromagnets pull down levers writing on smoked drums (kymographs) whenever contact is made. In an earlier experiment, instead of allowing the insect to wander freely inside a rotating chamber, Ghidini (1947) harnessed it just above a horizontal, freely revolving cylinder at the end of which was a wheel with metal teeth that made contact with mercury in a bowl beneath. Any loco-motory movement of the legs of the fixed insect caused the cylinder to rotate and the faster it revolved the more frequently were the contacts made and broken.

An aktograph which records the time, rate and duration of walking-movements and oviposition of moths has been described by Makings (1956). The working principles are similar and depend upon the moth being suspended so that it rests or walks in a normal position on a light wheel with the tip of the abdomen above, or resting on, the edge of a horizontal circular plate. When the moth walks the wheel is turned like a treadmill and moves a lever which operates a recording pen on a revolving chart. An electric contact on the pen arm actuates a counter which records the number of revolutions of the wheel and hence the distance walked by the moth. The circular plate also revolves: a large filter paper resting on it provides a convenient surface on which the eggs are deposited and cemented down by the moth, thus forming an automatic record of the time of deposition.

The first work on the recording of insect activity by means of akto-graph apparatus was carried out by Szymański (1914) who used an aktograph composed of a cage at the end of a long lever pivoted on a knife-edge. The cage was counter-balanced by a weight beyond which was a pointer writing on a revolving smoked drum. This registered any movement of the insect in the cage.

A modification of this is the aktograph of Gunn and Kennedy (1936) which was originally constructed for the investigation of kinetic re-sponses to humidity. It consists essentially of an arena or box pivoted on a knife-edge about its median transverse line. Any movement of one animal along the longitudinal axis tips the box and is recorded by a long lever balanced by an adjustable counterpoise and writing on a smoked drum. The box is cast in aluminium with walls 3 mm. thick and its internal measurements are 20 × 10 cm., 6 cm. deep. A small ledge above the true floor carries a false floor of perforated zinc. The true floor is divided by transverse partitions 1 cm. high and 1.5 cm. apart, into a number of troughs in which the humidity-controlling fluid or solid is placed. The partitions prevent gross movements of fluid when the box tips: the lid is of glass and is sealed with vaseline. A rod passing vertically downwards below the centre point of the box carries a weight which serves to bring the centre of gravity of the whole arena below the fulcrum. This can be screwed up or down in order to alter the sensitivity of the balance, while below the weight a transverse vane is immersed in a fluid so as to damp oscillations. This apparatus has been used by the writer in some of his studies on diurnal rhythms in terrestrial arthropods (Cloudsley-Thompson, 1952a, 1953b, d, 1955b, 1957a, etc.). Instead of the original long writing lever, however, a short rod is connected with a gymbal lever and a clockwork barograph drum employed as a kymograph in place of a 12-in. motor-driven drum. The object of these modifications is to reduce the overall size of the apparatus so that it can be placed in a large incubator and the light and temperature controlled artificially. The sensitivity of the apparatus renders it suitable for most arthropods weighing not less than 30 to 40 mg.

The apparatus can be considerably simplified where it is not necessary to control the humidities in the arena. Park (1935) and the writer have used simplified and less sensitive versions without a false floor for heavier animals, such as giant tropical millipedes. This apparatus is constructed of sheet metal with a plastic cover, the area of which is oval in shape, measuring 12 × 6 cm. (It is an advantage to eliminate corners in which animals tend to aggregate.) The arena can be adjusted by moving a small weight on a rod counterbalancing the writing needle. It is pivoted on two steel bolts ground to a fine point and mounted on a wooden frame (Cloudsley-Thompson 1951b). In the experiments on giant millipedes the arena was lined with damp humus which provided food and maintained a saturated atmosphere.

The writer has also constructed a simple aktograph of 'perspex', of similar dimensions, that has proved suitable for recording the diurnal rhythm of locomotory activity of cockroaches and locusts (Cloudsley-Thompson, 1953a, b, d) as well as in large beetles, scorpions and scolopendras (1956c). A short rod at the end of the arena is again connected with a gymbal lever. In this apparatus it is not necessary to damp oscillations by means of a vane at the bottom of the vertical rod which bears the weight that lowers the centre of gravity.

The rectangular and oval arenas described above are not sufficiently sensitive for use with very small insects. The leverage can be increased, however, by having a narrow and very much longer cage, although this possesses the disadvantage of ends with corners in which insects tend to come to rest as a result of their thigmotactic reactions. D'Aguillar (1952) has described an aktograph, the arena of which is triangular in cross-section and made of plastic. The apparatus differs essentially from others in bearing a writing point formed of a horse hair cut in half and itself carried by one or two bristles fixed to the material of the cage which is suspended below a short bamboo rod pierced by the pins on which it is pivoted. A sliding block at the end opposite to the writing lever allows for adjustment and the introduction of the insects.

A similar principle has been employed by Larsen (1949) who used a very simple aktograph consisting of a cellophane cylinder mounted on a rocking device with a stylus at one end writing on a revolving smoked-paper kymograph drum.

Sensitive micro-aktographs have been constructed by the writer to test the orthokinetic response of small millipedes, etc., to dry air or moist surfaces. In these the arenas are made from a thin strip of celluloid glued in a circle with a top and bottom of cellophane or filter paper (Cloudsley-Thompson, 1951a). They measure some 10 cm. in diameter and 1 cm. deep, and are pivoted on two fine entomological pins stuck through a straw glued across the upper transverse axis. The points of these pins rest on glass slides supported by the wooden framework of the apparatus. A thin fuse wire is threaded from one end along the centres of each of these straws until it reaches the middle of the arena, where it passes downwards into another straw glued to the under surface along the longitudinal axis. The wire is threaded through the second straw, at the end of which it is connected to a piece of fine platinum wire. When the aktographs tilt about their horizontal axes, contact is made and broken between these and other pieces of platinum wire attached to the frames of the apparatus. Balance is adjusted by means of very small pieces of plasticine attached to the rear-ends of the longitudinal straws. Batteries connected in series with the platinum wires to electro-magnets pull down levers writing on smoked drums, which thus record the movements of any animals in the arenas. The relative humidity in the arenas can be altered by pumping air, bubbled through water or sulphuric acid mixtures, through a hole at one side level with the fulcrum and sucking it out through a similar hole at the other.

For testing responses to moisture the filter-paper floors or lids of the aktographs can be damped with distilled water. In the experiments referred to the millipedes soon came to rest on the damp surface, but as the filter paper dried a great outburst of activity was recorded.

Chauvin (1943, 1944) describes a micro-aktograph similar to those of D'Aguillar and Larsen already mentioned. This is suitable for registering the diurnal rhythm of activity in small insects, but does not allow either the number of oscillations to be counted or the distance travelled by the experimental animal to be computed, since small and large movements cannot be differentiated. A fragment of mirror is attached at an angle to the top of the little tubular cage containing the animal. A beam of light focused on this is reflected on to photosensitive paper attached to a rotating drum. Movements of the experimental animal cause oscillations of the tiny arena and these are detected later when the photographic paper is developed. Naturally this method is suitable only for use in a dark room.

Hammond (1954) also uses a photo-electric method to magnify and

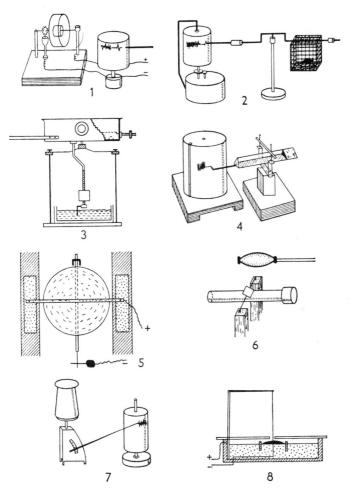

FIG. 2. Aktograph apparatus. (1) Revolving chamber aktograph (after Ghidini, 1948). (2) Rocking arena aktograph (after Szymanski, 1914). (3) Cast aluminium aktograph (after Gunn and Kennedy, 1936). (4) Elongated rocking aktograph (after D'Aguillar, 1952). (5) Micro-aktograph (after Cloudsley-Thompson, 1951a). (6) Micro-aktograph (after Chauvin, 1943). (7) Aktograph for jumping insects (after Everly, 1929). (8) Aktograph for climbing insects (after Brian, 1947). Not to scale. (After Cloudsley-Thompson, 1955b)

record the oscillations of a micro-aktograph containing insects weighing as little as 3 mg. The insect is placed in a chamber in the form of a balanced hollow beam 9 in. long and having a pendulum with a vertical slit. This slit swings in the path of a ray of light and an image of the slit is projected by a lens to the focal plane of a camera. In the focal plane is a horizontal slit across which the film is continuously moving. By this means a point of light records the movement of the chamber on the film, whilst time is recorded by the speed of film travel. The chamber was made by wrapping a piece of acetate sheeting round a length of wood of the required cross-section. The joint was glued with cement made from clippings of acetate dissolved in acetone. This balance is so sensitive that it requires completely draught-proof conditions.

Everly (1929) investigated the jumping reactions of grasshoppers which were placed in a cylindrical cage 2 in. high and covered with transparent celluloid. The cage rested on a spring-balance letter weight to the needle of which was attached a long stylus writing directly on a revolving kymograph drum.

Lutz (1932) studied diurnal rhythms of locomotory activity in crickets by means of a cage consisting of two small compartments connected by a narrow runway. In the middle of the runway was a delicately counter-balanced treadle which was depressed when the insects crossed it so that the wires at its ends dipped into mercury, completing an electric current through an electro-magnet. This magnet pulled aside a recording pen which was otherwise tracing a straight line on a kymograph drum.

Certain insects, such as wire-worm beetles, run up and down the stems of plants when they are active. Advantage can be taken of this to record their locomotory activity. Brian (1947) used an artificial stem of galvanized iron with a blade of copper spring fixed across the top. This is bent downwards at right angles and, when depressed about 2 cm. by the weight of an insect, dips into mercury and completes a circuit powered by a dry cell in which an electric buzzer records on a smoked drum. The iron stem is set in wax for rigidity and the mercury is placed in a shallow bowl so that the sensitivity of the instrument is not affected by temperature variations. The copper spring can be so adjusted that several quiescent beetles are unable to effect circuit closure, while one beetle moving about or dropping off causes sufficient disturbance.

In order to study the movements of fishes, Spencer (1939) used an "ichthyometer" in which a fine thread from the fish's tail moved a very light lever which gave a kymograph tracing. Spoor (1941, 1946) has used a method by which the water currents, generated by the movements of a fish, move a light weight paddle of aluminium foil suspended from a fixed support by 44 gauge copper wire. A silver rod in the suspension of the paddle passes through a hole in a fixed silver plate. As the

paddle is moved, contact between the silver rod and plate is made and broken, thus activating a sensitive relay with which the silver contacts are in series. The relay in turn operates a signal magnet or counter permitting quantitative measurements of the activity of the fish. The method is applicable to the investigation of basal metabolic rates, since activity and oxygen consumption can be measured simultaneously when the aktograph is combined with a continuous water-flow system.

More recently, Harder and Hempel (1954) have described an apparatus for registering the time when flat-fishes are resting on the bottom of an aquarium. A secondary bottom, made from a celluloid-lattice, is suspended from a balance and when a fish swims upwards from this, the weight on the balance is reduced and an electrical contact in series with an electro-magnet attached to a stylus is closed. When the fish is resting quietly on the bottom, no record is made on the smoked drum.

The method for obtaining a controlled daily temperature cycle described by Howe (1956) may profitably be employed in the investigation of diurnal rhythms in terrestrial animals. The apparatus is based on the type of bimetallic strip thermostat which has for many years given satisfactory control of constant temperatures in the laboratory. The hour hand of a 24-hour clock is linked with a thermostat by a connecting rod so that the contact moves slowly backwards and forwards. The two joints are fitted with washers so that the screws holding them can be tightened while still permitting free movement of the rods at the joints. The shape of the curve of the temperature cycle produced by this apparatus can be expressed as a mathematical formula: nearly constant relative humidity can be obtained even with the widest temperature range by means of a commercial paper humidistat. Howe uses a small dish of water containing a 125W heater to boil off water vapour and a pump to bubble a stream of air through a column of water into the incubator. Either method alone is normally satisfactory but the two are operated simultaneously as a safeguard against the failure of either.

Bailey and McCabe (1957) have described an instrument, based on a synchronous time-switch motor rotating once every 24 hours, that will brighten and dim a light source and control its "on" and "off" timing. To the spindle of the motor is attached an arm carrying a contact brush which is drawn across the faces of two "commutor blocks" connected to a tapped resistence circuit. By varying the angle between these, the total period of illumination is adjusted and by changing the position of the contact brush along the length of the revolving arm, the brightening and dimming periods are adjusted.

The means of testing for endogenous rhythms must differ with nocturnal and day-active animals. The former are often inhibited by light and their rhythm must therefore be measured in constant darkness when, if persistent, it will continue unchanged, since darkness is not a positive factor. This is not true of continuous light, however, which may affect an animal so that its activity shows a regular, constant and definite alteration which varies as we have seen, with the intensity of the light. The solution to this problem, according to Aschoff (1958), is to use continuous dim light which alters but little the normal activity pattern of day-active animals (see p. 155).

THE STATISTICAL ANALYSIS OF RHYTHMIC DATA

In few of the many publications on rhythms has any attempt been made to analyse data statistically. In most cases this is maybe because there is little to be gained from such treatment beyond the fact, clearly apparent from graphical or mathematical tabulation, that a rhythm is indeed involved.

However, not only is it possible to combine two or more simple harmonic motions of different period, amplitude and phase, but there are also means of analysing complicated wave forms to their component harmonies: this process is known as 'harmonic analysis'. The same analysis is possible for any periodic motion, however complicated, and the equation, called "Fourier's series" may be written:

$$y = a \sin 2\pi nt + b \cos 2\pi nt + c \sin 4\pi nt + d \cos 4\pi nt + e \sin 6\pi nt + f \cos 6\pi nt + \ldots$$

in which y is the displacement of the moving point and t is the time. The fundamental frequency n and the constants a, b, c, d etc. must be calculated from the given wave form or the data from which it is plotted, which may be a very laborious process.

However it is claimed that Fourier analysis is of limited use and auto-correlation provides a more elegant means of separating random from periodic elements. Details of harmonic analysis and autocorrelation are given in many standard mathematical text books.

In order to test for correlation between successive intervals, Gunn, Jenkin and Gunn (1937) made the following calculation:

If there are n intervals in a particular case, the first $n - 1$ intervals are put down as a column of x, and the last $n - 1$ as a column of y; $\bar{x}$ and $\bar{y}$ are the averages of x and y respectively. The sum of $(x - \bar{x}) y$ and the sum of $(x - \bar{x})$ are worked out for each case giving the correlation

$$b = \frac{\Sigma S (x - \bar{x}) y}{\Sigma S (x - \bar{x})}$$

Significance is then tested by the expression:

$$\left[\frac{1}{n} \frac{b \Sigma (x - \bar{x}) y}{\Sigma (y - \bar{y})^2 - b \Sigma S (x - \bar{x}) y} \right]^{\frac{1}{2}}$$

A translation of Prof. V. Volterra's (1926) important paper on variations and fluctuations of the number of individuals in animal species living together appears as an appendix to Chapman's (1931) book on animal ecology. Other mathematical concepts and their conclusions are discussed by Nicholson (1933), Solomon (1949), etc. Finally, the mathematics of relaxation oscillations are discussed by van der Pol (1926).

CHAPTER 2

Periodicity from Cells to Communities

RHYTHMIC or cyclic phenomena can be observed on all levels of biological organization, from cell, tissues and organs, to organisms and communities. Many of them comprise "physiological" or "personal" rhythms whose period or frequency in no way reflects the influence of meteorological or cosmic periodicities (Calhoun, 1944-46; Jores, 1937; Reinberg and Ghata, 1957).

REPETITION AND RELAXATION PROCESSES

One of the fundamental characteristics of all cyclic and rhythmic phenomena is repetition. Kalmus (1953) has defined this as "the phenomenon that a certain stage is repeated again and again in the course of a chain of biological events whether in most features or only in a few". It is not essential that the repetitions should be identical in every detail or that comparable phases should follow each other in equal or even approximately equal intervals of time. Repetition in some form or other occurs in every biological process. For example, there are no known cells, whether they be bacteria, algae, Protozoa or parts of multicellular organisms, which have not arisen by cell division. And repetition applies not only to the cell as a whole but to all its parts as far as they can be distinguished as separate units. It occurs in the cytoplasm, the nucleus, the nucleolus and such specialized cellular organs as the chloroplasts, the basal granules of cilia, the flagella and many others.

Of particular interest is the process by which the units of heredity, the genes, are repeated. Usually the reproduction of a gene results in two daughter genes with identical chemical or physiological properties although occasionally, at a rate statistically specific for each particular gene, unlike genes or mutations arise. Thus repetition is at the root of inherited variability. Two possibilities can, in principle, be envisaged as to the manner in which two genes might be produced from one. The first is simply a division of all the parts of the gene, which is somewhat difficult to understand if one thinks of the gene as a giant molecule. The second and more interesting possibility that Kalmus (1953) suggests may be visualized as "a sort of minting process by which is produced from a coin, the gene, first a negative cast and then a second coin or gene, indistinguishable but for an occasional mutation, from the original. Haldane (1941) has drawn attention to a possible relation between genes and antigens which might very well stand in a relationship of positive and negative. A similar sort of repetition might also underlie the production of antibodies through the action of antigens".†

All this may appear to be somewhat beyond the scope of this book, but it is often useful to compare events on a macro-scale with molecular models not only because they are generally familiar and the human mind tests every observation and hypothesis by comparing it with a series of models or "engrams" that the brain has already learned, but because the behaviour and arrangement of its molecular components often affects the behaviour and structure of the whole.

PERIODICITY IN CELLS

The free-living Protozoa show rhythmicity in many of their processes and some of these, such as that of division in *Paramoecium* (Kalmus, 1935) have been shown to be environment-dependent. On the other hand, Fauré-Fremiet (1948) studied the tidal rhythm of *Strombidium oculatum*, a ciliate associated with symbiotic *Chlorella*, which encysts at the time of high tide after having been free-swimming in rock pools. It remains encysted for 18 hours and then becomes free-swimming, even in the absence of tidal conditions. Clearly any individual whose rhythm gets out of phase with the tidal periodicity will be eliminated and doubtless the pressure of environmental selection ensures synchronization. When this selective elimination is suppressed under laboratory conditions, individual variations in periodicity are asserted and the collective rhythm gradually disappears.

Another rhythmic phenomenon concerning the animal cell is exemplified by the secretion and discharge of the contractile vacuole in Protozoa. The rate of secretion of contractile vacuoles is known to be controlled in accordance with osmotic conditions, but the vacuolar cycle has two other characteristics: the ultimate or maximal diameter and the frequency of discharge. All three may vary, but only two may vary independently. For instance, in Peritrich ciliates the frequency, ultimate diameter and rate of secretion all increase with a greater osmotic inflow of water from the external medium into the organism. If changes in the rate of excretion found their expression entirely in a change of frequency or of ultimate diameter a simple hypothesis could be devised, but this is not the case. Kitching (1954) therefore concludes that, under constant conditions, either there is a particular ultimate

† For a further discussion of the template theory of the relation of genes to antigens, see Haldane (1954).

B

diameter at which, for mechanical reasons, the vacuole contracts, but that this critical diameter is modified by a change of conditions, or that "there is a rhythmic process causing systole at regular intervals, but that the rhythm is subject to modification".

In *Amoeba* the contractile vacuole discharges when it reaches and makes the necessary contact with the plasmalemma, so that it is possible to suppose that it may be effected by surface tension, or body turgor, or the elasticity or contraction of the vacuolar wall as soon as these are given an opportunity to act. In some ciliates however, each contractile vacuole remains attached to its pore for a large part of the vacuolar cycle yet only contracts when fully grown. Moreover, in one animal there may be several vacuoles, yet only the full one contracts. Body turgor would affect them all alike and surface tension would exert the greatest effect on the smallest vacuole so that here again there must be some other mechanism by which systole is initiated.

Systole is known to occur in *Paramoecium* when the body is partly shrunk and in *Discophrya* when the body is wrinkled as Kitching has shown, so that in these cases at any rate body turgor is not necessary. It seems possible that the vacuolar apparatus may be affected in such a way as to contract protein molecules to a globular state which might initially produce an increase in tension in the wall of the vacuole causing a rounding prior to systole. As the protein molecules become globular and pass into the surrounding hyaloplasm, surface tension might take over and complete the process of systole.

The connection between frequency of contraction and rate of secretion could be due to a common source of energy or common component in the two mechanisms, to the fact that the small changes in volume which probably control the rate of secretion also affect the consistency of the pore plug or the structure and properties of the vacuolar wall, or that extension of the vacuolar wall increases the tendency to discharge and so accelerates the cycle (Kitching, 1954). In many Protozoa an increase in temperature causes an increase in vacuolar frequency. This increase may perhaps be ascribed to an increase in the velocity of some chemical reaction promoting contraction and solation but it is accompanied by a temporary fall in the rate of output, followed by a rise to a new level higher than the original. Perhaps the timing mechanism has been accelerated but available water is running short.

After a sudden fall of temperature the contractile vacuole continues to grow in volume at a fairly rapid rate, but systole is delayed so that the ultimate diameter is much greater than usual. By analogy with over-shoot in a chain of chemical reactions, Kitching has suggested that the fall in temperature drastically slows down a chemical process upon which contraction depends, but that as a result of this the products of earlier reactions in the chain pile up and by the law of mass action once more accelerate the periodicity.

Amongst the most prominent examples of periodicity in parts of cells are the cilia. These usually move independently of nervous impulse and even in multicellular organisms are only rarely controlled by the co-ordinating system of the body. Their beat is often continuous throughout the life of the animal and the stimulus for this arises endogenously in the protoplasm of the cell under the control of the basal granules. It probably does not occur unless at least a part of this modified protoplasm is attached to the cilium. In the ctenophores, however, the beat of the fused cilia which form the combs is controlled by impulses coming from the sensory hairs of the statocyst and in a few other animals there is evidence that the ciliated cells may be supplied by nerves which control the beat of the cilia.

In a snail, *Physa* sp., it has been shown that cilia on the lips which are normally at rest can be caused to beat if the nerves which supply the ciliated cells are stimulated, but the beat ceases after a few minutes unless the stimulation of the nerves is maintained. Again, in aeolid veliger larvae the cilia of the velum are under nervous control and beat inter-mittently. The stopping of the beat is believed to be due to impulses reaching the cells by nerves which end between or within them (see discussion in Carter, 1951a).

Cilia are found throughout the animal kingdom with the exception of certain groups such as nematodes and arthropods. In most cases they beat in a regular manner known as "metachronal rhythm"; the beat of the first cilium is followed by that of the second and so on. Each bends slightly after its neighbour, the first one setting the pace and the others following in time but increasingly out of phase. The effect is similar to that produced when a row of toy soldiers falls to the ground, or when a gust of wind blows across a field of corn. The interval between cilia is never more than a fraction of the whole period of their movement and according to the position of the cilia and the direction of their beat, the wave may pass towards the effector or recovery side or at right angles to the direction of movement.

The theories which have been put forward to account for the mech-anism of the beating of cilia are numerous, but all the observed forms of movement might result from contraction in a sheath of protoplasm surrounding a more solid, non-contractile core. Physiological study of the cilium suggests that its activity, in the cells of multicellular animals, reacts to changes in the external environment in much the same way that the contraction of muscle reacts. It is probable that each cilium is stimulated to beat by some stimulus provided by the beat of the cilium next to it, but the nature of that stimulus is still uncertain.

PERIODICITY IN TISSUES AND ORGANS

Many tissues, both plant and animal, exhibit periodicity. The peristaltic movements of the stomach and alimentary canal are caused by the contraction of the walls which is propagated from muscle fibre to muscle fibre at a rate of about 5 cm. per sec. Other cycles concerned with digestion occur in the pancreas, the liver and the intestinal glands. The concentric rings found on the shells of molluscs and the scales and otoliths of fishes are indications of periodicity of growth. Indeed, in all organisms growth tends to be a cyclical process, periods of rest alternating with activity. In no animals however is it more marked than in the arthropods, whose development is punctuated by a series of moults or ecdyses, each of which is preceded by a period of active growth and followed by one of apparent inactivity. All parts of the integument are moulted together, independently of nerve supply. The stimulus for this is hormonic in nature, metamorphosis too being controlled by hormones.

It is found almost everywhere in the nervous system that if a nerve cell is stimulated, a propagated impulse is set up either completely or not at all. At the same time conduction occurs without decrement whatever the distance travelled, but the size of the impulse is determined by the structural characters of the nerve cell as well as by the activity of its protoplasm. It is less when the activity of the cell is reduced by narcotics and other treatment and may be reduced to zero when the cell ceases to conduct. The rate of conduction varies too, in different types of nerve and may be as high as 100 m. per sec. in the axons of mammalian nerves. In the coelenterate nerve net it ranges from 4 to about 120 cm. per sec. and considerable delay occurs at each synapse.

After an impulse has passed through a nerve cell, the protoplasm is, for a short time, insensitive to further stimulation. This is known as the "refractory period". In the nerve-net the arrival of an impulse at a synapse reduces for a bit the hindrance at that synapse to the passage of a later impulse even though the first impulse does not cross the synapse. This phenomenon is called "inter-neural facilitation". Almost all natural stimulations last longer than the refractory periods of nerve cells, so that continued stimulation of a nerve results in the initiation of a series of impulses at intervals which may be nearly as small as the refractory period of the nerve, or may be much longer depending on the sensory receptor organ or the nerve termination in contact with it.

When the refractory period of a nerve cell has ended, the sensitivity of the cell is the same as before. The effect of fatigue on nerves is negligible because their metabolic rate is low. Thus if the jelly-fish *Cassiopea* sp. is stimulated at one point, an impulse sets out in both directions meeting finally at a point opposite the start, each impulse having travelled half-way round the circle. On meeting, the two impulses mutually extinguish one another: but if by applying ice to one side of the region stimulated the impulse on that side is diminished, the other will make a complete circle and continue for many hours to do so (Mayer, 1914).

These points are clearly illustrated by Pantin's (1935) classical research on the nerve-net of the Actinozoa in which he showed that if a point at the base of the column of a sea-anemone (*Calliactis* sp.) is stimulated electrically and the contraction of the sphincter muscle which lies round the edge of the disc is recorded, it is found that the response to a single shock is slight or non-existent. But if a series of shocks are given at intervals of 0.5 to 1.5 sec, the response to each shock increases gradually, producing a "staircase effect" (Fig. 3). When this is compared with the potential of

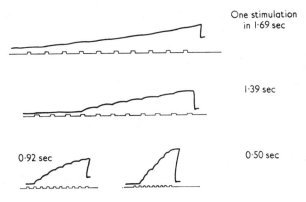

One stimulation
in 1·69 sec

1·39 sec

0·92 sec   0·50 sec

Fig. 3. Facilitation in the responses of the nerve-net of the sea-anemone, *Calliactis parasitica*. (After Pantin, 1935). Compare with Fig. 32 (p. 189)

a neon lamp under the influence of a similar, regularly spaced series of impulses (see p. 189), the analogy between the two is immediately apparent. The staircase effect in *Calliactis* results from neuro-muscular facilitation. The shorter the intervals between the shocks (until a minimum of about 0.5 sec. determined by the refractory period of the nerve cells) the more rapid is the increase in the response: but the energy of the electrical shock has no effect on the response as the nerve cells conform with the "all or nothing" law of conduction.

Innumerable other examples of periodicities in living tissues could be listed but, as already explained, it is quite impossible within the scope of this volume to be in any degree comprehensive. At the same time much will be found in later chapters relevant to the subject now under discussion. Special mention should however be made here of the work of Sir James Gray on the physiology of animal locomotion. From a physiological point of view one of the central problems of behaviour is whether an animal can initiate and maintain patterns of co-ordinated muscular movement without reference to the outside world. When frogs, and especially toads, walk on land they bring into play a set of proprioceptive reflexes that depend on the contraction of the muscles against an external resistance. Now a fully de-afferentated toad still swims actively, provided that its membranous labyrinths are intact; but no swimming movements have ever been observed after complete de-afferentation and bilateral labyrinthectomy. Again, a spinal dogfish shows a persistent rhythm of swimming movements which can be sustained after severence of a surprisingly large number of sensory nerves; yet it is abolished when de-afferentation extends beyond a critical number of spinal segments. The degree of dependence of swimming rhythms on peripheral sense organs is still uncertain however, and the whole problem of central versus peripheral control of muscular activity is obviously extremely complex. For any particular observer there must nearly always be some element of bias in favour of the view which provides the most satisfactory picture of the particular material with which he is familiar.

As Gray (1950) concludes in his extremely lucid review, "To my mind, the role of the proprioceptors in amphibian ambulation seems to be sufficiently clear to doubt the necessity of introducing conceptions of central control for which there is at present no direct experimental evidence. How far we are justified in attempting to extend this picture to mammals is more doubtful. For present purposes, however, the main conclusion must be that the existence of centrally controlled patterns of locomotion should be regarded as non-proven". (p. 124).

Certainly, however, the brain is not a passive mass of tissue: throughout the life of its possessor it drives along, running through a sequence of activities. In lower animals these are largely innate and instinctive, but in the higher mammals and man its activity is controlled by learning. A new born child sleeps most of the time; its numerous brain cells firing in unison. Actions at first random develop into little sequences as development proceeds. In response to any disturbing influence, the brain initiates sequences of action that tend to return it to its rhythmic pattern. If the first action fails to do this, other sequences are tried and the brain runs through all the "rules" it has learned one after the other, matching the input with its various engrams until unison is somehow achieved. Thus, as Young (1951) has suggested, a normal person learns the rules of seeing by connecting some parts of the sensory input with motor acts that lead to satisfaction such as naming and the fulfilment of communication. He at first learns to sweep his eyes along lines instead of in all directions at random.

A man born blind, when he is given sight, has to learn to interpret what he sees. At first this is only a mass of colours, but gradually he learns to distinguish shapes, although to begin with they can only be recognized in the same colour and at the same angle. From these brief remarks, it will be seen that the basic cyclic nature of the physiological activity of nervous tissue is ultimately responsible for behaviour itself, a point to which we shall be returning later.

No doubt further investigation will bring about a synthesis of the present dichotomy of views, since reafferent excitation and proprioceptive feed-back can be separated only by experimental operation and are inextricably entwined in the entire organism.

Periodicity in Organisms

As an example of periodic responses in the orientation and behaviour of Protozoa, the well known reactions to stimuli of the ciliate *Paramoecium* will now be considered. As long ago as 1906, Jennings demonstrated the occurrence of a number of aggregation reactions in Protozoa in which the direction of motion could not be related to the direction of the stimulus. Such reactions are undirected and orientation is influenced by the frequency of turning or rate of change of direction of the animal: at any particular instant its direction of movement is random. Thus if *Paramoecium* swims into a hot region or some obstacle it backs for a short distance, turns the body through an angle of about 30° and then resumes forward movement in the new direction. If it again reaches the hot region, the backing and turning are repeated, and so on until it can swim forward freely. This type of avoiding reaction, or klino-kinesis, is clearly distinguished from the normal, nearly straight movement of the animal and its frequency can easily be measured by observation.

Identical reactions are shown when *Paramoecium* swims into solutions of certain chemicals and thereby the animals tend to aggregate in regions of weak acidity. This response has the biological advantage of bringing the ciliates into regions where the breakdown of decaying vegetation by bacterial action is at its height, and food consequently plentiful. They swim at random, getting into the acid largely by chance and not by a directed movement. When they reach the boundary on the way out, however, they turn and so tend to return into the acid region within which, away from the edges, they turn little or not at all. The animals are not *attracted* by a favourable stimulus, but they avoid zones where a repellent is present or a favourable stimulus recently experienced is absent.

If a *Paramoecium* is transferred from a culture medium to one slightly more acid the frequency of turning immediately increases but after a few minutes it tends to fall again to the basic level. On the whole, the greater the change in pH, the greater the rise in rate of change of direction and the longer the time taken to revert to the basic level (Gunn and Walsh,

1941). In a similar way the orientation to light of flatworms and several of the responses of arthropods to other physical and chemical stimuli have been interpreted as klino-kinesis.

The avoiding reaction is a rhythmic phenomenon occurring at fairly regular intervals and klino-kinetic orientation behaviour is achieved not by altering the intensity or direction of the response, but by altering its frequency.

In the following chapters are considered some of the innumerable rhythmic responses of animals to periodic changes in their environments. These include the diurnal, tidal, lunar and seasonal or annual cycles which so greatly influence the conditions of life on earth.

PERIODICITIES IN EXPERIMENTAL COMMUNITIES

Regular cyclical changes in population numbers are frequent in animal ecology and are important in the study of evolution. In some cases such periodicities may be due to the inherent conditions of competition, but it is usually difficult to be sure that an observed rhythm is not the result of cyclical changes in non-biological factors external to the competition, so that even where cycles appear at regular intervals of time they are probably usually environment-dependent and not due to the inherent rhythmicity of the system.

Mathematical analysis indicates that under certain conditions two forms living in the same homogeneous environment and competing directly may be expected to live together for an indefinite time undergoing rhythmic cyclical changes in population density. Theoretically, as one species increases in numbers at the expense of the other, the second species which constitutes the food of the first will decline at the same time. This in turn will result in a decrease in the numbers of the first species owing to starvation and as the pressure of predation is relaxed the prey species will again increase in numbers (Volterra, 1926, 1931). In most experiments however the stronger species has been found to eradicate the weaker and then die out itself from starvation. Thus if *Paramoecium caudatum* and *Didinium nasutum* are cultured in a medium containing bacteria as food for the former, the *Didinium* feed on the *Paramoecium* which are soon eradicated. After this the *Didinium* inevitably die of starvation.

Homogeneous environments are rare in nature, however, and if in the experiments the weaker species can escape from the stronger in part of the environment, the results of competition may be somewhat different. Thus Gause (1934) found that he could provide a refuge for *Paramoecium* living in a mixed culture with *Didinium*, by allowing sediment to collect on the bottom of the culture tube. In these conditions the *Paramoecium* was sometimes eradicated, the refuge being inadequate, sometimes a few individuals managed to survive by escaping and then greatly increased in numbers after the elimination of their predators by starvation; and occasionally a mixed population of both species persisted for a while.

In an example of competition where the predator had a less deadly action on the prey than *Didinium* on *Paramoecium*, however, Gause actually found that rhythmic changes in numbers occurred without interference from outside. This example was provided by *Paramoecium aurelia* grown in culture with the yeast *Saccharomyces exiguus* as food and it

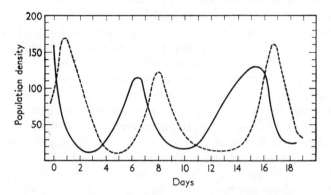

Fig. 4. Fluctuation in population density of *Paramoecium aurelia* (broken line) and yeast, *Saccharomyces exiguus* (solid line). (After Gause, 1934)

was found that both the *Paramoecium* and the yeast increased and decreased in numbers rhythmically. In one culture Gause observed three of these cycles in *Paramoecium* and two in *Saccharomyces* and theoretically the periodicity might have persisted indefinitely so long as the yeast had adequate food and waste products were removed (Fig. 4).

POPULATION CYCLES, IRRUPTIONS AND EMIGRATIONS IN NATURE

Few animal populations remain constant in size for long; their numbers fluctuate according to the state of the moon, the season of the year or some other factor. This is especially marked in the case of short-lived invertebrate animals such as insects and many of the inhabitants of fresh waters, but of course it applies also to the vertebrates whose numbers reach a maximum at each breeding season. In addition to seasonal and reproductive rhythms, which will be discussed in greater detail later, there is another type of population variation which is seen especially in the mammals and birds of the arctic and cool temperate regions of the world. This is the cyclic variation in numbers shown by creatures such as lemmings, voles and snow-shoe rabbits which are followed by fluctuations in the numbers of predators such as the lynx and snowy owl.

Two or three main cycles seem to occur. First, there is a 4-year cycle in the numbers of various mammals and birds of the tundra centring on the lemming; secondly, there is a 4-year cycle in the animals of the open forest with grassland, found particularly in the belt between the tundra and the main coniferous forests. This is based on the vole. Thirdly, there is a 10-year cycle in the snow-shoe rabbit and other animals of the northern forest regions of North America. The extensive literature on 4-year cycles has been reviewed by Elton (1942) and others, and the significance of the problem has been discussed by Lack (1954) who suggests that the dominant rodent interacts with its vegetable food to produce a predator-prey oscillation, and that when the rodent numbers decline the predatory birds and mammals decrease themselves and thereby allow an increase in the gallinaceous birds. The regularity of the cycles may be because the basic predator-prey oscillations are less disturbed by other factors than in other parts of the world.

Beyond this, it is not at present possible to draw any generalized conclusions. The weakness in Lack's argument lies in his basic assumption that natural selection cannot favour a smaller litter or clutch size. But the most fecund are not necessarily the fittest and natural selection does not act upon the individual more than it does on whole populations. Again, where numbers increase to the point of overcrowding, irruptions or emigrations occur. The apparent paradox that the individuals which actually emigrate seldom survive, so that there seems to be a continual selection against emigration can only be explained by supposing the instinct to emigrate benefits the population as a whole. Consider, for example, two separate populations of the same species, one possessing an emigratory instinct, the other without. When numbers increase beyond the normal control of predators and parasites over-crowding will result and conditions become unfavourable. In the non-migratory population disease and starvation may take a drastic toll, possibly even resulting in extinction: but in the population possessing the necessary instinct, emigration will reduce the population density and thus decrease the spread of epidemics and the effect of food-shortage (see discussion in Cloudsley-Thompson, 1957b). A similar hypothesis has been proposed by Koskimies (1955).

As Carter (1951b) has pointed out, cyclical fluctuations in numbers are a means by which animal populations are adjusted to periodic changes in environmental conditions. Until the population has reached the maximum density that the habitat can support the full effects of predation, starvation and epidemic disease do not come into play. Starvation and epidemics, at least, will weaken all the members of the population and it may be better for the species that a part of the crowded population should migrate and allow those that are left to form a healthy, but less numerous population. If so, emigration is the price that a species with greatly fluctuating numbers pays for the rapid rate of reproduction that allows it to take full and quick advantage of improvements in the environment. Cyclic fluctuations in numbers have two main advantages to a species; they permit correlation of numbers with changes in environmental conditions, and they allow evolutionary change to be more rapid than it would be in a species with constant numbers. This is because while the numbers of a population are increasing, selection is weak since a larger proportion of individuals are able to survive than when numbers are constant: consequently the population becomes more than normally variable. When it reaches its maximum however, this variable population is subjected to natural selection. Any variations that happen to be advantageous are then selected into the genotype. Thus a biological advantage accrues to species whose numbers tend to fluctuate cyclically, in addition to any incidental increase in distribution caused by emigration.

Unless cyclical fluctuations in animal populations have an ultimate biological significance, it is difficult to understand how the phenomenon can persist in nature. The ultimate factors already discussed may, however, be quite different from the direct causal, or proximal, factors which may have been evolved as a result of natural selection and have a more direct influence upon individual animals or groups (Koskimies, 1955). Whereas, in the case of Arctic forms, food may be the ultimate factor that determines the general level of population numbers, Siivonen and Koskimies (1955) have suggested that the regularity of the fluctuations may be governed through an adaptive proximal response to the lunar cycle.

All attempts have failed to find a cause for these rhythms by correlating them with weather conditions, sun-spots and other cosmic factors. Siivonen and Koskimies, however, have described a theoretical mechanism based on the lunar cycle, which makes it possible to explain both the 10-year fluctuation and the 3- to 4-year fluctuation on a common basis. The length of the lunar month is 29.53 days. As the total of the 12 whole lunar months in one year (365.25 days) is 354.4 days or 10.9 days less than a year, the lunar cycle runs each year 10.9 days ahead of that of the preceding year. Thus each moon occurs 10.9 days earlier than its equivalent in the previous year. After a certain number of years, a given phase of the moon must return to the same date as at the beginning of the period. Owing to the length of the lunar cycle, a given phase returns to within 6 days of the same date at intervals of 3–4 years and to within one day every 9.6 years (Fig. 5).

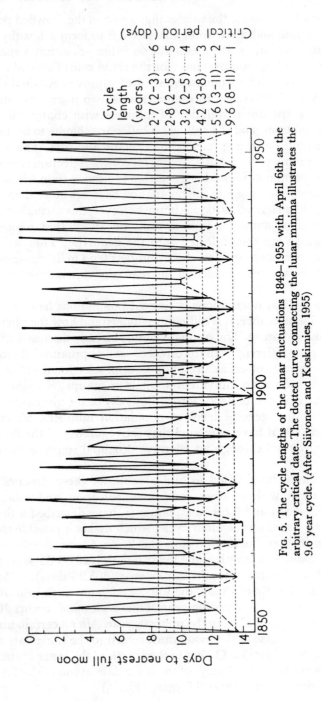

Fig. 5. The cycle lengths of the lunar fluctuations 1849–1955 with April 6th as the arbitrary critical date. The dotted curve connecting the lunar minima illustrates the 9.6 year cycle. (After Siivonen and Koskimies, 1955)

If it is assumed that a certain lunar phase occurs at the time of a certain critical period, depending each spring upon the photoperiod, this would explain the correlation of lunar cycle with the population fluctuation already observed. In view of the known influence of the moon on breeding rhythms discussed in Chapter 3, this hypothesis is by no means unwarranted.

The observed 10-year fluctuation of the varying hare in Canada has, over a century, followed the theoretical lunar fluctuation. Likewise, the 3- to 4-year lemming fluctuation in Norway since the beginning of the present century and the 3- to 4-year fluctuation of game birds in Finland during the past 20 years have shown perfect correspondence with lunar fluctuations.

To summarise: having briefly considered a number of rhythmic and cyclical phenomena at all levels of biological organisation, the only conclusion that can be drawn with any certainty is that although periodicities are apparent throughout living matter, there does not appear to be any common ground between them. It is dangerous to lump together a number of unrelated phenomena under ill-defined names such as rhythmic or cellular activity—a trait as seductive as it is misleading.

CHAPTER 3

Diurnal Rhythms and Animal Ecology: a Review

General Considerations

THE ecological aspects of periodism in animals have been discussed in detail by Allee *et al.* (1949) who point out that the major phenomena of the earth are cyclic. There are geological rhythms in erosion and deposition: study of the annual growth of trees discloses evidence of cycles of climate over the last few thousand years which is supplemented by the deposition of varve clays during the late Pleistocene and early post-Pleistocene periods and there is a rather confusing body of evidence relating to a variety of earthly events from annual precipitation and bird migration to the positive and negative correlation of sun spot cycles. In addition, animal communities show complex seasonal, lunar and tidal rhythms and many periodicities associated with the cycle of day and night. It is with the latter that we shall be concerned in the present chapter.

Diurnal periodicities of the physical environment affect organisms in a number of ways. For example, there is a variation depending on latitude so that in equatorial regions the hours of daylight and darkness are relatively constant throughout the year, while nearer the poles the hours of daylight increase during the summer months and decrease in winter. This aspect of photoperiod is of particular importance in the initiation of diapause and the regulation of breeding cycles. It is also correlated with leaf fall and the fruiting and flowering of plants, thus indirectly affecting herbivorous animals and through them, the carnivores. In addition, length of daylight is associated with light intensity, temperature, relative humidity, rate of evaporation and so on. There are also marked variations in timing and extent of the changes according to locality and habitat. In a continental desert, for example, the difference between day and night temperature may vary considerably, but in the wetter parts of the tropics it is no more than a few degrees. Again, in the upper layers of lakes and oceans the change in light intensity is comparable with that on land, but the temperature remains relatively constant. All these factors play an important part in animal ecology.

Diurnal rhythms of activity in terrestrial animals may be associated with changes in light and darkness, temperature, moisture, food supply etc.; but of these light intensity is usually the most consistent and reliable. Consequently it is not surprising that light often acts as a token stimulus which leads animals to places where other environmental conditions are favourable. In addition to the direct responses of animals to physical changes of the environment, the biological advantages to a species of rhythmic behaviour are often determined by secondary factors. Thus a species may become nocturnal as an adjustment to competition from other species or to escape being eaten: there are many nocturnal forms in tropical forests where competition during the day is particularly severe. As a short-term adjustment, game animals tend to nocturnal habits when much hunted, and rabbits do not come out until nightfall in areas that are often shot over. Conversely, predators must be nocturnal if their prey comes out only at night or they may take their prey at a time when it is least able to defend itself.

The nocturnal habit confers several advantages: enemies are more easily avoided and food more easily obtained; losses of moisture are reduced because the air at night is more nearly saturated; and inter-communication between members of the same species is facilitated, because odours are more readily conveyed. The carnivorous habit is less hazardous, too, at night, and competition is reduced when nocturnal carnivores, such as Carabid beetles prey on sleeping diurnal animals such as butterflies (Floersheim, 1906).

The habits and characteristics of nocturnal animals have been out-lined by Crawford (1934): specialisations involve differences of degree rather than of kind. Luminescence and some adaptations of vision provide the only examples of modifications that are not also useful by day. Absence of light is the most characteristic feature of the nocturnal environment and consequently nocturnal animals show refinements of the sense organs correlated with this. Scent becomes especially important at night for the congregation of individuals, sex attraction, following the prey, location of enemies and so on; hearing and sound-production for communication, the detection of enemies or victims; light production for sex attraction and warning; while eyes may show adaptation such as the development of a reflecting tapetum, a retina rich in rods, an iris with a vertical aperture and so on.

Nocturnal species are frequently primitive. This is particularly apparent in the case of Onychophora (Alexander, 1957) and of insects, of which cockroaches, silver-fish, bristle-tails, stick-insects and crickets are typically nocturnal forms: and the primitive species of more advanced orders are frequently nocturnal also (Kennedy 1928). The same is true, I think, of spiders and other arachnids. Scorpions are markedly nocturnal yet they are extremely resistent to high temperature, drought and other climatic rigours (Cloudsley-Thompson 1956c), so it is probable that their nocturnalism is correlated with ecological rather than physiological requirements. Primitive insects tend to have a lower metabolic rate than more advanced forms; they are usually slow and retiring and live in cool, shady or even dark environments. More highly evolved insects are quicker-moving, diurnal and live in hot light environments.

Again, many nocturnal animals such as elephants, hippopotami, sloths, lemurs and millipedes have long fossil records. So there may be an evolutionary aspect to the problem of nocturnalism (Park, 1940); but studies of the physiology of the vertebrate eye suggests here that diurnality and nocturnality come and go as mutation and ecological expediency direct. The few species which normally live in constant environments such as underground caves and wells are usually non-rhythmic, or at any rate do not show any overt rhythm of activity.

Kennedy (1928) concluded his paper by pointing out that a number of questions arise from this generalisation. For example, if primitive insects are correlated with low environmental intensity, were the Mesozoic tropics cooler and darker than the tropics of today? How did primitive groups cross tropical regions and what type of insects occupied hot tropical situations? The answer, I believe, is that in each case the more primitive species have become secondarily adapted to a nocturnal habitat as a result of competition with more efficient types. They may well have evolved from diurnal forms and there is no need to postulate that the tropics of the Mesozoic period were cooler than those of today. Indeed, this would seem to be extremely unlikely (Cloudsley-Thompson, 1953c, 1954a, 1956b).

Clark (1914) pointed out that strictly nocturnal birds and mammals tend to have a larger size than diurnal types and have zoogeographical affinities quite different from those of diurnal forms which occupy the same area. He also draws attention to the fact that predacious mammals and birds may become secondarily nocturnal and capture their prey at a time when it is least able to defend itself, while many herbivorous mammals are nocturnal in habit, thereby avoiding water-loss, overheating and the attentions of diurnal blood-sucking insects such as *Simulium* spp. *Glossina* spp. and Tabanidae.

Not only are many factors involved, but these may influence one another. Some nocturnal animals are never active in the daytime, while others can alter their habits in different circumstances. Thus the African buffalo was very abundant until, in 1890, a terrible epidemic of rinderpest almost exterminated them in many places. Whereas previously the animals used to feed in herds in the open by day, the survivors retired to forests and dense swamps, feeding only at night. After a number of years, however, buffaloes increased considerably and returned to their former diurnal behaviour. The change produced in the habits of game animals by hunting has already been mentioned.

Another factor to be considered is that although many species are active during a certain period of the day or night and are quiescent for the remainder of the 24-hours, others exhibit different kinds of activity at different times. Many normally diurnal birds migrate at night. The water-skater *Gerris rufoscutellatus* spends the daytime on the surface of ponds and streams, but flies from one locality to another mostly at night. Apparently there must be a certain amount of light during these migrations which is in agreement with the fact that the species is positively phototactic. There is no evidence that the insects migrate on dark nights, but only in moonlight or starlight (Riley, 1925). Similarly many other aquatic insects such as water beetles fly mostly at night, but swim actively throughout the day. Many Acrididae, which have definitely diurnal habits, are attracted to light and must therefore fly at night (Rockwood, 1925).

Despite the complexity of the numerous ecological aspects of the phenomenon of diurnal periodicity in terrestrial animals, it is possible nevertheless to draw certain general conclusions. Animals may be nocturnal as a response to the physical conditions of the environment and thereby avoid the rigours of the daylight hours. This is especially apparent in desert regions where climatic changes between day and night are particularly great (Buxton, 1923; Cloudsley-Thompson, 1956a; Williams, 1954). Thus many desert animals such as centipedes, spiders, scorpions, mites, ants, beetles and other insects, snails, lizards and snakes avoid the extreme mid day heat, drought and ultra-violet light by hiding under rocks and stones or in cracks in the ground. They soon die if taken from their burrows and placed on the hot sand. Birds take refuge in the leaf-base and young shoots of palm trees, or in bushes and camel scrub.

The second main ecological factor responsible for nocturnal habits is probably competition, as a result of which vulnerable and primitive forms especially, tend to become nocturnal.

Finally there is a smaller group of highly specialised animal, whose food is more readily available at night, which has acquired a nocturnal behaviour pattern in response to this.

In the case of aquatic animals the ecological significance of diurnal rhythms is far less clear. In most cases it is probably related to the vertical migration of the plankton which is considered elsewhere (p. 46) and to other aspects of food chains. Most sea-shore animals have a marked rhythm correlated with the state of the tide and therefore related to the lunar day of 24 hours 50 minutes (see p. 35), but obviously the time of day of exposure at low tide will have a considerable effect upon the littoral fauna.

DIURNAL RHYTHMS IN LOWER ANIMALS

Whereas, according to Calhoun (1944), no studies have been conducted primarily dealing with diurnal locomotory rhythms in the Protozoa, there exists some data concerning cyclic reproductive and feeding habits which are important to note in seeking a homogeneous explanation of the existence of 24-hour physiological or locomotor activities. For example, in continuous darkness *Paramoecium* shows an increasing rate of division during the day with a peak in late afternoon and a minimum just before sun rise. This curve of division exactly parallels that of the temperature curve of the water: experiments have shown that an increase of temperature causes an increase in division-rate irrespective of the time of day (Kalmus, 1935). The rhythm is therefore environment-dependent, and depends upon compensation factors of individual growth such as cell plasma relationship, relative surface and so on.

In fact, nearly all protozoan rhythms have been shown to be exogenous, although a few cases of apparently endogenous rhythms have been recorded. Thus Pohl (1948) found that *Euglena gracilis* has a rhythm of phototactic sensitivity which persists in continuous darkness and this has been confirmed by Bruce and Pittendrigh (1956). The environment-independent diurnal rhythms of *Gonyaulax polyedra* are discussed below (p. 194).

The striking periodicity of reproduction found in several species of *Plasmodium* has naturally led to speculations regarding its nature and mechanism. The problem has been complicated, however, by the diversity of periodicities found in different species or strains. Some show little or no periodicity, others have cycles of 48, 36, 24 or 12 hours. No doubt the length of the cycle is largely determined by the genetical constitution of the parasite, but the time of segmentation and the synchronism of reproduction are determined by the host. That there may be some interaction between host and parasite is indicated by the fact that if only the host factor were involved, all parasites would show 24-hour rhythms, whereas if the host played no part, each strain might be expected to have a different type of infection. In fact, most strains of malaria have synchronous rhythms which are multiples of 24 hours.

The literature on the subject has been reviewed by Stauber (1939) who has studied the factors influencing the asexual periodicity of three strains of *Plasmodium cathemerium* and one strain of *P. relictum* var. *matutinum*, parasitic in the blood of the canary *Serinus canarius*. As a result of this work it was shown that the synchronous periodicity of reproduction of the malarial parasite was affected by alternate 12-hour periods of high and low temperature. It was also indirectly influenced by the effect of light on the eyes, but not on the body surface of the host, since birds have a diurnal cycle of temperature which rises during the hours of light and drops during the dark, or rest period.

Stauber found that when the host was subjected to normal light conditions, *P. cathemerium* showed a peak of segmentation at the beginning of the dark period; but if parasites from this host were innoculated into canaries which had been subjected to reversed lighting for 15 days, the peak of segmentation immediately become synchronised with the new dark period. When the host was kept in continuous light for two weeks or more, the rhythm of reproduction in the parasite tended to disappear, but it reappeared if the birds were subjected to rhythmic feeding periods, because then their times of rest also became rhythmic.

The periodicity did not appear to be directly affected by the feeding of the host, and it was concluded that in all probability the host furnishes a set of critical temperature conditions, dependent upon its period of rest, which are responsible for orienting the time of segmentation of its parasite. It has also been found that lengthening a bird's day artificially to 28 hours results in an increased period between the peaks of segmentation, but the time of the peak shifts from the late evening to early morning hours.

An interesting parallel is afforded by the microfilaria larvae of *Wuchereria bancrofti*, the organism responsible for elephantiasis. The adults of this nematode worm inhabit the lymphatic vessels of man, whereas the microfilariae inhabit the blood-stream. They are rarely found in the blood during the day, but towards evening appear in increasing numbers. By midnight there may be as many as 40 or 50 millions in the circulatory system of the patient. The number decreases during the later part of the night and by about 9.0 a.m. they have again disappeared from the peripheral blood. This diurnal periodicity may be maintained with the utmost regularity for ten years or more, but if the patient is made to sleep during the day and remain awake at night the rhythm of the microfilariae becomes reversed in three or four days. This has also been demonstrated in *Dirofilaria immitis* by Hinman (1936).

Hawking and Thurston (1951a, b) have recently shown that periodicity of microfilariae in the blood of monkeys naturally infected by a worm of the genus *Dirofilaria* is due to the fact that during the day time the parasites disappear from the blood stream and accumulate in the lungs. Earlier theories by which the periodicity was explained by postulating cyclical parturition of the female filariae with a daily destruction of all the embryos synchronised by rhythmic changes of temperature in the host are now recognised as untenable, for the periodicity persists when microfilariae are transferred intravenously into a new host so that no adults are present (Hawking, 1953). The increase of microfilariae in the blood at night is not a spurious effect due merely to congregation of the organisms in the capillaries of the skin, but is a true increase affecting all the circulating blood. Accumulation in the lung, the active phase, is due to an active response of the microfilariae to some unidentified stimulus provided by the 24-hour physiological rhythms of the host. In the passive phase, the microfilariae are distributed throughout the blood.

In patients infected with *W. bancrofti*, the microfilarial count at night is rapidly diminished by the breathing of oxygen, by muscular exercise and by hyperventilation. With *Loa loa* on the other hand, the count is not affected by these stimuli (McFadzean and Hawking, 1956).

Filarial periodicity has yet to be satisfactorily explained. Hawking (1955) has suggested that the optimum site for microfilariae consists of the capillaries and small vessels of the lungs. Here the parasites hold themselves during the active phase of their 24-hour cycle and they are liberated and distributed throughout all the circulation, thus appearing in the peripheral blood stream. The accumulation of microfilariae in the pulmonary vessels and their discharge depends upon an active response to some stimulus provided by the small physiological changes which occur in most of the constituents and systems of the body during its 24-hour cycle, but the actual physiological change involved is not yet known. That the orientation of the cycle of *L. loa* microfilariae to the patient's daily habits, rather than to the movements of earth and sun, is illustrated by the fact that the microfilarial cycle of patients from Kumba town, British Cameroons, is about four hours later than that of prisoners in the local jail who get up and go to bed earlier than the townsfolk.

The 24-hour periodicity of microfilariae is clearly an adaptation to the biting cycle of the insect vector. Thus *Loa loa* which is transmitted by diurnal blood-sucking horse-flies, *Chrysops* spp., circulates in the peripheral blood by day and migrates to the lungs at night, whilst *W. bancrofti*, of which the intermediate host is the nocturnal mosquito *Culex fatigans*, circulates in the peripheral blood at night. At the same time some strains of *W. bancrofti* are non-periodic and others show reversed periodicity where the intermediate host is a day-biting mosquito. For example, in the Philippines, Fiji and Samoa, the vector of the parasite is the diurnal mosquito *Aedes variegatus* and in these regions the larvae of *W. bancrofti* are present in the peripheral circulation both during the day and at night, although 43 per cent occur between 18.00 and 02.00 hours and practically none from 10.00 to 14.00 hours. (Belding, 1941; Manson-Bahr, 1948). For the same reason it cannot be that the movement of the microfilariae through the cutaneous blood-vessels is obstructed least when the body is fatigued, as some authors have suggested.

This would indicate that the vector may determine the rhythm of the parasite, and that the rhythm persists when the latter is transferred to its vertebrate host. Harker (1958a) suggests that it is possible that both vector and host affect the rhythm and that the host will have the over-riding effect if normal conditions are altered. In that case, the reversal of the parasite rhythm by reversal of the host's rhythm is no different from the many cases in which rhythms continue with precision over long periods in an unchanged environment, and yet can be altered by new environmental conditions.

Daily periodic changes in the frequency of swimming movements have been found in the medusae of Coelenterates, although the rhythmic contraction of the umbrella is associated with respiration and is in-dependent of day and night. The sea-anemone *Actinia equina* is non-rhythmic in places where the tides are small; when uncovered at low tide it shows an activity rhythm which persists for several days under constant conditions provided the fluctuation of the environmental factors exceeds a threshold value (see discussion by Calhoun, 1944). Indeed, most sea-shore animals have a marked rhythm correlated with the state of the tide as we shall see in the following chapter. At low tide they are inactive and they are activated by the force of the waves. In the laboratory a rhythm of sensitivity to mechanical shaking persists in periwinkles, *Littorina* spp., for several days. The little green flatworms, *Convoluta roscoffensis*, which owe their colour to the presence of symbiotic algae in their tissues, come to the surface of the sand in great numbers during high tide. At low tide they descend into the sand as it dries. When placed in an aquarium in which vertical glass tubes are substituted for their burrows, their reversal of geotaxis continues unabated for as long as eight days in close co-ordination with the changes of tide in the ocean (Bohn, 1903). A similar endogenous rhythm has been demonstrated in marine annelid worms such as *Nereis diversicolor*. Tidal rhythms in the chromatophores of Crustacea are discussed below (Chapter 6).

It is readily observable that earthworms are nocturnal in habit and tend to avoid the light. Their rhythm of activity has been established experimentally by Baldwin (1917) and Szymanski (1918a), and persists in both halves of a worm that has been bisected, but it has not yet been determined whether or not the rhythm is endogenous. Leeches, *Glossi-phonia stagnalis*, too, have been shown to be active at night and inactive during the day, but under constant conditions they at once become arhythmic.

Recently, Ralph (1957) has investigated the oxygen consumption of *Lumbricus terrestris* and described both diurnal and lunar cycles, while Arbit (1957) has shown that the diurnal cycle plays a significant role in the rate at which worms can learn to turn to the left or right when placed in a T tube. One arm of the tube was lined with sand-paper and contained copper wires through which an electrical shock of one volt could be administered, the other led into a beaker containing moist earth and moss. A group of worms trained between 20.00 and 24.00 hours learned significantly more quickly than a group trained between 08.00 and 12.00 hours. There was little evidence of a neurological pacemaker as occurs in lug-worms (see p. 167).

In general, the Mollusca do not show marked rhythms of activity and rest. In slugs and snails exogenous rhythms of activity have been shown to be correlated with environmental factors, especially temperature and humidity, and disappear immediately under constant conditions. There is a tendency towards arhythmicity or at least prolonged activity. The periods of inactivity that do occur tend to be associated with unfavourable conditions (Calhoun, 1944).

More recently, Dainton (1954) has shown that in the slug, *Agrolimax reticulatus*, activity is induced by falling temperatures and suppressed by rising temperatures between 4° and 20°C. Temperature changes as slight as 0.1°C per hour are appreciated. The daily rhythm of activity and rest thus follows the normal diurnal rhythm of falling temperature by night and rising temperature by day, except when daytime mists and showers impose a minor fluctuation and result in daytime activity. No activity is observed on continuously wet days, which are normally without such fluctuations. Between 20° and 30°C activity is induced by rising temperatures and suppressed by falling temperatures. This response is not nearly so sensitive as that to falling temperatures below 20°C. It does, however, enable the animals to escape a rapidly rising temperature that might be caused by the midday sun, and which could otherwise soon become lethal. Thus slugs are normally active at night when atmospheric humidity rises. Experiments proved that no response to humidity occurs, and this was confirmed by field observations. But since slugs are found at rest in damp situations beneath stones and vegetation it is hardly possible that they could be aware of humidity changes occurring in the air above. It is also difficult to envisage how any form of hygroreception could register anything but saturation on a wet-skinned animal. Clearly a land snail withdrawn into its shell or a contracted slug can be likened to an arthropod with a water-proof wax-layer (see p. 52), whilst its water-relations when it is crawling about will resemble those of a woodlouse.

DIURNAL MIGRATIONS IN PLANKTON

Diurnal movements are a characteristic feature of the behaviour of free-swimming, planktonic animals. In contrast to the various aspects of 24-hour periodicity discussed above, the vertical diurnal migrations of planktonic organisms are so well documented and understood that I do not propose to consider them more than briefly. For further details the reviews of Cushing (1951), Kikuchi (1930), Rose (1925) and Russell (1927) should be consulted.

In general it may be said that most planktonic animals avoid strong light, each species showing a preference for a certain strength of light to which it is adapted. For this reason, few animals are to be found on the surface layers of the sea during the hours of daylight but are distributed at various depths according to their specific light responses. On the approach of dusk, however, they all begin to swim upwards to the surface layers. That is why fish like herrings, which prey on plankton, also come to the surface of the sea at nightfall. Consequently this is the time when fishermen shoot their drift nets. Later, when all is dark and there is no light stimulus, planktonic animals tend to scatter. They migrate to the surface again at daybreak and later move downwards as the light strengthens.

The first published account of the diurnal migrations of planktonic animals may be that of Baron Cuvier (1817) who wrote in his book *La règne animale* that in the morning and evening and even on cloudy days, Daphniae generally station themselves on the surface, but that during the heat of the day they seek the depths of the water.

As Russell (1927) described the situation: "It would seem that in fairly homogeneous waters light intensity may be the factor of prime importance governing the distribution of the different species, though other factors such as temperature and salinity may play their part, perhaps in altering the sensitivity of the animal to light. Rate of movement must be an important factor in the various sudden changes in vertical distribution exhibited, and the distribution of food is not to be ignored".

That the physiological responses to these different factors may affect one another has been known for several years. For example, McGinnis (1911) found that after exposure to darkness varying from 12 hours to 6 weeks, *Branchipus serratus* still responded positively to light showing positive geotaxis. In darkness, however, the animals exhibited negative geotaxis. An avoidance was also shown of temperatures outside the range 14 to 17°C.

Again, Dice (1914) studied the reactions of *Daphnia pulex* to various factors such as light, gravity, temperature, chemicals, mechanical stimuli and so on in relation to vertical movements. He found that an increase in temperature has a tendency to cause a decrease in positive phototaxis, while a decrease tends to make the animals more strongly positive. Below 12°C individuals are positive to all intensities of light. Increase of light intensity with high temperatures causes a tendency towards positive geotaxis, while decrease in light intensity and low temperatures engender negative geotaxis. As a result of this work, Dice concluded that reversal of geotaxis with change of light intensity is a predominating cause in affecting the diurnal vertical movements of *Daphnia pulex*. He regarded phototaxis as an accessory factor which determines the upper and lower limits of vertical distribution.

A few years later, Eyden (1923) observed that *Daphnia pulex* was to be found in greatest abundance at the shallow margin of a pond just before sunrise, but was most scarce in this water 2 hours earlier. She established that the specific gravity of the animal varies at different periods of the day and night, attaining a maximum shortly after sunrise and reaching a less defined minimum about midday, and concluded that changes in specific gravity must be taken into consideration when investigating the causes of the vertical distribution of plankton.

Fox (1925) showed that *Paramoecium* sp. and Echinoid larvae under certain environmental conditions swim downwards in light and upwards in darkness, the most effective rays being the ultra-violet. He therefore concluded that the phenomenon of vertical migration already described by various authors in arthropods exists not only among animals swimming by muscular movements, but in organisms moving by ciliary action.

Diurnal migrations occur even among deep water animals, as Welsh, Chace and Nunnemacher (1937) have shown. These authors found that the movements of the most abundant species in the Sargasso Sea are obviously related to day and night. Moreover, the lower limit of the penetration of daylight of an intensity significant in determining the vertical distribution of animals (*c.* 1,000 m. in clear water) is correlated with marked changes in temperature, salinity, oxygen and phosphates. They concluded that a combination of factors is doubtless responsible for keeping the majority of the macroplankton above 1,000 m. in this region but did not speculate as to which, if any, is the most important.

In an important and extensive article, Rose (1925) placed the various factors responsible for diurnal migration in the following order: 1. Light which clearly dominates under average conditions; 2. Temperature which becomes very important and can even overwhelm the effect of light when it exceeds 20°C; 3. Other factors such as salinity, aeration, etc.

The actual mechanisms by which organisms keep themselves at the optimum level may be phototaxis, geotaxis or acceleration or inhibition of movement. It may be a combination of all. From the evidence of laboratory experiments, it would seem to differ in different species. "The important point is that the mechanism, whatever it may be, brings the animals into their region of optimum illumination; and by illumination is meant composition as well as intensity of light, owing to the selective absorption of the water." (Russell, 1927).

In a recent review of vertical migrations in planktonic Crustacea, Cushing (1951) has shown that the cycle consists of four parts: ascent from the day-depth, midnight sinking, and dawn rise, followed by descent to the daytime depth. These different aspects of migration are part of a single, continuous process. Ascent in the evening and descent in the morning are related to decreasing and increasing penetration of daylight. The midnight sinking is probably the result of the passive state of the organisms in full darkness while the dawn rise represents a return by the animals to optimum light intensity. This is supported by the fact that the order in time of arrival at the surface for some fresh-water species is the same as the order in depth at which they are found in full daylight. Migration between periods of complete darkness may be occasioned by photokinesis, phototaxis or by a combination of these mechanisms.

Harris and Wolfe (1955) have recently shown that a population of *Daphnia magna* in a tank filled with a suspension of indian ink in tap water, will undergo a complete cycle of vertical migration. A 'dawn rise' to the surface at low light intensity is followed by the descent of the animals to a characteristic maximum depth. The animals rise to the surface again as the light decreases and finally show a typical midnight sinking. The light intensities at the level of the animals are of the same order as those reported in field observations (Fig. 6).

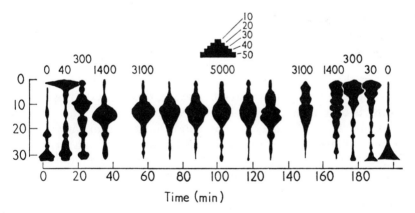

FIG. 6. The distribution of fifty individuals of the water flea, *Daphnia magna*, through a laboratory cycle of vertical migration. Figures below the diagram represent time in minutes from the start of rise of voltage; those above indicate the intensity at the surface in lux. Each polygon is the sum of five observations separated by 1 minute intervals, and thus represents 250 positions measured. A cycle of 3 hours with a maximum light intensity of 5,000 lux. (After Harris and Wolfe, 1955)

The upward and downward movements which follow the lowering and raising of the light intensity are both active responses and the downward movement is not merely a passive sinking.

In light of low intensity, as at 'dawn', a photokinetic response which leads to the rise of the animals in the water is not associated with the direction of the light source. At high light intensity, however, there is an orientation response superimposed upon an alternating photokinetic phase and a negative phase during which movement is inhibited.

Animals from which the eyes have been removed still exhibit the photokinetic response including an inhibition of movement at high light intensity, but no phototactic response. Consequently such animals can carry out a vertical migration determined solely by light intensity (Harris and Mason, 1956). Nevertheless, there is no evidence to show any endogenous factor in the rhythm.

It is probable that the diurnal periodicity of movement in planktonic animals is largely, if not entirely exogenous. Obviously many different factors are responsible for these movements. As Russell (1927) points out in his review, each planktonic animal probably has its own vertical zone in which it finds conditions most favourable. This zone varies, not only for different species, but for individuals of different ages and stages of development of the same species. The distribution of any one species may vary too, from place to place, season to season and day to day.

He adds, "The question of a physiological rhythm is of interest. It seems, however, almost to be expected that such should occur, but it is, of course, brought on primarily by the periodic changes of the environment. The physiological rhythm is not responsible for the diurnal movements; it is the environmental changes that bring about the periodic movement and thereby set up in the animal a physiological rhythm. It is, therefore, natural to expect such 'habits' to show themselves for a period in the laboratory after the stimuli of the external environment have been removed. One would not imagine, then, that the physiological rhythm is of much importance in nature except in that it makes the animal 'ready' for the environmental changes when they occur."

I have quoted this paragraph in full because, although written over 30 years ago, it coincides exactly with my own outlook on the subject of the biological advantage of many physiological 24-hour periodicities.

It would seem that the diurnal migrations of planktonic animals, primarily in response to changes of light intensity, are ecologically related to the movements of phytoplankton which forms the base of their food chain. This, in turn, is related to the optimum light intensity for photosynthesis.

Optimum light intensity may be an important factor in influencing the vertical migration of planktonic organisms, but a number of other factors are also involved. Some animals which usually stay down in the daytime may occasionally be seen at the surface in bright sunshine. And it is clear from the results of tow-netting at different levels that not all individuals in a population react in the same way to one particular set of conditions. Even though the majority may migrate upwards, a proportion usually remains below.

Hardy (1956) discusses the matter in some detail and suggests that vertical migration may have been evolved because it gives the animal concerned a continual change of environment which would otherwise be unattainable for a passively drifting creature. Water masses hardly ever move at the same speed at different depths, for the surface areas are nearly always faster travelling than the lower layers. So, although by swimming in a horizontal direction an animal will not get much change of environment in the sea, by moving upwards and downwards it may achieve an extensive degree of horizontal movement.

Hardy (1956) has also proposed an hypothesis of "animal exclusion" to account for some of the observed phenomena of plankton migration. According to this, the distributional relationship between animals and plants may be due to a modification in the vertical migration of the former in relation to dense concentrations of the latter. Most animals, it is supposed, would come up to feed in the dense phytoplankton zones for a short time only, possibly because of some antibiotic effect, and would therefore tend to become distributed in larger numbers in other areas. On the other hand, the animals which stay up longest in the phytoplankton would naturally remain more concentrated in these regions. This explanation is largely hypothetical, although certain flagellates are known to have a poisonous effect.

Alternatively, animals may become concentrated by modified vertical migration in regions rich in phytoplankton, graze there for a while, and then move to other areas by vertical migration. That the vertical diurnal migration of plankton has important adaptive functions is clear from its ubiquity, but the exact nature of these has yet to be assessed.

DIURNAL RHYTHMS AND WATER-RELATIONS
IN TERRESTRIAL ARTHROPODA

The terrestrial Arthropoda can be roughly divided on an ecological basis into two main groups. The first includes woodlice, centipedes, millipedes and their allies which, in dry air lose water rapidly by transpiration through their integuments (Cloudsley-Thompson, 1950; 1956c etc.; Edney, 1957). Consequently they are restricted by reflex behaviour mechanisms to damp, dark habitats which they leave only at night when the temperature falls and the relative humidity of the atmosphere increases (Cloudsley-Thompson, 1954a, b; 1955a; 1956b, d; 1958a, b, etc.).

The second group includes most insects and arachnids; these are comparatively independent of moist surroundings because their integument possesses an impervious layer of wax which prevents desiccation. They are discussed below (p. 57).

Many nocturnal terrestrial forms such as woodlice, centipedes and millipedes possess a clear endogenous 24-hour periodicity and emerge from the comparatively constant conditions within their daytime retreats under stones, bark, logs and fallen leaves, under the stimulus provided by some internal physiological chronometer.

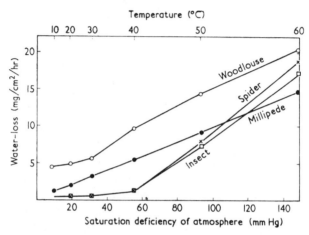

FIG. 7. Rate of water-loss in dry air at different temperatures, and corresponding saturation deficiencies, from a woodlouse (*Porcellio*), millipede (*Oxidus*), spider (*Lycosa*) and insect (*Pieris* larva). In the woodlouse and millipede the rate of water-loss is proportional to the saturation deficiency of the atmosphere, but in the spider and insect it is negligible below about 40°C, the critical temperature at which their epicuticular wax-layers become porous. Rate of water-loss is expressed in milligrams per square centimetre of surface area per hour. (After Cloudsley-Thompson, 1955a)

In the case of the small British millipedes *Blaniulus guttulatus* and *Oxidus gracilis*, an exogenous diurnal rhythm is primarily a response to light and darkness, the degree of nocturnal activity being correlated with the stimulus of falling temperature at dusk (Cloudsley-Thompson, 1951a, b) and no endogenous activity has been observed. In the large West African species *Oxydesmus platycercus* and *Ophistreptus* sp., however, aktograph experiments have demonstrated an endogenous rhythm independent of fluctuating light and temperature and persisting for as long as 19 days in constant light and temperature. Locomotory activity is stimulated both by increases and by decreases of temperature and it is suggested that temperature fluctuations may be of primary importance in the synchronisation of the animals' activities with day and night, for the effect of light on their activity is slight and is perhaps an insignificant environmental factor in their natural gloomy habitat in tropical forests.

On the other hand, in the woodlouse *Oniscus asellus* an endogenous diurnal locomotory rhythm is correlated primarily with alternating light and darkness, and not with fluctuating temperature or humidity (Cloudsley-Thompson, 1952a). In this case, light is the 'clue' or 'synchroniser' which keeps the rhythm of the animal in phase with that of the environment. These points have been discussed in greater detail elsewhere (p. 5). Here it will be sufficient merely to indicate that in different nocturnal species occupying the same type of habitat during the day, emergence at night may be achieved by different types of physiological mechanism which serve the same function of bringing the animals into the open when darkness has fallen, temperature is lower and relative humidity higher than during the day.

By means of choice-chamber apparatus it has been found that the intensity of the humidity response of the woodlice is less in darkness than in light and still less in the nocturnal phase: it increases with desiccation.

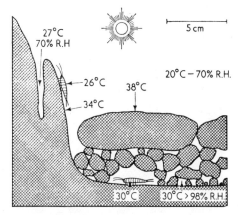

FIG. 8. Vertical section of the base of a red sandstone cliff and shingle inhabited by the marine woodlouse *Ligia oceanica* (diagrammatic) to show the microclimatic conditions and internal temperatures of the animals at 14.00 hrs. G.M.T. in August 1951. (After Edney, 1954)

Movement away from light is more marked in animals which have been in darkness for some time, and is still initially shown in dry air, whereas control animals move towards the light where humidity is sufficiently reduced. Finally, the active phase is correlated with increased sensitivity to external conditions such as the carbon dioxide content of the air.

These experimental results can be related to the nocturnal ecology of the species. Woodlice are often to be seen wandering in dry places at night: as we have seen, they spend the daytime under stones, logs and in other damp, dark situations where environmental conditions are relatively constant. If nightfall involved only a reduction of the factors which normally operate to restrict them to their daytime habitats, it seems unlikely that they would have any occasion to leave them. The endogenous diurnal rhythm, however, will engender locomotory activity in some individuals at least at nightfall when they are especially sensitive and easily disturbed. Even if the majority are exposed to daylight only occasionally, this may be sufficient to maintain their periodicity and keep it in phase with the 24-hour cycle (Cloudsley-Thompson, 1952a).

Field observations on *P. scaber* have indicated a shortening in the time of activity as the days lengthen to midsummer and also a lack of any clear relationship between activity and changes in temperature or relative humidity (Brereton, 1957).

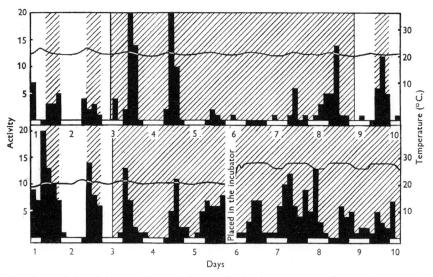

Fig. 9. Activity of the woodlouse *Oniscus asellus* in damp surroundings under natural lighting and in darkness at room temperature; and later in darkness at room temperature followed by artificially fluctuating temperature reaching a minimum during the day. (After Cloudsley-Thompson, 1952a)

The decrease in the intensity of the humidity response at night enables woodlice to walk in dry places where they are never to be found during the day, and the increased photo-negative response after they have been conditioned to darkness ensures that they get under cover promptly at daybreak and thus avoid many potential predators. On the other hand, if their daytime habitat should dry up, the woodlice are not restrained there until they die of desiccation since they tend to become photo-positive in dry air and thus are able to wander in the light until they find some other damp hiding place and again become photo-negative (Cloudsley-Thompson 1952a).

Even the desert woodlouse, *Hemilepistus reaumuri*, has a 24-hour periodicity and water-relations essentially similar to those of woodlice from temperate regions. Although this species can withstand hot, dry conditions for some considerable time there is no 'critical temperature' to indicate the presence of a cuticular layer of water-proofing wax (Cloudsley-Thompson, 1956c).

The rate of water-loss by transpiration in a number of British species of woodlouse has been investigated by Edney (1951, 1954, 1957). They have been shown to stand in the following order: *Philoscia muscorum* > *Oniscus asellus* > *Porcellio scaber* > *Armadillidium vulgare*.

At temperatures just above freezing the intensities of the reaction to humidity of all species are much reduced and do not differ significantly from one another. At higher temperatures (30°C) the humidity responses of *Ph. muscorum* and *O. asellus* are again somewhat reduced, and it is suggested that this may be associated with a lower thermal death point and the need to effect a reduction in body temperature by evaporation (Cloudsley-Thompson, 1956b).

The humidity responses of woodlice are shown to be correlated with

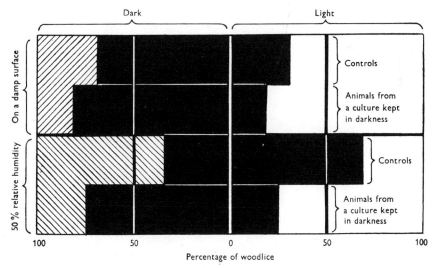

FIG. 10. Responses of *Oniscus asellus* to light, on a damp surface and at 50 per cent relative humidity. Controls and animals kept in darkness for some days previously (in the nocturnal phase of activity). The latter are more strongly photo-negative and do not become photo-positive in dry air. (After Cloudsley-Thompson, 1952a)

saturation deficiency rather than with relative humidity. The specific sense organs are concerned with the appreciation of humidity and the response is probably engendered as a result of desiccation. It may result from the influence of increased concentration of the body fluids stimulating proprioceptors (Waloff, 1941).

Ph. muscorum is the most strongly photo-negative of the four species and there is a graduation through *O. asellus* and *P. scaber* to *A. vulgare* which is the least so. *Ph. muscorum* has been shown by means of aktograph apparatus to be the most intensely nocturnal in habit, *A. vulgare* the least. It is therefore suggested that the degree of nocturnal activity may be correlated with the ability to withstand water-loss by transpiration (Cloudsley-Thompson, 1956d).

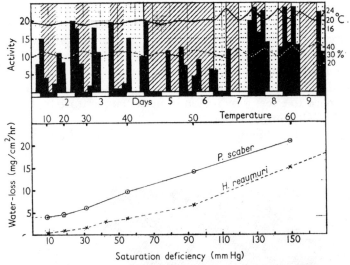

FIG. 11. *Above.* Diurnal rhythm of the desert woodlouse *Hemilepistus reaumuri* at first in normal daylight and darkness, then in constant darkness and finally under conditions of artificial lighting in an 18-hour cycle and a 24-hour cycle of reversed illumination. *Below.* Rate of water-loss in mg./cm.²/hr. in dry air at different temperatures and saturation deficiences of *H. reaumuri* compared with *Porcellio scaber.* (After Cloudsley-Thompson, 1956c)

Finally, it has been shown by measurements with a sensitive anemometer that the nocturnal emergence of woodlice in nature is inhibited by wind. This may well be because air currents tend to remove the shell of moist air that surrounds the transpiring animal (Cloudsley-Thompson, 1958c). The relationship between wind-speed and the number of woodlice wandering abroad at night applies only above a minimum threshold temperature of about 5.5°C, however.

Insects and arachnids, which possess an impervious epicuticular layer of wax, are mostly active in the daytime. But an integument completely impervious to water vapour would also be impervious to oxygen and carbon dioxide. A respiratory mechanism has therefore had to be evolved which permits gaseous exchange without excessive water-loss. Indeed, each aspect of adaptation to life on land affects and is affected by other aspects. For example, if the integument is rigid and provides support, then growth becomes impossible except by moulting and this limits size. Size is also limited where the respiratory system consists of tracheae and tracheoles The physiology of nutrition and excretion are closely concerned with water conservation. Superimposed upon such basic morphological and physiological requirements are the numerous concomitants of behaviour and ecology, for orientation and behaviour mechanisms must also be evolved to retain organisms in environments to which they are suited, to find food, mate and, indeed, carry out the functions essential to their continued existence.

The conflict between the incompatible requirements of respiratory exchange and prevention of water-loss has been illustrated by a comparison of the spiders *Amaurobius* (= *Ciniflo*) *ferox* and *A. similis* (Cloudsley-Thompson, 1957a). Although there is some overlap in their territories, *A. similis* tends to inhabit somewhat drier environments than *A. ferox*.

Aktograph experiments indicate that both species are nocturnal in habit, over 90 per cent of their activity taking place during the hours of darkness. When their water-relations are considered, however, it is found that there is a critical temperature at approximately 35°C above which both species quickly lose water by evaporation in dry air, but below this *A. ferox* loses water more rapidly through its lung-books than does *A. similis*. The rate is almost doubled in both species when 10 per cent carbon dioxide is present, as this keeps the lung-books open. Conversely, the length of time of survival in air of 50 per cent relative humidity and in dry air is longer in *A. similis* than in *A. ferox*, death ensuing when from 20 to 25 per cent of total weight has been lost by evaporation.

A. similis 'tires' more rapidly than *A. ferox* when forced to run at full speed without stopping, but both species can run for long periods when supplied with oxygen. *A. ferox* becomes anaesthetized more quickly in ether vapour and has the larger number of leaves in its lung-books. Its greater 'stamina', therefore, depends upon a proportionately larger respiratory surface acquired at the expense of greater dependence upon environmental humidity.

Diurnal rhythms of locomotory activity in animals are especially marked in desert regions where the climatic changes between day and

c

night are particularly great (Buxton, 1923, 1924a, b; Cloudsley-Thompson, 1954a, 1956c; Kachkarov and Korovine, 1942; Williams, 1954 etc.). Microclimatic readings have indicated a considerable reduction in temperature fluctuations in the daytime retreats of deserticolous forms. For example, Williams showed that in August whilst the surface of the sand in a wadi near Cairo varied from 17.5° to 58.2°C, at a depth of 18 cms. the range was only 29.3° to 37.8°C; whilst the effect

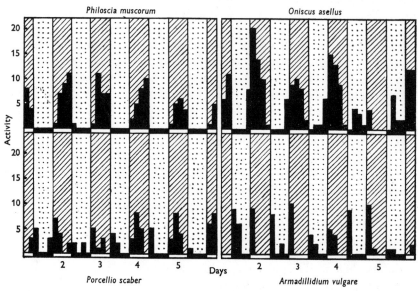

FIG. 12. Locomotory activity of woodlice in aktograph exposed to alternating light and darkness. The light periods from 18.00 to 06.00 hrs. are indicated by stippling, the dark periods from 06.00 hrs. to 18.00 hrs. by hatching. The percentage of locomotory activity that took place during the periods of darkness, based on at least five 5-day experiments with different individuals of each species was *Ph. muscorum*, 92%; *O. asellus*, 77%; *P. scaber*, 71% and *A. vulgare*, 60%. (After Cloudsley-Thompson, 1956d)

of shading was to lower the surface temperatures some 20°C. Buxton found that the surface of clay desert in southern Israel rose about 20°C beyond the shade temperature and quoted a daily range of temperature from —0.5° to 37.2°C in December at Bir Milgha in Southern Tripoli. Further examples of this kind can be obtained from the publications referred to above.

In addition to the considerable reduction in temperature extremes between day and night, only a few centimetres down a hole or within a small cave, a time-lag occurs in these sheltered habitats so that when their inhabitants emerge at dusk they may actually be leaving a warmer for a cooler environment.

In hot climates, survival depends upon avoiding desiccation and keeping cool. Consequently where water is in short supply, there must inevitably be a conflict between the requirements of conserving water for vital purposes and of transpiring it for cooling. Arthropods are too small to withstand transpiration for long and therefore can exist only by avoiding extreme desert conditions. Their physiological adaptations to desert habitats involve changes in degree rather than the evolution of new mechanisms. Thus, the behavioural responses and water-relations of the desert woodlice, *Hemilepistus reaumuri*, and of centipedes such as *Scolopendra clavipes* of North Africa are essentially similar to those of species from temperate regions.

Scorpions, however, present a more difficult problem. *Euscorpius germanus* from Italy and the Tunisian species, *Scorpio maurus*, *Buthus occitanus* and *Androctonus australis* are all markedly nocturnal and experimentally show well marked periodicity even under constant conditions. They can be arranged in a series as regards their rate of water-loss and time of survival in dry air and this series is in agreement with what is known of their ecology. The integuments of the three Tunisian species are extremely effective in preventing water-loss and their cuticular wax-layers have a critical temperature as high as 65°C. It is difficult, therefore, to ascribe any ecological function other than the avoidance of enemies to the markedly nocturnal behaviour of these animals which may be quite capable throughout much of the year of surviving the high temperatures and low humidity encountered on the surface of the desert sand during the daytime (Cloudsley-Thompson, 1956c).

According to Vachon (1952, 1953) scorpions were not originally characteristic of desert regions; they represent the remains of an ancient fauna which lived under quite different conditions of temperature and humidity and managed to survive in conditions of heat and drought because of their subterranean habitat and nocturnal habits. They are responsive to micro-climatic variations and each species seems to have to live and reproduce within characteristic ecological conditions varying within close limits (see also, Cloudsley-Thompson, 1958a). No doubt the better an animal is adapted to adverse physical conditions of the environment, the greater will be the influence of biotic factors in determining its time of activity.

Of course, it might be argued that scorpions are protected by their poisonous stings. Poison is not always a deterrent to large and powerful enemies, however, which might well trample a scorpion under foot, just as deer will stamp on a snake. Again, baboons and other monkeys often become adept at catching scorpions without themselves getting stung. Elsewhere I have argued that the 'pectines' are sensory receptors for vibrations of the ground and serve more for the avoidance of enemies than for the detection of prey (Cloudsley-Thompson, 1958a) and a number of mammalian predators of scorpions including rats, shrews, mongooses and hedgehogs have been recorded under laboratory conditions.

However, biotic factors cannot be the only ones affecting the rhythms of scorpions for the tropical African *Pandinus imperator* is intermediate between temperate and desert species as regards its water-relations (Cloudsley-Thompson, 1959d). Biotic factors are of prime importance, but they may be reinforced by physical conditions.

Desert beetles also show marked diurnal rhythms of locomotory activity and although the figures for water-loss from British and North African species are in the same order of magnitude, it may be not only that there has been some adaptation of the water-relations of the latter to desert life, but also that the types found in the desert are those whose physiology and behaviour are already such as would enable them to colonize arid regions (Cloudsley-Thompson 1956c). It must be remembered, however, that the ability to lose *some* water by evaporation and thus achieve reduction in temperature may be an important factor for all Arthropoda.

Buxton (1924a) comments upon the diurnal and seasonal appearance of desert beetles and has shown that many large Tenebrionidae, such as *Adesmia* spp. which are conspicuous in North Africa and Israel at all times of the day in March and April, seek shelter under stones and bushes in May and June. Bodenheimer (1934) has also shown that the time of maximum activity of desert beetles varies with the season.

It could scarcely be expected that the time of activity of terrestrial arthropods should be rigidly correlated with their rate of water-loss. Temperature tolerance, rate of water-loss in dry air, time of activity and the microclimatic conditions of the habitats in which they live are all factors of importance to be considered when assessing the adaptations of the various species to terrestrial life. Nevertheless a number of broad correlations can be drawn.

The vertebrates probably migrated to land by way of tropical swamps where the oxygen content of the water was low so that the inhabitants became pre-adapted to air-breathing. In the case of invertebrates the course of evolution is less clear, but it is by no means improbable that the route via the littoral zone may have been the one most frequently followed. The ancestors of the terrestrial arthropods may at first have been restrained by behaviour mechanisms to damp environments. Later some of their descendants, woodlice, centipedes and millipedes, exploited still further this form of terrestrial life; while others, the arachnids and insects, acquired waterproof integuments and the other physiological and morphological mechanisms that must accompany them. In the absence of more direct evidence, physiology and ecology can merely suggest the course that evolution may have followed (Cloudsley-Thompson, 1955a; 1959b).

DIURNAL RHYTHMS IN INSECTS

If the suggestion made above is correct (that Insecta and Arachnida, possessing waterproof integuments are primarily diurnal in habit) some explanation of nocturnal behaviour in these groups is required. Certainly the more primitive orders such as scorpions, whip-scorpions, spiders of the families Dictynidae, Dysderidae, cockroaches, stick-insects and so on, if not always active at night, may have become secondarily adapted to their nocturnal habits as a result of competition with more efficient species. At the same time, many primitive species are large and somewhat vulnerable and may need to escape the attentions of potential predators in this way (Cloudsley-Thompson, 1954a, 1956b; Kennedy, 1928).

In general, larger forms tend to reach maturity more slowly than their smaller relations, because they have to grow more. Consequently their rate of evolution must be slower and inevitably those that survive will tend to be primitive by comparison. Thus Rau and Rau (1929), finding that some species of giant Saturniid moths show a more deeply seated activity rhythm than others, concluded that those more markedly nocturnal were phylogenetically older. Nevertheless, certain ecological niches will favour larger species which may, however, only be able to exploit them at night.

Although a great deal of descriptive work on insect rhythms has been published, comparatively few people have attempted any assessment of the ecological significance of their observations.† This criticism is more easily expressed than answered, for although it can easily be appreciated in theory that selection pressure will favour organisms capable of adapting their functions to the periodicity of their surroundings, it is often by no means easy to determine the minute ecological factors tending to make one part of the 24-hour period especially favourable to any particular activity.

Of course, activity is not necessarily *confined* to a particular time of day. For example, Everly (1929) showed that grasshoppers, *Melanoplus differentialis*, show a maximum period of activity during the daylight hours but they are also active at other times.

Again, Edney (1937) observed great variation in the amount of activity shown by different individual migratory locusts, *Locusta migratoria migratorioides*, and in the activity of any one individual in each

† Rau and Rau (1916) and Rau (1938) have reviewed the phenomenon of sleep in insects and add many original observations. These are largely anecdotal, however, and no attempt has been made to correlate and integrate the data that has been assembled.

stadium, the highest level occurring about half-way between moults. The insects were also shown to be capable of very intense activity immediately before a moult. Diurnal periodicity was induced in insects reared under alternating 12-hour periods of light and dark, but the periodicity was retained for only a few days in constant conditions. The effect of starvation and the presence of fresh food appeared to have a greater effect than fluctuations in light intensity. Nevertheless, aktograph experiments with individual adult locusts, *L. migratoria migratorioides* and *Schistocerca gregoria* have shown that activity takes place at all hours of the day and night. But when the records from several days are lumped together, it can be shown that under experimental conditions locusts tend to be active mostly in the light and when the temperature is higher. The rhythm is chiefly exogenous, the effect of light largely over-riding that of temperature. Nevertheless, spontaneous activity occurs at all hours of the day and night, a result conforming with accounts of observations on locust swarms in the field (Cloudsley-Thompson, 1953a).

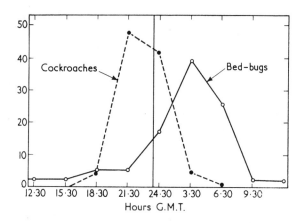

Fig. 13. Comparison between the periods of activity of the cockroach, *Blatta orientalis*, and the bed-bug, *Cimex lectularius*. (After Mellanby, 1939, 1940)

By means of traps in an animal room infested with bed-bugs, *Cimex lactularius*, Mellanby (1939) found that adult bugs appear to feed on an average once every 5 or 6 days when the temperature is in the region of 20 to 27°C (68 to 80.6°F). In the animal house the bugs were most active between 03.00 and 06.00 hours, the rhythm apparently being endogenous.

In contrast, the rhythm of activity of cockroaches in the room showed a peak just before midnight (see Fig. 13). The activity occurred only in the dark and was almost entirely prevented by quite low artificial illumination. Darkening the room during the day did not cause the cockroaches to appear unless it had been artificially illuminated during the previous night (Mellanby, 1940).

The diurnal rhythm of activity in cockroaches has been studied extensively and is referred to in detail elsewhere (p. 169) (Cloudsley-Thompson, 1953d; Gunn, 1940; Harker, 1956; Mellanby, 1940; Szymanski, 1914 etc.). More recently, Janda and Mrciak (1957) have shown that the activity rhythm is paralleled by a rhythm of oxygen consumption.

Nocturnal ecology, with especial reference to insects has been studied for some years by Park and his co-workers. In their early papers (Park, Lockett and Myers, 1931; Park and Strohecker, 1936) are described observations on the ecology of nocturnal animals in two beech-maple forests in North-eastern Ohio, from which it was concluded that the activity of nocturnal species tends to increase with increased relative humidity, decreased evaporation rate and air temperature. The nocturnal activities of the American forest cockroach *Parcoblatta pennsylvanica* and of eight species of beetles one of which, the fungus beetle, *Boletotheros cornutus* maintained its rhythm for 3 months in constant darkness and humidity, were analysed by Park and Keller (1932) and that of the mycetophagous beetle *Megalodacne heros* by Park and Sejba (1935). In his later papers, Park has concentrated on analysing the components of the nocturnal community in tropical rainforests. (Park 1938, Park, Barden and Williams, 1940) and other environments, and on the investigations of the activities of individual animals in aktograph apparatus (Park and Woods, 1940; Park, 1940; 1941a, b; 1949a). From this work he has formulated the analysis of periodicity discussed above (p. 7).

The interesting suggestion that nocturnal activity would be progressively inhibited in poikelothermic animals as the polar regions are approached (Park, 1941b) is expanded in a later paper (Park 1949b) in which it is shown that the nocturnal American Carabid beetle *Dicaelus purpuratus* reaches a greater size in the southern part of its range. This is correlated with shorter nights further north which results in smaller larvae, as there is less time for them to find food. On the other hand, it should be noted that Krumbiegel (1932) obtained evidence of an opposite situation in the predatory beetle *Carabus nemoralis*, the northern races of which are strictly nocturnal and have a low optimum temperature tolerance, while the southern races are more or less diurnal in habit. In a similar way, according to Wheeler (1913) the northern races of the ant *Myrmecocystus mexicanus*, which ranges from Mexico City to Denver, Colorado, are nocturnal while the southern races are darker in colour and diurnal or crepuscular in habit.

In the course of an investigation on the activity of Noctuid moths,

Larsen (1943) reached the important conclusion that the intensity of activity is governed by the factor that comes nearest to the minimum demands of the insects. "Since light passes below the minimum demand every 24 hours, it is the factor that sets its mark on the activity as a whole, while the other significant factors, humidity, temperature and force of wind, are in the main decisive for the degree of intensity. If during a period of some length one or some of these factors lie below the minimum in the night, the hunger of the animals will be so intense that the whole picture of their activity will change phase and the obstacle presented by the light will be overcome."

Parallel field and laboratory experiments made with *Plusia gamma* in Denmark tended to confirm this observation. The preferred temperature of this moth was determined experimentally as 25° to 30°C, considerably higher than that of other Noctuidae, and its activity was negligible below 18° to 20°C. *P. gamma* was active in the laboratory both in light and darkness, regardless of the time of day, but it showed a preference for activity in the dark and was especially responsive to a change from light to darkness. Feeding activity in the field showed two peaks, a temperature dependent one at midday and a light-dependent one at dusk. When evening temperature inversion occurred and feeding activity ceased, the moths rose into the upper, warmer air layers, where they continued flying until after midnight (Larsen, 1949).

The number of adult mealworm beetles, *Tenebrio molitor*, of both sexes and of full grown larvae on the surface of the bran in which they live depends upon light intensity. When the surface of the bran is exposed to daylight and darkness, the insects show a diurnal periodicity and come to the surface at night: young larvae tend to move downwards. Aktograph experiments with individual adults and larvae have demonstrated an endogenous 24-hour periodicity, correlated with light and darkness. The distribution of the insects in the medium in which they live is thus regulated by their reactions to light and gravity. Adults and full grown larvae move upwards and come to the surface when this is not exposed to light. Smaller larvae move downwards into the lower levels of the bran (Cloudsley-Thompson, 1953e).

These observations are supplemented by the experiments of Michal (1931) who found a daily oscillation in the oxygen consumption of mealworm larvae which reaches a maximum during the night when the insects are asleep.

The season is often an important factor influencing 24-hour periodicity. Bodenheimer and Klein (1930) for example, observed that the activity pattern of the ant, *Messor semirufus*, is modified by the season environmental complex and especially by temperature changes. From November to March activity is stopped by cooler temperatures and in summer and autumn by warmer temperatures. There are individual variations, but in general the peak of activity tends to fall about noon during the winter, during the evening in spring, during the entire night in summer and during the first part of the night in autumn. The activity pattern appeared not to be modified by rain, dew, moonlight or wind.

A distinct diurnal rhythm of mating has been observed in the common Indian housefly, *Musca domestica nebulo*, by Ilse and Mulherkar (1954). Two peaks of mating activity were observed, one in the morning and the second in the afternoon, the exact time of each peak differing slightly in different months: the rhythm is upset by darkness or 'reversed' lighting.

Kennedy (1939) has correlated diurnal behaviour of the desert locust *Schistocerca gregaria* with microclimates and finds that in the concentration zones, older hoppers and adults do not remain inactive on the vegetation, but display a diurnal regime determined largely by temperature differences and change, and involving prolonged basking on the small patches of bare, sheltered and sunlit ground among the vegetation.

The time of emergence of adult insects from their pupae, discussed in detail below (p. 120) from a physiological viewpoint, is also of considerable ecological significance. Bremer (1926) showed that diurnal insects usually emerge in the morning, nocturnal ones in the afternoon and evening.

Corbet (1952) found that the emergence of the dragonfly, *Pyrrhosoma nymphula*, is also restricted in time and shows a marked periodicity. Unfavourable weather conditions at the peak period 08.00 to 09.00 hours postponed emergence until the following day. Dunning (1956) found a clear diurnal rhythm in the emergence of the beet fly *Pegomyia betae* from the soil, a peak occurring daily between 06.00 to 07.00 hours, when the soil temperature at a depth of 2 inches and the air temperature are at about their minimum, or are just beginning to rise, and the humidity is at its maximum. These are the optimum conditions for the appearance of the flies at the soil surface: if they emerge at midday when the temperature is high and humidity low, they may fail to expand their wings properly, owing to premature drying and hardening.

On the other hand, Lewis and Bletchly (1943) showed that temperature does not affect the emergence rhythm of the dung fly, *Scopaema stercoraria*, which reaches its peak between 09.00 to 14.00 hours daily although they suggested that the normal daylight rhythm is at least contributory in controlling the time of emergence.

In discussing the periodic emergence of Chironomidae as an adaptation to nocturnalism, Palmén (1956) wrote: "Nocturnalism is generally considered to be an adaptation of the organism to the cyclic change of the physical and biotic environment, brought about by natural selection.

According to this hypothesis, it would seem possible to correlate the evolution of the timing mechanism ensuring the emergence of the majority of a given Chironomid species around midnight with the selection effect of those environmental factors which exhibit a diel cycle.

"Of these factors, the relative humidity of the air, combined with diel changes in air temperature, would seem to be the most important. Every individual emerging during the night will immediately encounter conditions where the danger of rapid loss of water is practically absent owing to the high relative humidity and the usually low temperature . . . the negative selective effect of the low humidity of the daytime would seem to be readily understandable, particularly if combined with comparatively high temperatures (sunshine).

"Another factor acting in the same direction is the wind . . . calmness is distinctly more frequent during the night than during the daytime; against the background the advantages of nocturnal emergence appear obvious. Days when the wind ruffles the water surface and when the delicate midges are in danger of being carried away from their localities are definitely less favourable than calm periods. Hence the diel changes of wind conditions would seem to act in the same direction as the cyclic fluctuations of the relative humidity and temperature, i.e. in favour of those species or mutations which have their periodicity of emergence adjusted to nocturnalism."

Measurements of the time of activity of insects also often show big variations depending upon weather conditions. The diurnal rhythm of the Colorado beetle *Leptinotarsa decemlineata*, for example, normally active in daylight, is affected by the duration of the light, whereas the nocturnal Carabid *Pterostichus vulgaris* shows a much more marked endogenous rhythm (Brehm and Hempel, 1952).

D'Aguilar (1952) found that the activity of adult wireworm beetles, *Agriotes* spp., is a function of temperature, the optimum being 5° to 20°C, although the diurnal rhythm is a response to daylight and darkness. Again, Brian (1947) found that the nocturnal *Agriotes obscurus* is positively correlated with temperature, activity in the morning is correlated positively with temperature and negatively with the hours of sunshine, but most activity takes place in the evening. He concluded that cloud might be an important factor in the beetle's life.

A study of Vesperine wasps (Gaul, 1952) has shown that these insects awake in the morning when both temperature and humidity reach certain threshold conditions which are specific for each species. Bruns (1954) recorded the diurnal rhythm of predation by artificial and natural colonies of *Formica rufo rufopratensis*. He found that the activity of the ants showed a peak maximum in the afternoon.

Nielsen (1938) has studied the activity and song of three European species of grasshopper, *Tettigonia viridissima*, *T. cantans* and *Decticus verrucivorus*, by means of recording apparatus. He found a marked exogenous rhythm of activity and, to a lesser extent, of song. This was regulated by the illumination and could be initiated or stopped at will, simply by removing or reinstating the source of light. In crickets, on the other hand, the rhythm is endogenous and will persist for weeks under constant conditions (Cloudsley-Thompson, 1958d; Lutz, 1932).

Corbet and Tjønneland (1956) have recently shown that flight activity is bimodal in many East African Trichoptera, the main flight occurring at dusk with a smaller peak at dawn. They suggest that in insects with a short adult life, flight behaviour is probably closely connected with the need for the sexes to meet. It is likely that most sexual activity occurs during the evening flight, since copulation and oviposition are observed at this time and fewer females are caught later in the night. "Whether such acute synchronisation is biologically necessary can only be elucidated by further work, but it is interesting to note in this connection that insects responding to crepuscular light intensities will have shorter periods of activity in tropic than in temperate regions, twilight being more protracted in the latter."

In temperate regions, insects with aquatic larvae having an adult life span of less than a year, usually fly at restricted and well defined periods of the season. By reducing interspecific competition in a limited habitat and by synchronising the appearance of the reproductive stage, this has adaptive value (Corbet, 1952).

It is well known that in nature fire-flies become active, fly about and emit flashes of light with the onset of darkness. The subject has been reviewed by Buck (1938). This author found that in the field the time at which males of the fire-fly *Photinus pyralis* begin to flash, is correlated with temperature and light intensity but not specifically with the time of day and a change from light to darkness always induces flashing. He demonstrated experimentally, however, the presence of an endogenous rhythm superimposed upon the flashing response to exogenous factors of the environment (Buck 1937).

Under natural conditions swarming of the chafer, *Melolontha melolontha*, also begins at dusk and the time of its beginning changes from day to day, keeping pace with the change in the time of sunset so that it always coincides with a definite light intensity. The rhythm is apparently exogenous, for swarming can be induced experimentally by artificial darkness and its regularity is lost if the beetles are kept in constant conditions (Meunier, 1928).

Harker (1953) measured the activity of nymphs of the may-flies *Ecdyonurus torrentis*, *Heptagenia lateralis* and *Baetis rhodeni* by recording their movements during 10 minute periods every hour over a series of 24-hour periods. She found endogenous diurnal rhythms under conditions of natural daylight and darkness in all three species at different times. She did not attempt to assess the ecological significance of any particular time to the species concerned. There need not necessarily have been any for, as McClure (1938) has pointed out, competition between different species will be reduced if their activity does not take place at the same time. In the same way, distinctive colour patterns which reduce or prevent hybridization between related species are an advantage, irrespective of the actual colours involved.

Robertson (1939) has investigated the nocturnal family of crane-flies of the sub-family Tipulinae by analysis of the captures in a light trap operated at Rothamsted Experimental Station, Hertfordshire over a period of 4 years. He found that activity was greatest just after sunset and a gradual decrease was interrupted by a slight secondary maximum near midnight. The only exception to this was *Tipula paludosa* which showed no maximum at midnight and a definite rise in activity towards dawn. Nocturnal activity was favoured by a high minimal temperature and a small diurnal range. Both cloud and moonlight affected the number of captures, optimum conditions being complete cloudiness and absence of moonlight.

By means of counts of mosquitoes feeding on *Tanacetum vulgare* in Denmark, Larsen (1948) showed that there is a regular diurnal rhythm with maximum activity in the morning and evening at the lowest wind strength and highest atmospheric humidity. She was unable to distinguish, however, whether the rhythm was endogenous or merely an exogenous response to these environmental factors.

Field observations on the wheat bulb fly, *Leptohylemyia coarctata*, have also indicated a diphasic 24-hour periodicity with maximum numbers occurring in the crop in the very early morning and the late evening, which suggests a daily flight dispersion followed by a general or localised return of the flies to the crop. The daily temperature rhythm is found to be only partly responsible for this (Long, 1958a). In laboratory cultures a daily oviposition rhythm was observed in which egg-laying was restricted to the afternoon and evening with a maximum 2 hours before nightfall. This coincides with the daily flight rhythm, was maintained for 24 hours in the absence of light and therefore appears to be partly inherent (Long, 1958b).

Some of the Chironomidae common about sewage farms, such as *Spaniotoma minima* and *Metriocnemus* spp., are diurnal swarmers while *Chironomus dorsalis* is crepuscular. Each species has a characteristic altitude zone based on the ground or on some raised object, within which the swarmers seek maximum light and therefore swarm at the greatest height permitted by the wind. Discrete swarms are thus the result of a conflict between these factors (Gibson, 1945).

Again, in a study of swarming behaviour of *Aedes cantans* and other mosquitoes, *Chaoborus crystallinus* and certain Chironomids, Nielsen and Greve (1950) observed swarming to take place at about sunset and sunrise. Evening swarms appeared to be formed in response to decreasing light intensity and to disperse at a light intensity of about 7 Lux, the same as that at which the morning swarms began to form. Low temperatures tended to delay swarming and it did not occur below 10°C, but atmospheric humidity had no effect.

The work of Haddow and his colleagues has shown that the biting cycles of mosquitoes in Bwamba County, Uganda, are dependent upon features of the microclimate, especially temperature and relative humidity. Forest mosquitoes migrate to banana plantations at night (Haddow 1945a).

When the biting cycle of the strictly diurnal *Aedes simpsoni* was studied, it was found that this species is most active on warm cloudy days: activity is inhibited by cold, wind and direct, hot sunshine. *Aedes africanus* is definitely crepuscular, as is shown by the fact that 42 per cent of the total catch was taken in the hour following sunset (Haddow, 1945b), but this species too is particularly susceptible to the influence of weather conditions and low temperature may partly, or even completely inhibit its biting activity in the sunset period (Haddow and Mahaffy, 1949). On the other hand, Lumsden (1952) found that the peak activity of a number of crepuscular species is largely controlled by changes in light intensity about the time of sunset.

Gillett (1957) analysed the age of mosquitoes coming to bite at different times during the biting cycle, by inspection of the insects caught with larvae of water mites attached to them. This ingenious method provides information as to age much more quickly and simply than inspection of the ovaries by dissection of each mosquito caught. Analysis of three 24-hour catches by this method indicated that young adult mosquitoes make up a constant proportion of the total number of *Taeniorhynchus africanus* coming to bite hour by hour.

The complexity of mosquito biting cycles is not, however, fully indicated by catches confined to one level. Where catching goes on simultaneously at several heights above the ground, marked qualitative differences may be found in different species. Broadly speaking peaks of activity are shorter but more intense in the forest canopy than in the under-storey, and in the under-storey than at ground level (Haddow, 1956).

Mattingly (1949, 1952) also discusses the cyclical behaviour of various African mosquitoes and suggests that the number of insects taking a blood meal (the biting cycle) merely reveals changes in the general activity of the insects. The subject of nocturnal activity and biting cycles has been reviewed in some detail by Muirhead-Thomson (1951).

It is of great significance that when specimens of *Aedes africanus* were confined in an unchanging micro-environment in a closed, sound-proof chamber they remained inactive during the day but became active at dusk at the very time when their peak biting period occurs in nature. Evidence was produced that the activity of mosquitoes does not, or does not wholly depend on the changing microclimate, but that it is inherent to the particular species of mosquito. This inherent rhythm is most evident in very young mosquitoes and eventually may be modified by contact with the environment (Bruce-Chwatt, 1950). Gillett, Haddow and Corbet (1959) believe that although the cyclical oviposition rhythm of *Aedes aegypti* breaks down in constant light, an endogenous 24-hour rhythm is present which only becomes apparent in the presence of alternating light and dark time clues.

Kettle (1957) comments on the lack of quantitative data on the effects of weather conditions on the activity of biting flies in Britain. In a 24-hour study of weather conditions and the biting and flying activities of the clegs *Haematopota pluvialis*, *H. crassicornis* and the midge *Culicoides impunctatus* on open moorland at Kinlochewe in Western Ross, he stressed the importance of high light intensity and warmth in relation to the activity of *Haematopota* spp., and of low light intensity and calm conditions on the activity of *C. impunctatus*. Observations in the field readily demonstrate the effect of wind in inhibiting biting flies of various species (Cloudsley-Thompson and Sankey, 1957).

On clear, warm days, *Drosophila pseudo-obscura* exhibits, in California, a diurnal activity cycle which involves early morning and late afternoon periods of activity. The character of this cycle varies with the season, the active periods being longer and less definite in the early spring months, shorter and more definite in late spring, summer and autumn. The rhythm is not affected by relative humidity, whilst temperature variations influence the degree but not the time of activity which results from a behavioural response to a particular light intensity (Mitchell and Epling, 1951).

Dyson-Hudson (1956) obtained comparable results in England with *D. obscura*. In the summer, this species invariably has a marked peak of activity in the evening and usually a small peak in the morning correlated with light intensity, for activity drops sharply below and above 6.5 candles/sq. ft. In the evening no effect of temperature can be detected, but in the morning, below 15°C, activity is primarily dependent on temperature. In contrast, *D. subobscura* begins to be active at dawn; activity increases as temperature and light intensity increase and ceases at nightfall. Thus it seems that *D. obscura* may respond to low light intensity and low temperature, but has a wide range of tolerance of both, while *D. subobscura* appears to respond to low and possibly high temperatures, but primarily to have a very definite light optimum.

At first sight it may appear curious that the Drosophilidae should be crepuscular because the remaining flies of the sub-order Schizophora are mainly day-flying insects. The Drosophilidae have apposition eyes which are usually associated with good directional vision in daylight, and *D. subobscura*, in particular, cannot mate without light, at least in the laboratory. However, in wild-type *D. melanogaster* which have a similar periodicity there is a shift in the spectral sensitivity of the eye to shorter wave-lengths when light intensity is low and this tends to increase efficiency at dawn and dusk.

The Drosophilidae are highly susceptible to desiccation and those that live in humid, sub-tropical forests have a more flexible periodicity than those found typically in open country. For this reason, Taylor and Kalmus (1954) have made the interesting speculation that *Drosophila* spp. may have become adapted to increasing daytime aridity, not by increased resistance to desiccation, as must have happened to most other Schizophora, but by increased visual efficiency in low light intensities together with a shift in flight periodicity to climatically less extreme but darker times of day. This suggestion is not incompatible with the reasoning expressed in the preceding section of this chapter.

The study of aphids shows that there is a diurnal periodicity of flight and a nocturnal quiescence at crop-level; and that the supply of insects to the upper air depends on the extent to which this diurnal supply coincides with convection and turbulence. That the rhythm is reflected up to heights of at least 2,000 ft. above ground has been shown by the work of C. G. Johnson (1951, 1952 etc.) and his co-workers in their elegant field experiments using suction traps which automatically segregate the catch into hourly samples, attached at various heights to balloon cables (p. 12). Continuous operation of these traps during the summers of 1947, 1948 and 1949 at Rothamsted Experimental Station, Hertfordshire showed that the greatest aerial densities occurred between 09.00 and 21.00 hours and that most species showed a double peak of abundance each day. Large night and early morning catches were observed only when a species was present in unusually large numbers (Eastop, 1951).

The subject has been reviewed in detail by Johnson (1951, 1954) to whose work the reader is referred for further details.

Many nocturnal moths are inactivated by light and the number caught in light traps and at bait is greatly affected by moonlight. This is especially marked in the Noctuidae which have their maximum activity at midnight, less in species that fly chiefly at dusk and dawn (Williams, 1936 etc.).

The possibility that the reduction in numbers of insects caught on moonlight nights may be due to a reduction in the efficiency of light traps at full moon, when the brightness of the light in the trap relative to the surrounding area is less than on dark nights, has been suggested by Williams, Singh and el Ziady (1956). The use of suction traps did not support the suggestion that there was any regular lunar cycle in the number of insects caught. There is thus no evidence of any effect of moonlight on the activity or distribution of night-flying insects, except in the case of some aquatic species where the influence appears to be on emergence from the water and so on the size of the adult winged population (Hartland-Rowe, 1955; see also p. 91).

In his review of insects and climate, Uvarov (1931) concluded that the daily activities of insects are influenced by combinations of several meteorological factors. This can only be partially true. Biotic factors certainly cannot be neglected for every species and, even where they are relatively unimportant, attempts to explain the daily cycle by a single factor have little chance of success.

The above examples have been selected entirely from insects, but comparable results have been obtained with various Arachnids and other terrestrial arthropods, of which only a few will be cited here. Lees and Milne (1951) have described a diurnal pattern of behaviour in active sheep ticks, *Ixodes ricinus*. A higher proportion end a phase of activity on the tips of blades of grass during the evening than at any other time of day. A diurnal rhythm has also been demonstrated in the fall of engorged ticks, *Boophilus microplus*, the majority dropping from their host between 06.00 to 10.00 hours (Hitchcock, 1955).

Norgaard (1951) has shown that the behaviour of the spider, *Filistata insidiatrix*, in southern Europe, is related to environmental factors, particularly temperature. The spider stays in its heat-insulated tube during the hottest hours of the day and thus avoids the high temperatures outside. It comes out at night when woodlice, its chief prey, are most numerous. Thus temperature and the periodic food-supply probably reinforce each other in adding to the ecological significance of the observed rhythm.

The diurnal rhythm of colour change in fiddler crabs is discussed in detail in Chapter 6 from the point of view of its physiological implications. In nature, no doubt it serves the function of protecting the animals from the bright sun and from predators. The same is true of the chromatophore rhythms of insects and spiders. Although this chapter has been concerned primarily with locomotory rhythms it should be remembered that these are naturally associated with numerous physiological rhythms, many of which may have direct ecological significance.

This brief survey of a few of the publications that have appeared within recent years on the subject of diurnal rhythms of activity in insects will be sufficient to show that the factors involved are so numerous and diverse, even within individual species, that few generalizations can be made. Each species must be studied on its own account; any conclusions reached will not necessarily apply even to closely related forms.

DIURNAL RHYTHMS IN VERTEBRATES

Scattered through the literature are numbers of diverse observations on daily rhythms of activity in vertebrate animals. In general, on account of their larger size, primary factors of the physical environment such as light, temperature and humidity tend to be less directly important to vertebrates and secondary considerations, especially of predation and the availability of food, are governing factors in the time at which activity takes place.

It is well known that aquarium fish can be trained to observe particular times for feeding, but little critical work has been carried out on the subject (Thorpe, 1956). Some fishes tend to follow the vertical diurnal movements of the plankton on which they feed, others that inhabit shallow water, streams and rivers, tend to be less rhythmic.

Spencer (1939) made records on a number of species of fish in America and concluded that the sunfish, *Eupomotis gibbus*, is diurnal in habit, the mud minnow, *Umbra lima*, usually nocturnal. Young carp, *Cyprinus carpis*, are also nocturnal but they become arhythmic as they grow older, perhaps because the pressure of predation is less on larger individuals. The majority of species tested, including *Lepomis pallidus*, *Ambloplites rupestris*, *Perca flavescens*, *Huro salmoides* and *Ameiurus melas* were found to be arhythmic.

This is probably related to the fact that physical changes from day to night are far less marked in the aquatic environment than on land and consequently there is less selection pressure in favour of rhythmic activity.

The common goldfish, *Carassius auratus*, has been shown by Szymanski (1914) and Spencer (1939) to be markedly diurnal, the rhythm persisting in constant conditions for longer than in most fish species. An interesting ecological observation was made by Schuett (1934) who observed that activity was less in groups of four fishes than in larger groups or individuals, although during any 24-hour period the oxygen consumption per individual was the same regardless of the size of the group. In this study the activity of only one individual of the group was measured for a single hour out of the 24-hour period. Consequently the differential results obtained from the measurements of one hour of activity of one goldfish among groups of different sizes may have resulted from a shift towards arhythmicity in the medium sized groups. In this way intensity of activity over a short period of time during the day would seem less in an arhythmic than in a day-active group when activity was measured only for such a brief period (Calhoun 1945).

A weak endogenous rhythm of retinal pigment migration has been described in the catfish *Ameiurus nebulosus* by Welsh and Osborn (1937). In this fish the rods and cones of the eyes are lengthened at night thus exposing a greater surface to the diminished light. During the day they contract. Under continuous lighting there is no detectable change in the position of the visual elements, but in constant darkness, constant temperature and running water the rhythm of extension and contraction was maintained for 2 days even in hypophysectomised fish.

Diurnal rhythms of colour change by means of chromatophores in fishes, amphibians and reptiles, are reviewed by Parker (1948). Their ecological significance in the attainment of concealment are obvious and should not require further stress (*see* Cott, 1940).

It might be supposed that larval Amphibia, being aquatic, would tend to be arhythmic, whereas adults would be active at night when water-loss by evaporation is reduced. In fact, Kalmus (1940) found the reverse for *Triturus* sp. adults are arhythmic though the larvae possess a well-developed, endogenous nocturnal activity pattern. This also persisted after removal of the hypophysis.

On the other hand, Szymanski (1914) found that under normal environmental conditions the European tree frog, *Hyla arborea,* showed a bimodal pattern of activity with a peak at noon and another after dusk. As Calhoun (1945) points out, it would appear most unlikely that hunger contractions of the stomach initiate these activity periods.

The only careful analysis of 24-hour activity under controlled conditions in Amphibia is that of Higginbotham (1939) who found that under normal light cycles the majority of individuals of the toad species, *Bufo fowleri* and *B. americanus,* are nocturnal with a major peak of activity occurring just after the beginning of the dark period. The rhythm is endogenous and persists for weeks in constant darkness. With an increase of 10°C there was a doubling or tripling of the amount of activity but no alteration in the frequency of the period (see p. 177). Occasionally an individual was consistently diurnal and others usually nocturnal from time to time exhibited a day-active periodicity. Park, Barden and Williams (1940) found that another toad, *Bufo marinus,* in the Panama rain forest is also preponderantly day-active when placed in mechanical recording apparatus under natural conditions. These observations are contradictory to the conclusions of Walls (1942) who claims that the presence of yellow oil droplets in frogs' eyes accounts for their more arhythmic type of activity and suggests that the early Amphibia, the Stegocephalia had yellow oil droplets and were diurnal: in becoming respectively nocturnal and secretive, toads and salamanders have lost the yellow oil droplets in their eyes.

It is well known that turtles are normally diurnal in habit, little activity occurring in the afternoon and almost none during the night. This has been proved in the case of *Geomyda amulata* by Park *et al.* (1940). The necessity for daytime activity in turtles is pointed out by Walls (1942) who claims that turtles have practically pure cone retinae with slow and slight retinal migrations or none at all, which limits them to diurnal vision and makes them dependent on olfaction in muddy water. Red oil droplets enable them to see through the surface glare of a tropical sea. Nevertheless, the majority of turtles oviposit at night (Park, 1941b).

Since amphibians and reptiles are poikelothermic, temperature and humidity fluctuations must be considerably more important to them than to birds and mammals. Probably most lizards and snakes are diurnal, seeking their prey during the hottest period of the day and nocturnal activity takes place only in very warm weather. There is comparatively little precise experimental data on the subject, however.

Field observations on the American lizard, *Cnemidophorus sexlineatus*, in its natural sand dune habitat showed it to be active in the daytime only and even then not until the sand had been warmed by the morning sun. Laboratory experiments with aktograph recording apparatus confirmed this activity pattern. At 29.4°C (85°F) however, 13 per cent of activity occurred during the night. Of the day time activity, two-thirds came before noon. The rhythm persisted under continuous conditions (see p. 3).

Park (1938) obtained diurnal activity patterns with the lizards *Mabuya mabuya*, *Basiliscus basiliscus* and *Anolis frenatus* in aktograph apparatus, and Kayser and Marx (1951) found that *Lacerta agilis* and *L. muralis* are active between 10.00 and 16.00 hours (p. 178).

In contrast, geckoes such as *Thecadactylus rapicaudus* are strictly nocturnal, whereas *Sphaerodactylus lineolatus* is diurnal (Park, 1938). Of these reptiles, Walls (1942) writes: "The geckoes have such excellent pupillary control of sensitivity that they are practically arhythmic though tending to feed more at night." In practically all species that have been investigated the bulk of nocturnal activity takes place before midnight and before temperatures have begun to drop much.

From an extensive survey of the reptiles of California, Klauber (1939) has shown that the strenuous high temperature conditions in deserts lead to a change from diurnality to nocturnality in coastal species which have invaded the desert and he lists several diurnal snakes that are apparently limited to the coastal region by their inability to assume a nocturnal pattern of activity.

Of the homiothermic animals, most birds, larger mammalian herbivores and their predators tend to be day-active, smaller mammalian herbivores and their predators, which include owls, weasels, stoats, polecats, civets and other Viverridae, are mostly nocturnal in habit.

Many of the activities of birds show a morning peak, afternoon trough and minor evening peak. This is true, for example, of the song of the European wren, *Troglodytes troglodytes*, described by Whitehouse and Armstrong (1953).

The fact that birds, with the exception of nocturnal or crepuscular forms such as owls, goatsuckers and some herons, are the most strikingly diurnal group of organisms is reflected in the structure of their eyes. Besides possessing a nearly pure cone retina, which endows them with keen visual acuity, there are several types of oil droplets which act as filters. The red droplets are of value during early morning or at sunset, during midday the yellow droplets are of service and in midmorning and midafternoon the orange droplets are of maximum importance (Walls, 1942). Thus, late-rising birds such as hawks have fewer red droplets than song birds.

A. J. Marshall (1938) found that during the perpetual light of the Arctic summer, birds such as the Arctic tern, *Sterna macrura*, show periods of quiescence which may be correlated with meteorological conditions. On the other hand, species like the fulmar petrel, *Fulmarus glacialis*, show no peak of activity but rest only when replete or fatigued. Local weather conditions such as sudden sunlight or icy winds may abruptly curtail activity.

A number of examples of diurnal rhythms of activity and basal metabolic rate have been described in birds and are reviewed by Calhoun (1945) and Harker (1958a). Others are discussed below (p. 139) from a physiological viewpoint. The importance of an internal chronometer or biological 'clock' in the celestial navigation of birds is also mentioned later (p. 137).

There are few parts of the world, except hot deserts, in which mammals and birds are forced to become nocturnal in habit so that they may avoid the daytime heat. Whereas large mammals such as camels, sheep and goats resist extreme conditions by sweating, small species such as the African jerboas or the American kangaroo rats *Dipodomys* spp. can avoid extremes of temperature and dryness by living in burrows from which they emerge to feed only at night.

The microclimates within the burrows of kangaroo rats have been investigated by Schmidt-Nielsen and Schmidt-Nielsen (1950) who found that even during the driest season of the year the soil in the Arizona desert contains enough water to keep a closed air space in the ground at a depth of 30 cm. saturated with water vapour.

The air space within the burrows of desert rodents is not saturated, but its moisture content is from two to five times as high as the atmosphere outside. These rats can exist indefinitely on perfectly dry food and no water. They do not sweat and the formation of metabolic water leads to an ultimate gain in moisture so long as the animals breathe the moist air in their burrows during the daytime. For if they were breathing the air outside the burrows with its low moisture content, the rate of evaporation from their lungs would exceed the rate of formation of metabolic water.

Except in desert regions, predation and the availability of food are probably the chief ecological factors in mammalian 24-hour periodicity. As Hediger (1950), referring to animals in captivity, points out: "The importance of timing is also a consideration in the presentation of food. Most birds are adapted to seeking food by daylight while many mammals prefer to feed at twilight or by night. Many nocturnal animals can undergo a considerable change in habits in the physiological, optical sense, whilst the opposite in birds, for instance, is impossible since they cannot see well enough in the dark."

Some mammals are rigidly diurnal, nocturnal or crepuscular but others are able to change their habits quite easily. The buffaloes already cited (p. 40) were able to revise their habits and in man the degree of specialisation to a nocturnal or diurnal existence is not particularly marked.

Like most young animals, the human baby is comparatively non-rhythmic during the first year of life, as parents are only too well aware, but gradually there is an increasing range and regularity of the 24-hour physiological rhythms of body-temperature, urine secretion and so on as the child becomes progressively adapted to a normal rhythmic existence.

In the eyes of nocturnal animals a reflecting mechanism or tapetum is usually present so that any light passing through the retina is reflected back and there is a double chance for a given ray to stimulate a rod or cone. Associated with a very efficient retina, as in the opossum, a tapetum results in such sensitivity that bright light is avoided at all times, even though a slit pupil very greatly reduces the amount of light penetrating to the retina and ensures some protection by means of its fine control.

The larger terrestrial mammals—ungulates, elephants, lions, bears and so on—have eyes that are not particularly specialised either for day or night vision. They have a tapetum and sufficient rods for reasonable visual acuity and yet have many cones also. These, coupled with a large eyeball, ensure good resolution of detail. In consequence, vision is relatively good both at night and by day, even where senses of scent and hearing are acute and the animals are not markedly nocturnal or diurnal.

Nocturnal forms often have an iris with a vertical pupil aperture, and adaptations may also occur in the lens. For example, flying squirrels, *Glaucomys* spp., are nocturnal and have colourless lenses, whereas true squirrels, *Sciurus* spp., are diurnal and have yellow lenses. Both types inhabit the same forests in many localities and their different periods of activity are correlated with the light-filtering properties of their eyes.

Yellow filters cut out much of the violet light and some blue. These are the colours responsible for most chromatic aberration. At the same time they enhance contrast and do not impede natural hues. A combination of a yellow diurnal lens or yellow droplets with a tapetum would result in poor vision at all times and does not occur in nature (Walls, 1942).

There is an Arabian fable concerning an argument between the horse and the lion as to which had the keener sight. The lion could distinguish a white pearl in milk on a dark night, but the horse could see a black pearl in a heap of coal in the day. The matter was submitted to arbitration and the judges rightly pronounced in favour of the horse. No doubt they realised that the acuity of the cone vision in Perissodactyla is greater than that of the nocturnal rods and tapetum of carnivores!

Within recent years the daily cycle of activity of small mammals, such as woodmice, voles, shrews and moles, has attracted attention. The literature has been reviewed by Southern (1954). Crowcroft (1954) has investigated the activity patterns of the common shrew *Sorex araneus*, the pygmy shrew *S. minutus* and the water shrew *Neomys fodiens* in captivity. The single water shrew studied had a 24-hour rhythm characterised by a peak just before sunrise. Nine common shrews showed bimodal 24-hour rhythms with major peaks at 20.00 and 04.00 hours and a minor peak between 07.00 and 11.00 hours when light was controlled and the hours of darkness were from 17.00 to 05.00. A single pygmy shrew kept under similar conditions showed a 24-hour rhythm similar to that of the common shrew, but differed in that the major peak occurred during the 'day'.

Although the common and pygmy shrews exhibited short-term physiological rhythms of the order of 2 hours' periodicity and the longest periods of rest and activity in the water shrew were 3.4 hours, the most frequent periods of rest and activity were much shorter. A short-term rhythm, generally called the "feeding" or "hunger-motivated" rhythm has been found in all small rodents investigated so far, and the period tends to decrease with decreasing size of the animal.

That this is not brought about by periodic stomach contractions has been shown by removing the stomach and cutting the nerves connecting it with the nerve centres. It is probably caused by a cycle of physiological changes within the animal including the accumulation of fatigue products as well as nutritional requirements.

In the common shrew, at least, the form of the 24-hour rhythm may well relate to the frequency of refection, or rectal feeding. (See discussion by Crowcroft, 1954).

In this connection, Southern (1942) has shown that there is a diurnal periodicity of refection in the wild rabbit, the number of stomachs containing soft pellets being greatest amongst rabbits shot between 06.00 to 19.00 hours, least among rabbits shot at night.

Godfrey (1954) has recently shown that the mole *Talpa europaea* resembles *Sorex* and *Microtus* spp. in that it is active throughout both day and night but it differs in that it has a short term rhythm of apparently 8 hours instead of $2\frac{1}{2}$ hours although the proportion of the 24 hours spent at rest is no greater. Digging occupies between one and two thirds of the $4\frac{1}{2}$ hours activity, the remainder of the active period being spent in moving about: $3\frac{1}{2}$ hours of each 8-hour cycle is spent in rest.

Kalabukhov (1939) found that under normal conditions the activity rhythms of *Apodemus sylvaticus* and *A. flavicollis* are almost identical. When subjected to continuous darkness, however, *A. sylvaticus* rapidly loses its rhythm and activity becomes more or less equally distributed throughout the 24-hours. On the other hand, the rhythm of *A. flavicollis* persists in its original form for 100 to 130 days. Thus, in the absence of external clues one species is shown to have an exogenous, the other an endogenous, rhythm. It would seem that persistence of rhythm is not necessarily of great ecological importance in the natural environment.

Miller (1955) made simultaneous recordings of the feeding activities of the woodmouse *Apodemus sylvaticus* and the bank vole *Clethrionomys glareolus* in response to day-lengths of 8, 12 and 16 hours, the nights being 16, 12 and 8 hours in length respectively. He found that both species were nocturnal but their rhythms were modifiable according to day-length: he suggested that the role of activity rhythms in the community relations of the species is an extremely critical one and that it is an important feature of any competition between them (see p. 39).

It may be concluded that among small mammals, a considerable amount of daytime activity probably occurs only in shrews, *Microtus* spp. and other forms that feed mainly within dense cover and have great food requirements. No doubt predation is the significant ecological factor responsible.

Although, as an individual, man is markedly periodic, and those who have to work night shifts take a long time to become adjusted, nevertheless social communities as a whole are less periodic the larger they are. Thus the isolated family or hamlet may be completely rhythmic, but in a small town there is usually someone awake at night, if only the policeman. In larger cities there is a considerable degree of night life of various kinds (Park, 1941). An interesting parallel is afforded by ants and some other social animals.

Since in man it may take several days before the normal metabolic curve with its daytime peak is reversed, it has been suggested that greater individual and communal efficiency might result if night shifts were lengthened to several weeks or months, so that the rhythm might have time to become completely reversed. Of course, means of recreation and other facilities would have to be available at night too, for the scheme to work.

There is a considerable amount of literature on the subject of shift workers, their physiological and psychological problems.

Lewis and Masterton (1957) studied the influence of the polar environment on 29 men during the British North Greenland Expedition of 1952–54. Its effect was studied on the sleep pattern of men accustomed to a diurnal cycle, observations being made on the number of hours slept over the seasons, the effect of specific duties and the relationship of disturbed sleep to the taking of naps. The time of going to sleep and getting up varied greatly, especially during midwinter (continuous darkness) and midsummer (continuous light) without preference to any particular hour. During the periods of continuous darkness and continuous light, slightly more of the 24 clock hours were used for sleep but there was no great difference between months of outdoor activity and months when the men were confined to their hut. The winter months were characterised by many interruptions of sleep and by the taking of naps, but there was no relationship or coincidence between interrupted sleep and naps.

The effect of specific routine duties on sleep showed how men varied when there was need to conform to a social pattern. For example, one radio-operator took about a third of his sleep before the 06.00 hour duty and the remainder afterwards, including a great number of naps at haphazard times. In contrast, the second radio-operator went to bed about midnight, woke just before 06.00 hours to transmit the report and then promptly went back to sleep for two hours before breakfast. After that he was up for the whole day and only rarely took a nap. Yet the background and Service discipline and training of the two had been identical.

During the second winter at Northice, the first radio-operator carried out his duties in the main laboratory where over 20 men were working under conditions of greater communal organisation. Despite this change of environment, his sleep pattern was disrupted as in the previous year. If, however, the expedition had exerted social pressure on the member's off-duty times, he would probably have conformed to the community timetable.

The mean duration of sleep throughout the expedition was 7.9 hours from which it is concluded that the approximate period of 8 hours taken in temperate climates represents a normal demand. Detailed experimental work on the physiology of human rhythms is discussed in a later chapter (p. 153).

CHAPTER 4

Lunar and Tidal Rhythms

TIDAL RHYTHMS OF ACTIVITY, ETC.

IN addition to the rhythm of daylight and darkness, another natural period that appears to be used conspicuously by organisms in the measurement of time is the period of the lunar day of 24.8 hours. The lunar day is the period elapsing between two consecutive times when the moon is at its zenith and this occurs about 50 minutes later each solar day. As Brown (1957b) points out, compared with the sun, the influence of the moon on illumination, temperature and humidity is slight. But in the intertidal regions of the shores of the oceans, the influence of the moon is twice as great as that of the sun.

The tides of the ocean are produced predominantly by the gravitational attraction of the moon so that tidal cycles are of lunar frequency. To a lesser extent the tides are also affected by the gravitational influence of the sun and at 15-day intervals, the sun's and moon's influences are additive to produce the extra high, so-called 'spring' tides. "It is generally conceded that the greater part of the evolution of all animals and plants occurred in the littoral regions of the oceans. Hence, probably for many hundreds of millions of years, ancestors of all present-day living things were subjected to the rhythmic ebbing and flowing of the tides" (Brown, 1957).

Early in the present century it was reported that a number of littoral organisms showed cycles of behaviour which persisted under constant laboratory conditions with the same frequency as that of the tidal events occurring in the areas from which the organisms had been collected.

For example, Gamble and Keeble (1903, 1904) studied the emergence onto the surface of the sand at low tide of the flatworm, *Convoluta roscoffensis*. These animals are restricted to the area between the outflow of tidal water and the high water level of the lowest neap tides. Here they may become so numerous as to form green patches on the sand, the green colour being derived from symbiotic algae in their digestive tracts. Each patch reaches its maximum size soon after its site has been exposed by the tide, and then slowly decreases until the tide comes in. When the water has come within a few feet, the last of the patch disappears suddenly. At night the colonies do not ascend: presumably during the daytime the symbiotic algae can make use of the increased light intensity for photosynthesis. When the tide returns, the flatworms retreat into the sand, and thus avoid the wave action of the incoming tide. This rhythmic behaviour persists in the laboratory.

Bohn (1904) reported that the polychaete worm *Nereis diversicolor* exhibited a persistent tidal rhythm that involved the emergence of the animal on to the surface of the sand as the tide rose. He also observed that the rough periwinkle, *Littorina rudis*, which normally inhabits the higher regions of the intertidal zone and consequently is covered by water only during the spring high tide, becomes active once every 15 days when maintained under constant laboratory conditions, the activity coinciding closely with the time of the spring tides.

During the first decade of the century, Bohn and Piéron described a tidal rhythm of expansion and contraction in the sea-anemone, *Actinia equina*. This rhythm is endogenous and persists for up to 8 days in constant conditions in an aquarium under water. It was claimed that these tidal movements were performed a little in advance of the actual tidal changes thus like many diurnal periodicities giving evidence of an anticipatory reaction. This work has recently been re-described by Piéron (1958).

A persistent rhythm of phototaxis in the hermit crab, *Clibanarius misanthropus*, collected in an area of considerable tidal amplitude, was described by Drzewina (1907). The crabs were negatively phototactic at times of low tide and positively phototactic at high tide. In contrast, hermit crabs of the same species collected in a region where the tidal variation was slight, did not exhibit a tidal rhythm of phototaxis.

Wheeler and Brown (1936) have observed a lunar periodic swarming of the prawn *Anchistioides antiguensis* at times when the moon waned from last quarter to the first quarter of the new cycle.

A year later, Gompel (1937) showed that several species of littoral animals display tidal rhythms of oxygen consumption which also persist under constant laboratory conditions. An endogenous tidal rhythm of locomotory activity has been described in the mud snail *Ilyanassa obsoleta* by Stephens, Sandeen and Webb (1953). If the activity of this snail is recorded mechanically, it is found that it reaches a maximum at the time of high tide and there is no diurnal component in the rhythm. Snails collected from localities with different tidal times showed activity patterns correlated with the times of high and low tide in their original habitat.

Rao (1954) demonstrated the occurrence of a tidal rhythm in the rate of water propulsion in mussels, *Mytilus edulis* and *M. californianus*, collected from under a variety of environmental conditions. This persisted in the laboratory for over 4 weeks in phase with the tidal cycle of the natural environment and independent of a wide range of temperature (9° to 20°C) and varying conditions of light and darkness: it even occurred in sub-tidal populations.

Specimens collected at Barnstable Harbor on Cape Cod and studied at Los Angeles, California—nearly 3,000 miles west—showed a rhythm in their rate of water propulsion which was out of phase with the local tidal cycle by 6½ hours. Some of these mussels placed in a wire cage and attached to the pier of Kerckhoff Marine Laboratory, California, for a week, showed a shift in their rhythm to synchronise with the local tidal cycle. They then continued to keep phase with the local tidal cycle for over 3 weeks in the laboratory.

The rhythm is thus clearly endogenous, but may be synchronised fairly rapidly with tidal changes in the environment. Rao suggests that the different findings of the many workers who have investigated rhythmic behaviour in sea-anemones may be due to the fact that the intrinsic rhythm becomes marked and measurable only when the fluctuations of the environmental factors reach a certain, but unknown, threshold value.

The rates of oxygen consumption in two species of littoral gastropods, *Littorina littorea* and *Urosalpinx cinereus*, have been determined continuously for 26 and 22 days respectively by Sandeen, Stephens and Brown (1954). In addition to a diurnal rhythm, a persistent tidal rhythm in oxygen consumption in *U. cinereus* involving minimal rates about 5 hours after low tide and maximum rates 2 to 3 hours before low tide, have been revealed. The data for *L. littorea*, although not conclusive, also suggests the presence of a tidal rhythm with minimum rates about an hour before high tides and intermediate rates at the time of low tide.

The physiological significance of such periodicities in littoral species can be recognised and correlated with their ecological requirements. In the case of the lunar cycles obtained from carrots, potatoes, salamanders, etc. the significance is less clear and the criticisms levelled in a later chapter (p. 114) may well apply.

Fiddler crabs, *Uca* spp., show a diurnal rhythm of colour change (p. 109). Within their daily rhythm of gross colour-change there is a certain amount of variation in the degree of daytime darkening, which varies with the time of day. Sometimes the crabs are darkest in the morning, sometimes at noon and sometimes in the afternoon. Occasionally they are darkest both early in the morning and in the evening of the same day. Now the time of greatest darkening tends to occur about 50 minutes later every 24 hours and corresponds with the time of low tide. The rhythm persists in darkness in the laboratory for many weeks (Brown, Fingerman, Sandeen and Webb (1953). Similar results have been obtained by Fingerman (1955) with the blue crab, *Callinectes sapidus*. The physiology of this response is discussed in Chapter 6.

The diurnal and the tidal rhythms coincide in phase about every 15 days. A low tide at 9 a.m. is not followed by one at the same hour until 15 days later. The tidal rhythm, like the diurnal one, has been found to be remarkably precise. Fiddler crabs from Woods Hole, Massachusetts, kept in darkness side by side with crabs from Martha's Vineyard, a few miles away, where the low tide comes 4 hours later in the day, maintain their darkest periods 4 hours earlier for long periods.

The 15-day tidal rhythm has been found to be independent of temperature, like the 24-hour rhythm and can be reset in a similar way by shifting the period of illumination (see discussion on p. 110).

Guyselman (1957) recorded the locomotory activity of three groups of crayfish, *Cambarus virilis*, in activity wheels kept in darkness and running water. He found a diurnal and lunar (12.4 hour) cycle of activity both at constant and at normally fluctuating atmospheric pressures.

More recently, Naylor (1958) has obtained similar results with the common European shore crab, *Carcinus maenas*, which shows a complex rhythm with diurnal and tidal components which persists in constant dim light at constant temperature, whether the crabs are kept in moist air or continuously immersed in water.

Persistent tidal cycles of spontaneous motor activity have also been described in *Uca pugnax* by Bennett, Shriner and Brown (1957). These workers recorded the movements of individual crabs placed with a small amount of sea-water in plastic saucers covered with a circular piece of cardboard. The saucers were supported on one side by metal bands and attached on the other by nylon threads to ink writing pens recording on kymographs.

It was found that the crabs showed two peaks of activity 12 to 13 hours apart within one solar day. The movement of these peaks across successive solar days at an average tidal rate establish the reality of a tidal cycle persisting under laboratory conditions.

This report appears to be the first example of a clearly overt locomotor rhythm of primary lunar or tidal frequency. The rhythm persisted in constant conditions for at least a week, but after this some displacement of the peaks occurred. A low amplitude solar rhythm of activity was also apparent upon the analysis of 29 days of continuous data. This rhythm is characterised by high activity between 06.00 and 12.00 hours. Thus it would seem that a primary tidal rhythm of locomotory activity has, superimposed upon it, a diurnal rhythm which can only be appreciated statistically. In Chapter 6 we shall see that fiddler crabs show an overt diurnal rhythm of chromatophore expansion and contraction superimposed upon which is a tidal rhythm which can only be discerned by statistical analysis of the data. These conclusions have a logical ecological explanation. The emergence of fiddler crabs from their burrows is obviously related to the state of the tide, but the adaptive significance of chromatophore expansion is equally clearly related to day and night irrespective of the state of the tide. Fiddler crabs, therefore, have two simultaneous rhythms of different frequency, lunar and solar. One is the predominant regulator of activity, the other of colour change.

Fingerman, Lowe and Mobberly (1958) have recently suggested that the phases of the tidal rhythm in *Uca pugilator* and *U. minex* are set primarily according to the time that the area where the crabs live is uncovered by the receding water, and secondarily according to the time required for the area to drain so that the sand is firm enough to support holes from the burrows to the surface.

A tidal cycle of opening and closing of the valves also occurs in the oyster, *Crassostrea virginica*, according to Brown (1954) who found that specimens collected in Long Island Sound and shipped 1,000 miles westward to Evanston, Illinois maintained, in the laboratory, a rhythm in the opening of their shells which coincided with that of the tide in their original habitat. The tidal maxima thereafter gradually shifted to coincide with the times of maximum lunar gravitational attraction in Evanston.

Finally, Bennett (1954) recorded continuously the opening and closing of the valve of the common quahog, *Venus mercenaria*. Analysis of the records revealed a persistent tidal rhythm, the times of minimal opening coinciding with the times of low tide in the area where the animals were collected. A lunar cycle of maximum opening was also present, major peaks occurring every 29 days with a minor peak about midway in the cycle.

A number of additional examples of tidal rhythms of activity, oxygen consumption and colour change in invertebrates are cited by Calhoun (1945), Caspers (1951) and Fingerman (1957).

A somewhat different type of rhythm is seen in the lunar time-sense of sand-hoppers. In Chapter 7, an account is given of the work of Papi (1955a) on the solar navigation of sand-hoppers, *Talitrus saltator*. These Amphipods possess an orientation mechanism based on the position of the sun and therefore involving an endogenous solar time sense. In an earlier paper, however, it was shown that in its nocturnal migrations *T. saltator* orientates itself in a similar way but by the light of the moon. Since it can maintain a steady direction it must be able to make the necessary corrections for lunar movement (Papi and Pardi, 1953; Pardi and Papi, 1953).

BREEDING RHYTHMS IN MARINE ANIMALS

Great numbers of marine animals and plants have bi-monthly or monthly lunar breeding cycles in which all members of the species within a particular region become sexually active. This synchronisation is essential to the maintenance of the species, since it ensures that reproductive cells are discharged in sufficiently high concentrations to provide a reasonable chance of fertilisation taking place.

Thus, in addition to its daily tidal rhythms, *Convoluta roscoffensis* exhibits a fortnightly lunar variation. Colonies increase to a maximum during spring tides and decrease during neap tides as a result of periodicity of reproduction. The majority of animals in a mature colony discharge their egg capsules at the onset of spring tides. In most cases the body is ruptured, the hind end remains in the sand and only the front part forms the green patch on the sand. Thus at neap tides the size of patches decreases and hence the size of the colony on the surface of the sand at low tide (Gamble and Keeble, 1903, 1904).

There are a number of references as to the effect of moonlight on the breeding of marine animals, many of them dating from antiquity. For example, Aristotle said that the ovaries of sea-urchins acquired a greater size than usual at the time of the full moon; Cicero noted that oysters and all shell-fish increase and decrease with the moon, and Pliny stated that careful observers attribute to lunar power the increase and decrease of the bodies of oysters and shell-fish. The same belief is common today in many parts of the world. The amount of edible matter in sea-urchins, molluscs and crabs is stated to vary with the phases of the moon and some gourmets maintain that their flavour varies also (Fox, 1922).

In Volume 2 of the '*Philosophical Transactions*' of the Royal Society (1667), travellers to the East Indies are asked to enquire (p. 419) "Whether those shell-fishes, that are in these parts plump and in season at the full moon, and lean and out of season at the new, are found to have contrary constitutions in the East Indies?" At Suez, sea-urchins and crabs are said to be 'full' at full moon and 'empty' at new moon; at Alexandria the same is said of mussels and of sea-urchins; the Tarentines believe that oysters are fattest at full moon, while at Nice, Naples, Alexandria and in Greece, sea-urchins are said to be 'fullest' at full moon. The part of the sea-urchin which is eaten is the gonad, while in the crab it is the muscles, so these tissues are supposed to vary in bulk with the phases of the moon.

As Fox (1923, 1956) points out, however, while the supposition is untrue of mussels, *Mytilus* sp. and sea-urchins *Strongylocentrotus lividus*, in the Mediterranean and of mussels, *Mytilus variabilis*, and crabs, *Neptunus pelagicus*, in the Red Sea, it is based on fact as far as the sea-urchins, *Centrechinus setosus*, found at Suez are concerned. In this species the gonads undergo a cycle of growth and development corresponding with the phases of the moon. They are at their greatest bulk just before full moon at which time spawning occurs. The shrunken gonads then gradually fill again with ripening sexual products to be discharged at the next full moon.

Fox suggests that the idea spread from Suez in ancient times, passed to Greece and has persisted in Mediterranean countries until the present time; but he was unable to ascertain the nature of the physiological synchronisation of breeding with the lunar cycle.

The best known case of lunar productive periodicity is probably that of the 'Palolo' worm, a Polychaete that lives in Pacific coral reefs. At the last quarter of the moon in October and November, the posterior parts of the worms, laden with genital products, become detached from the anterior portions and swim to the surface where they shed their eggs and spermatozoa. (For references, see Caspers, 1951; Korringa, 1947).

Although many descriptions of the phenomenon have been published during the last century, Burrows (1945) gives such a graphic account of this that I quote from it at length. He writes: "During my period as commissioner, stationed at Levuka, I have seen the 'rising' at Tokou on several occasions. Nearly every year there are two risings, the first known as *Mbalolo lailai* (small Mbalolo) and the second as *Mbalolo levu* (large Mbalolo); 'large' and 'small' do not refer to the size of the worm but to the quantity of the worms. Occasionally there is no *Mbalolo lailai*.

"In a normal year the *Mbalolo lailai* appears about the end of October and is followed by the second, and main, rising about two or three weeks later. The main rising always occurs at dawn, and, literally, the worm comes up with the sun. It is, also, always at the time of high water.

"The worm, when it comes to the surface, is headless, and it is known that the head remains alive in the reef. The parts shed are from ten to fifteen inches long when they reach the top of the water and continue to wriggle. There was one old Fijian living in the village of Tokou who was a foreteller of the day of rising . . .

"When the first light of dawn appears, great funnels of worms burst to the surface and spread out until the whole area is a wriggling mass of them, brown and green in colour.

"When the tropical sun rises perpendicularly from the sea the catch is in full swing, and hundreds of boats, canoes and punts are filling up kerosene tins and jars by the simple process of dipping them out with nets. The worms also provide an annual feast for the fish; for all round and between the boats big fish and sharks cruise quietly along, gulping them in, and take no notice whatever of the boats or their occupants.

"As the sun makes itself felt, a change begins to occur in the length of the worms. They begin to break up into shorter and shorter bits, until some three hours after sunrise the entire surface of the sea shows nothing more than patches of scum. Mbalolo is rightly prized as very good eating . . .

"A curious fact is that all fish caught in the neighbourhood of the rising are poisonous to human beings for about ten days or a fortnight after the event."

In the Atlantic, another species *Leodoce fucata*, swarm at about the third quarter of the June-July moon, but if this falls late in July there is, in addition, an earlier swarm at the first quarter (see below).

The lunar breeding of the luminous worm *Odontosyllis enopla* in the West Indies has an unexpected historical interest. This worm swarms at the surface of the Atlantic during the night at the third quarter of the moon and the shining light from the females attracts the males. The luminescent glow at the surface of the sea lasts only 5 to 10 minutes: females appear first at the water surface and emit a stream of brilliantly luminous secretion with the eggs. Males then rush in with short, intermittent flashes. Now, on 11th October, 1492 at 22.00 hours a mysterious light was seen from the poop of Christopher Columbus' ship, the *Santa Maria*, just in the region where this occurs. It was compared with the flame of a small candle alternately raised and lowered. On that night the moon was one day from her third quarter. Crawshay (1935) suggests that this may be a point of evidence of first importance towards settling the problem of the landfall of Columbus in the West Indies.

Newell (1948) has shown that in Britain, the lugworm *Arenicola marina* spawns during 2 weeks in early autumn in the period between spring tides. There is only one spawning period in the year and the actual dates vary with the phases of the moon.

For many years the physiological nature of the rhythm has been uncertain, and somewhat contradictory experimental results obtained. Consideration of the literature, however, lends support to the view that rhythmic breeding is a response to the light of the moon rather than to the state of the tide, though this may be a contributory factor.

Hauenschild (1955) found that the sexual form of the worm, *Platynereis dumerilii*, has a breeding rhythm dependent upon the phase of the moon. A lunar periodicity of metamorphosis persisted for a year or more in the laboratory, but could be suppressed entirely by constant lighting. On the other hand, an artificial rhythm could be induced by artificial lighting and even very low light intensities (0.02 to 0.26 Lux) were effective.

Korringa (1941, 1947) has investigated the production of oyster larvae in the Basin of Oosterschelde, Holland, which show a marked periodicity in the course of the breeding season. The swarming of oyster larvae is not limited to a few days, but is distributed over several weeks, showing more and less important peaks. Maxima occur about 10 days after full and new moon, however, and since *Ostrea edulis* is an incubatory species it can be inferred that spawning occurs at both of the spring tides.

One of the maxima in the production of oyster larvae predominates; during the years 1935–46, it was the one that appeared between June 26 and July 10. Thus a reliable method for long-term prediction of the greatest maximum in the production of oyster larvae could be established. Analysis of the data on the production of oyster larvae showed that fluctuations in water temperature are unimportant and that it is probably the sequence of spring and neap tides which engenders rhythmical reproduction in the oyster and that rhythmical differences in water pressure are the agent in this. However, in areas with little or no tidal amplitude, other factors must be responsible for lunar rhythms of reproduction.

In his important review of the moon and periodicity in the breeding of marine animals Korringa (1947) lists the following well documented species that spawn at both full and new moon spring tides:

Leuresthes tenuis *Enchelyopus cimbrus*	Pisces
Littorina neritoides *Ostrea edulis*	Mollusca
Platynereis dumerilii *Odontosyllis phosphorea* *Ceratocephale osawai* *Nereis japonica* *Spirorbis borealis* *Amphitrite ornata*	Annelida

In these, the breeding period is known to vary from 2 weeks to several months, maxima in swarming or egg laying occurring at complementary phases of the moon, either at new and full moon, at first quarter and last quarter, or at a fixed number of days after new and full moon. A tidal range of considerable magnitude occurs in each case except that of *A. ornata*, the least well documented.

There are a number of animals which show maxima in reproductive activities once in the course of a lunar cycle. Korringa lists, amongst others:

Chaetopleura apiculata *Acanthozostera gemmata*	Mollusca
Platynereis dumerilii *P. megalops* *Odontosyllis enopla* *O. hyalina* *Eunice viridis* *E. fucata* *Lysidice oele*	Annelida

D

These animals all show a marked periodicity in reproduction directly associated with the phases of the moon. The breeding season may vary from one month to the whole year and maxima in spawning and swarming may vary in duration from a single night or day to about a fortnight. The influence of nocturnal illumination is here the environmental factor affecting maturation, for all the species live in shallow water in areas with a modest tidal range and are nocturnal in habit, sheltering during the daytime. Only in *E. fucata* and *P. dumerilii* has it been demonstrated that tidal features may have some influence on breeding.

Korringa (1947) concludes as follows: "In order to analyse cases of periodicity in reproduction a clear distinction should be made between the annual rhythm (the length of the breeding season), the monthly rhythm (periodicity correlated with tidal sequence or lunar cycle) and the daily rhythm (concentrating spawning or swarming to a certain well-defined hour of the day, or to certain phases of the tidal cycle). In extreme cases these three rhythms in combination can lead to a most complete concentration of reproductive activities in the species concerned, so that an entire population may spawn simultaneously during one single hour a year."

There is still not much information regarding tidal or lunar rhythms in vertebrates (Bullough, 1951; Fingerman, 1957). It is believed that both the Californian grunion, a small smelt some 6 inches long, and the New Zealand whitebait spawn only at particular phases of the moon, the process being repeated during 2 or 3 successive months. The grunion, *Leuresthes tenuis*, deposits its eggs at night on the sand near the high-water line during spring tides. These little fishes come ashore on the top of a wave, lie for a moment on the sand, and drop back into the sea with the succeeding wave. The eggs develop in dry sand, hatching when next they are covered with water.

Spawning occurs from March to midsummer with a peak of activity in April and May, so it is obvious that the lunar rhythm must overlie a deeper seasonal rhythm. F. N. Clark (1925) demonstrated that the same individuals take part in reproductive activity every spring tide, and suggested that rhythmical gamete ripening is correlated with the tidal sequence.

From the above account it will be seen that, in many cases, tides do not appear directly to be a causal factor in lunar periodicity of reproduction. It is, however, a little difficult to understand how moonlight could be responsible since the intensity of the light of the full moon is only about 1/500,000 times that of sunlight. Various authors have pointed out that the light of the moon is partially polarised, but even so, very much more polarised light is incident on the earth during the daytime than on moonlit nights. Moreover, even if the polarised light of the moon could cause a reproductive rhythm, this would be a bilunar, not a lunar cycle for maximum polarisation is at the first and third quarters. For this reason Fox (1932) has suggested that the moon may perhaps cause a lunar cycle in reproduction, not through its relatively small intensity of light as compared with that of the sun, but by the additional total number of hours of illumination per 24 hours at full moon, over and above a threshold light value.

It may be significant, therefore, that the minimum light whose photoperiod is known to induce diapause in the Arthropoda has a threshold above the maximum intensity of moonlight (Lees, 1955).

In view of the wide occurrence of lunar breeding cycles in marine invertebrates, it appears reasonable to postulate that endogenous diurnal and tidal rhythms may play an important role in regulating the frequencies and actual times of these breeding periods, including not only the synchronisation of swarming, mating or spawning behaviour, but also the synchronous anticipatory preparatory processes involved (Brown, Webb, Bennett and Sandeen, 1954).

LUNAR RHYTHMS IN TERRESTRIAL ANIMALS

With the exception of marine animals very few organisms are known that show lunar rhythms of activity, as can be seen from the important monograph by Caspers (1951). However, Hartland-Rowe (1955, 1958) in Africa, has recently shown that adult mayflies, *Povilla adusta*, appear in large numbers only at about the date of full moon. Analysis of the dates of 22 swarms observed between March 1953 and April 1955 at Kaazi (near Kampala) and at Jinja, both on Lake Victoria, shows that such swarms only occurred within 5 days of full moon, with the greatest number of swarms on the second night after full moon. On three occasions, swarms were recorded simultaneously at Jinja and Kaazi which are 50 miles apart.

Again, Corbet and Tjønneland (1955) have suggested that the flight activity of certain Trichoptera in East Africa may be greater on moonlit nights resulting from a positive response to light of low intensity. However, as mentioned above (p. 72) Williams, Singh and el Ziady (1956) have argued that in such instances the influence of the moon appears to be on emergence from the water and so on the size of the adult winged populations.

In the case of birds, Wynne-Edwards (1930) has shown that the nightjar, *Caprimulgus europaeus*, exhibits an apparent periodicity. A series of observations was made during the breeding season of the time at which a single male became active in the evening and it was found to be as much as 20 minutes later than usual at the time of full moon. It is not surprising that moonlight should affect the habits of a crepuscular bird. Furthermore, it was noticed that the greatest delay occurred, not exactly at full moon, but a few days before and a few days after it. The full moon rises at sunset and sets at sunrise, and being low in the sky at midsummer has practically no effect on twilight. A few days before it is full, however, it is high in the sky and thus gives considerable light at sunset. A few days after full moon a maximum effect on the morning twilight is achieved. This cannot affect the evening waking time of the nightjar directly, but may influence its rhythm of activity. The 2 eggs are laid during the last quarter of the lunar cycle so that the chicks are reared during the next full moon when hunting can be continued all night.

Similarly, it has been shown that when the eggs of a nightjar are taken, a period of 3 weeks must pass before the bird can lay again, in contrast to other species that have been studied (Marshall, F. H. A., 1942).

Caspers (1951) reviews a number of alleged and observed correlations between lunar rhythm and menstruation rate, distribution of births, urine secretion and colour vision changes in man. Apparently the physiological significance and causal relationships, if any, between these phenomena are not understood. In most cases the data are too few to permit exact statistical analysis.

Although the light of the moon has been supposed, from early times to influence the human menstrual cycle and breeding habits, this has been disproved by the work of Gunn, Jenkin and Gunn (1937) who collected menstrual data from normal women by a postal method in which tests of reliability were possible. The 770 women providing periodicity data were divided into 209 reliable, 270 fairly reliable and 291 unreliable cases. It was found that 90 per cent of cases had an average interval between the onsets of successive menstruations lying between 25 and 36 days inclusive. Three per cent had an average of 37 days or over, 7 per cent of less than 25 days and only about 2 per cent had an average of less than 24 days.

The duration of one interval was not influenced by the duration of its predecessor, but there was a progressive decrease in the average interval with increasing age amounting to 1 day in 5 or 6 years. There was no tendency for the interval to vary with the seasons of the year and *no connection whatever could be detected between menstruation and the moon* in the data of over 10,000 menstruations. Consequently any approximate coincidences would appear to be fortuitous.

Ten years' records of services of cows by two Indian buffalo bulls kept for stud purposes at the Government of Madras Agricultural Research Station, Kovilpatti (latitude 9°N) have shown that most of these occur at the time of the new moon, more cows coming on heat on dark nights (Ramanathan, 1932).

Siivonen and Koskimies (1955) have shown that the nightly activity of three caged capercailzies near Söderhamn, Sweden, was related to the lunar cycle. They suggest that restlessness was associated with physiological reproductive readiness depending on a fixed seasonal photoperiodic rhythm. When this critical period fell close to a new moon, the reproductive stimulation was temporarily suppressed until the next full moon, when nightly activity was again resumed.

Again, Harrison (1952a, b; 1954a, b) has investigated the effect of moonlight on the pregnancy of Malayan forest rats, *Rattus* spp. by calculating the distribution of intra-uterine litters in the lunar month. He has shown that there is a strong tendency for conceptions to be more frequent in the period before full moon. This is true for the nocturnal forest rats and to a less marked degree for house rats and rats of an oil-palm estate, but not for diurnal forest squirrels. No such effect could be detected with town rats, however, but, over three monthly periods, there was a correlation with the number of wet days in the period.

Little is known of lunar influences on the breeding cycles of non-marine vertebrates. It is, however, not impossible that precise timing of the breeding season of bats, *Miniopterus* sp. in the New Hebrides, may be ensured by the moon acting as a 'clue' and imparting great accuracy to the timing of an internal rhythm with approximately a yearly periodicity (Bullough, 1951) and, as we have seen (p. 35) it has been suggested that a lunar rhythm may be responsible for cyclical fluctuations in animal numbers in the Arctic.

CHAPTER 5

Seasonal and Reproductive Rhythms

SEASONAL RHYTHMS AND ANIMAL ECOLOGY

SEASONAL rhythms are apparent in the lives of almost all animals and only a few examples can be selected in the present volume. In the case of invertebrates, the life-cycles of most species are of a year's duration. Nevertheless the timing of the rhythm may vary in different species. For example, in his paper on intrageneric isolation among spiders, Tretzel (1955) shows that different species may be isolated in time as well as in space. This temporal separation is manifest, not only in the daily rhythms of activity but also in the yearly breeding cycles. Thus interspecific competition is avoided. For example, in Germany *Lycosa amentata* matures during March and April, *L. pullata* reaches a peak in May whilst the majority of specimens of *L. tarsalis* do not undergo their final moult until June and July. Again, the greatest number of *Goelotes inermis*, *Zelotes latreillei* and *Agroeca brunnea* reach maturity in the spring with a very much smaller peak in autumn; whilst the congeneric *C. atropos*, *Z. pretensis* and *A. proxima* show a major autumnal peak, many fewer reaching maturity in spring.

Seasonal changes are apparent in the behavioural responses of many species. Thus, Perttunen (1953) has shown that a marked seasonal change occurs in the humidity responses of the millipede *Schizophyllum sabulosum* in Finland. The dry summer reaction is gradually reversed to moist in the autumn when the animals hibernate. This seasonal change corresponds well with the ecology of the species: whereas in summer it is often to be found in dry places, it always hibernates in moist surroundings. A reversal of the normal humidity response also occurs in females about to lay eggs. These show a positive reaction to moisture which takes them to the damp localities in which oviposition takes place (Perttunen, 1955).

Seasonal changes have also been observed in the humidity reaction of the common earwig, *Forficula auricularia*. In summer the animals show a clear and strong 'preference' for the drier side of choice-chamber apparatus, but in the winter they respond positively to moist air which causes them to burrow into the soil for hibernation (Perttunen, 1952).

Stephens (1955) has recently found that exposure of American cray-

94

fishes, *Cambarus virilis,* to rather low light intensities during the winter months is capable of inducing moulting in animals which would fail to moult if maintained in constant darkness. The tendency to moult increases with increasing length of the photoperiod or daily periods of illumination, but there is a threshold below which the response does not occur. This lies below a day-length of approximately $10\frac{1}{4}$ hours. Stephens concluded that it does not seem likely that photoperiodic response can provide a complete explanation for the timing of events in the moulting cycle, but it appears that they can contribute towards it. Furthermore a clear influence of day-length upon the viability of the animals was demonstrated.

More recently, Dehnel (1958) has shown that the oxygen consumption of two intertidal crab species, *Hemigrapsus nudus* and *H. oregonensis,* in British Columbia, is affected by photoperiod. In general it was found that at 15°C and 35 per cent salinity there was a significant increase in oxygen consumption in animals exposed to an 8 hour photoperiod, compared with that of crabs exposed to 16 hours daily illumination. This suggests that when crabs are exposed in summer to winter light conditions they adjust their oxygen consumption to winter conditions and vice versa.

In a study of the effects of light on the Jassid *Euscelis plebyus,* Müller (1956) has shown that various seasonal forms can be induced by differing lengths of photoperiod, but that the effect is enhanced by seasonal differences in temperature and relative humidity. Apparently these factors influence the allometric growth gradient of the top of the penis; their combined action, which depends both upon latitude and local topography, causing the appearance of polymorphic forms.

That the duration of the daily period of illumination may affect the fecundity of insects has been shown in the case of the Queensland fruit-fly *Strumeta tryoni* by Browne (1956). Flies kept in constant darkness laid no eggs. When the daily period of light was $7\frac{1}{2}$ hours, flies under 120 lm/sq. ft. laid fewer eggs than those under either 60 or 240 lm/sq. ft., but at an illuminance of 240 lm/sq. ft. the longer the daily period of illumination, up to $7\frac{1}{2}$ hours, the greater was the number of eggs laid. Light had these effects on fecundity by influencing the amount of feeding, the rate of maturation of eggs, the readiness with which these were laid and the rate at which the flies mated. In constant darkness they fed little, did not mate and laid few eggs even when gravid: these eggs did not mature. When the daily period of illumination was $7\frac{1}{2}$ hours, flies under a light of 120 lm/sq. ft. fed less, matured eggs more slowly and mated later in life than those under either 60 or 240 lm/sq. ft. It is probable that the effects of light on feeding and egg laying were due to its influence on activity.

Hoar (1956) has demonstrated that different light periods affect thermal resistance in goldfishes. Short-day (8 hour) photoperiod fish are more resistant to cold than long-day (16 hour) ones, and the reverse is true for heat adaptation.

From a study of rhythms in the breeding behaviour of the European wren, *Troglodytes troglodytes*, Whitehouse and Armstrong (1953) showed that there is a steady decline during the day in the activity of the female. This is shown by the decreasing number of sorties from the nest as the day advances. There is also a diurnal reduction in the number of trips made by parent birds to the nestlings during the last week of the nestling period. These declines are not due to fatigue but to seasonal physiological changes in the birds.

Eyster (1954) has recently compared the influence of photoperiod, temperature and season on the activity of the English sparrow, *Passer domesticus*, the white-crowned sparrow, *Zonotrichia leucophrys*, the white-throated sparrow, *Z. albicollis* and the slate-coloured junco, *Junco hyemalis* in Illinois. He has shown that the non-migratory English sparrow does not display nocturnal activity at any season while the other species all show nocturnal unrest during the migratory season. The different species responded variously to the influence of extended photoperiod. In continuous light, the junco's activity was fairly evenly distributed over the 24 hours, but since this species nests in regions having up to 21 hours of daylight, one might expect its activity to be dispersed over a long period. On the other hand, the two species of *Zonotrichia* when kept in continuous light confined 85 per cent of their activity to a 14-hour period. Since they nest at a maximum photoperiod of 17 hours, they would be more likely to require a daily period of rest. The English sparrow, normally having two peaks of activity per day, was much more active than the other species and its activity was again more evenly distributed. All four species exhibit an increase in daytime activity when a shortage of food occurs.

Again, Tembrock (1958) found that the daily rhythm of activity of the crepuscular red fox, *Vulpes vulpes*, and of the Arctic fox, *Alopex lagopus* shows characteristic changes during the year. The greatest amount of daytime activity occurs in midsummer when there is a decrease in total activity, whilst the dawn peak disappears in winter and reappears at the time of 'heat'. In fact, the whole cycle of activity parallels the sexual cycle. There is a difference of 2 months between the two species because the Arctic fox retains its ancestral breeding period. The *Zeitgeber* for the diurnal rhythm is the change from light to darkness, but no exogenous synchroniser could be determined in the case of the annual cycle, although it was certainly connected with the physiological reproductive cycle.

In his paper on activity rhythms in the woodmouse and bank vole referred to above (p. 79), Miller (1955) showed that the diurnal and feeding rhythms of *Apodemus sylvaticus* and *Clethrionomys glareolus* respond markedly in amount and pattern to day-length. Woodmice began storing food when the day length was decreased from 16 to 12 hours, and bank voles when it decreased from 12 to 8 hours. Progressive decreases in day length also produced parallel changes in nocturnal preference between the two species.

On the other hand, not every mammal responds to the length of daylight and darkness. Wolf (1930) subjected Japanese dancing mice, *Mus wagneri*, to constant temperatures of between 4.0° and 31.5°C and found that the two major nocturnal peaks of activity were retained in their usual position, whether under a normal light cycle, continuous light or continuous darkness. Above 31.5°C there was an increase in activity associated with a shortening in the length of the feeding periods and an increase in their number. Likewise, below 4°C there was a decrease in total activity, a decrease in the number of feeding periods, which became longer, and an increase in the length of time between feeding periods.

These brief examples indicate some of the ways in which animal behaviour, physiology and ecology all respond to seasonal changes in photoperiodicity. Specific physiological changes are discussed in the following sections. In all these cases an innate rhythm or time sense is necessary for the change in photoperiod to be appreciated, but the nature of this time sense is unknown.

PHOTOPERIODICITY AND DIAPAUSE IN ARTHROPODS

The possession of a resting phase enables many organisms to persist in inconstant environments and regions that would otherwise be unfavourable for permanent habitation. The dormant state of 'diapause' is usually characterised by the temporary failure of growth or reproduction, by reduced metabolism and often by enhanced resistance to climatic factors such as cold, heat or drought; but in borderline cases it is difficult to distinguish it from simple 'quiescence'. Despite the generality of the phenomenon throughout living organisms, it is among the Arthropoda where normal growth is essentially discontinuous, that examples are most numerous and varied. In the case of phytophagous insects the onset of diapause frequently coincides with some distinctive phase in the growth cycle of the host plant, yet experiments have revealed that there is no causal connection between these events.

Diapause usually occurs in that state of the life cycle which is best adapted to resist the rigours of the climate. Thus, among insects it may occur in the egg before the embryo has completed segmentation and also when the embryo is mature and apparently ready to hatch, as well as in a number of intermediate stages. For any one species, however, the stage is uniform. In the larva or nymph, diapause may occur at the close of any instar, but is more frequent in the early instars or the last one: it is also common in pupae and can occur in adults. The significance of diapause in relation to the ecology of insects has recently been reviewed by Andrewartha (1952) to whose work the reader is referred for further details.

In the case of eggs, diapause may be induced by comparatively simple changes in the physical properties of the medium surrounding the embryo. For example, the entry of water at the onset of diapause may be cut off by the deposition of a waxy layer over the surface of the hydropyle and the immediate cause of the growth arrest is lack of water, since adequately chilled eggs will not develop if the entry of water is prevented and diapause can be broken by immersing the eggs in wax solvents and then allowing them to take up water in carefully controlled quantities.

Many insects in a state of diapause die when exposed to temperatures that might normally be expected to favour development. It has been known for many years that temperature shocks and other stimuli sometimes cause growth to be resumed. The mechanism of diapause development may therefore be dependent on the interaction of two or more processes which have different positive growth coefficients and which compete for the same substrate, for subsequent growth is often promoted by exposure to temperatures that are too low to permit the growth of the non-diapause stages and it has been shown that the cytochrome-cytochrome-oxidase system is not concerned in maintaining metabolism in the diapause embryo. On the other hand, in most insects with facultative diapause the agencies which induce diapause cease to exert any action once growth has been arrested. Indeed, they are frequently divorced from the processes, often thermally controlled, which terminate the arrest of growth; but occasionally day-length is the controlling agency and growth arrest remains under the immediate control of the inducing factor. [For details of this research, see "The Physiology of Diapause in Arthropods" by Lees (1955).]

When diapause occurs in the post-embryonic stages of morphogenesis, these adjustments are co-ordinated by humoral means although the physiological responses are linked to external stimuli such as temperature and length of day which serve as an index of the season. As a device for measuring time, however, it is clearly necessary that the photoperiodic reaction should be independent of random diurnal fluctuations. Some significance may also be attached to the fact that the threshold of sensitivity to light seems to be just above the intensity of direct moonlight (Lees, 1955).

It has long been known that insects suffer an arrest of growth when deprived of the source of the moulting hormone, and it is not impossible therefore, as Hinton (1954) suggests, that a diapause hormone which arrests growth may be secreted by the sub-oesophageal ganglion and be inhibited by the prothoracic gland hormone. Diapause is brought about by the conjunction in time of two distinct events—a diapause hormone must arrest growth in most tissues and the prothoracic glands must cease to secrete. Thus diapause may be broken independently either by the secretion of the prothoracic gland hormone or by the destruction of the diapause hormone. It would be most interesting if a relationship could be shown to exist between this diapause hormone and the hormone, also secreted by the sub-oesophageal ganglion, that has been shown to control the diurnal rhythm of locomotory activity in the cockroach, *Periplaneta americana* (see p. 170).

Unlike many vertebrates, the majority of arthropods probably respond to the actual duration of the light and dark components of the cycle of illumination and not to the change in day length. For example, although in nature the winter females of the red-spider mite, *Metatetranychus ulmi*, appear in late summer as the days are becoming shorter, only summer females are differentiated if the developing mites are subjected to a long photoperiod falling each day by 7 minutes (Lees 1953). Similarly, in other insects diapause is not prevented by regular daily increments of light, provided that the insects experience a short day length during the sensitive period of larval development.

On the other hand, in the slowly developing dragonfly, *Anax imperator*, in Britain, the onset of diapause is influenced by the progression of the photoperiod (Corbet, 1957a). In this species, larval populations showed a wide measure of temporal variation, yet emergence was restricted regularly to a period of about 45 days each year between mid-May and mid-July. The first 14 days of adult life are spent away from water. After this, when sexually mature, adults return to the aquatic habitat for reproduction.

Duration of the larval stage is usually about 2 years, but exceptionally it may be completed in one, growth being restricted to the period from May to October. The thermal coefficient for growth is high, but two factors extend the duration of the larval stage: a high 'lower temperature threshold' for growth, and a diapause in the final instar. This diapause is facultative and only affects larvae entering the final instar after May. These do not undergo metamorphosis until the following spring. Thus, although in England *A. imperator* is chiefly a 'spring' species, a small proportion of the population exists as a 'summer' species and thereby obviates the necessity for full-grown larvae to prolong the life-history by one year (Corbet, 1957a).

In the 'summer' species, *Coenagrion mercuriale* and *Ceriagrion tenellum*, the eggs are laid in June and July and hatch about a month later. During the first winter larvae are about 4 to 5 mm. long. Most individuals pass the second winter in the penultimate instar, which they enter in the autumn. Ecdysis to the final instar occurs abruptly in spring and is followed closely by metamorphosis and emergence.

A facultative diapause may exist in the penultimate instar, but a synchronising factor operates between the resumption of growth in spring and emergence. Corbet (1957b) has suggested that this may be achieved by a rising series of lower temperature thresholds for successive developmental stages in spring.

Diapause is of value to the varied carpet beetle, *Anthrenus verbasci*, because it induces a rhythm in the life cycle which synchronises with the rhythm of the seasons and ensures that the adults are present when the environment is favourable for their activity. The cycle of active growth and rest persists when development takes place under constant laboratory conditions. Furthermore, an alignment of alternating active and diapause periods in individuals developing at different temperatures and therefore at different stages of their development, indicates an internal rhythm common to all, having a period of about 41 weeks compared with the annual rhythm of development under outdoor, fluctuating conditions. No doubt the shorter interval is basic, and in nature, although diapause may be completed, activity does not begin until a threshold temperature has been attained (Blake, 1958).

As Hinton (1957) points out, insects that have facultative diapause take account of certain attributes of the environment, especially day length and temperature, in such a way that at a much later stage of their life cycle, the brain ceases to inhibit the release of the diapause hormone. "The period of the life history that is sensitive to day length or other token stimuli of the environment may be short or long, but as a rule it is restricted largely to one stage or one instar, and sometimes the incidence of diapause is determined by token stimuli acting over a period of no more than 2 days or so in a particular part of a particular instar. Between the reception of the token stimuli and the response of the brain many days, weeks, or even months may elapse and in the meantime the insect may have developed to quite a different stage, say from egg to pupa. In other words, a 'time-keeping' process is here evident. This process is of course quite distinct from the processes that initiate, maintain and end diapause.

"The extreme accuracy of the 'time-keeping' is evident when we consider that diapause is nearly always initiated in each species in only one stage of development. The environmental conditions that determine that diapause shall be initiated always precede the initiation of diapause.

In the silkworm (*Bombyx mori* L.), for instance, diapause is determined in a late embryonic stage, the release of the diapause hormone is not initiated by the brain until the pupal stage, and the hormone does not take effect until the eggs of the next generation are one or more days old. In another moth, *Polychrosis botrana* Schiff., there is a pupal diapause that is determined in the egg stage. In most pupal diapauses, however, determination occurs in one of the larval stages, and in larval diapauses in an earlier larval instar or in the egg. But in many insects diapause occurs in the early embryo before the differentiation of the nervous or endocrine systems. It has been suggested that in all these, diapause is maternally determined as it is in the silkworm (Hinton, 1954)."

This 'time-keeping' has not been investigated and no evidence is available as to the part of the organism in which it occurs. "On very general grounds it might be provisionally assumed to be in the brain, but at present there seems to be no good reason to suppose that it is not in some other tissue or tissues." (Hinton, 1957). Certainly it is necessary to distinguish between the processes concerned with the determination of diapause and those concerned with its initiation.

In conclusion it can be stated that as a general rule the photoperiodic reaction in arthropods is independent of intensity and total light-energy provided that the intensity exceeds a threshold value. In most cases, no doubt in correlation with their short life-cycle, arthropods probably respond to the actual duration of light and dark rather than to changes in the length of the daylight.

BREEDING CYCLES IN BIRDS AND MAMMALS

It has long been known that the breeding seasons of birds and mammals (Marshall, F. H. A., 1910 etc.), like the flowering and leaf-fall of plants (Baker and Baker, 1, 1936; Kellerman, 1926 etc.), result from the interaction of two agencies: external environment and internal rhythm. In some organisms the environmental control of seasonal changes is all-important, while in others internal rhythm predominates, though never so completely as to make the organism quite free from environmental control.

Consequently the internal rhythm may be maintained, at any rate for a time, when an organism is brought from one hemisphere to the other. This was pointed out as long ago as 1910 by F. H. A. Marshall in his monumental work "The Physiology of Reproduction".

Thus, Baker and Ranson (1938) showed that most birds of the southern hemisphere breed there in spring and summer. Specimens of many species imported into Europe change their rhythm so as to breed in the spring and summer of the northern hemisphere, but the Northern Rosella parrot, *Platycercus venustus*, the budgerigar, *Melopsittacus undulatus* and the Gouldian finch, *Poëphila gouldiae*, have a rhythm that is not easily influenced by the environment, for, when imported into the northern hemisphere, they continue to breed in the same calendar months as the members of their species in their native land.

In view of the vast amount of carefully documented information regarding breeding cycles in vertebrates (Bullough, 1951; Marshall, F. H. A., 1910, 1936, 1942; Parkes, 1952) this aspect of seasonal rhythms will be discussed only briefly and especially in relation to the synchronisation of the internal endocrine sexual system with external environmental changes. The exteroceptive factors that modify the internal rhythm act through the agency of the central nervous system, and probably through the hypothalamus, upon the anterior pituitary gland, whose secretory functions vary according to the stimulation received.

In general, spring is the period of greatest sexual activity, but there is much specific variation and among ruminating mammals, autumn breeding is common.

Experiments with light and ultra-violet radiation indicate that with the majority of vertebrates breeding occurs in response to seasonal changes, of which increase of light is the most important. In the case of the red deer, however, a fall in temperature is essential to bring the animals into their full autumn rut. (For references, see Marshall, 1942.)

The first person to show experimentally that light was a cause of cyclical reproductive activity was Rowan (1926, 1929 etc.) who conducted experiments upon the migratory Canadian bunting, *Junco hyemalis*. By exposing the birds in mid-winter, in Canada, to ordinary electric light, despite the cold, he obtained an increase in the size of the gonads comparable to what occurs with the increase of daylight in spring. This work was afterwards confirmed with crows and canaries. Later, Bissonette (1930, 1933 etc.) extended it to the European starling, *Sturnus vulgaris*, in which he found that intensity and wave-length, as well as the daily period of light, were factors in promoting sexual activity. Similar results were obtained shortly afterwards (Bissonette, 1932 etc.) with ferrets, *Putonius vulgaris*, as well as with voles and other mammals, and it has been shown that hypophysectomised animals are unaffected by lighting and go into permanent anoestrus (Marshall, F. H. A., 1936 etc.).

Not only do sexual display and courtship phenomena among animals serve to keep the sexes together, but they have the further and more general function of promoting an effective synchronisation of the male and female reproductive processes, thus favouring successful procreation. The precise nature of the stimuli involved is variable, but the synchronisation achieved again acts through the intermediation of the hypothalmus as in the case of other stimuli (Armstrong, 1947; Marshall,

F. H. A., 1936, 1942; Marshall, A. J., 1954; Tinbergen, 1951 etc.). It may be not without significance that the acts of display which thus synchronise breeding rhythms are themselves usually rhythmical.

The relationship between latitude and the breeding season in birds has been discussed by Baker (1939) who shows that as one goes north from the temperate latitudes a general tendency appears for the egg-laying seasons of birds to start later and later, at the rate of some 20 or 30 days per 10° latitude. As one goes south from the temperate latitudes into the northern tropical and equatorial zones, however, one finds a general tendency for the Accipiters, Coraciiformes and, to a lesser extent, the Passeres to begin laying earlier. In the northern hemispheres, Charadriiformes, Grallae, Herodiones, Anseres and other aquatic birds tend to breed later in tropical and equatorial zones than in the sub-tropical and temperate.

The main proximate causes of the breeding seasons of birds in nature are thought to be temperature and length of day in the boreal and temperate regions, and rain and intensity of insolation near the equator. It is unlikely that the stimulus provided by the sun is its visible or ultra-violet light, and Baker (1938) has shown that the rainy seasons, which usually coincide with the overhead sun, are likely to be effective, especially perhaps in the case of aquatic birds. Much egg-laying occurs when the days are getting shorter but little when the length of daylight is below 11 hours and none when it is less than 10.

Baker (1939) continues: "Despite all the intensely interesting experiments on the effect of light on the reproduction of birds, for which we are indebted mostly to the pioneer work of Rowan (1929 and earlier and later papers), and of Bissonnette (1930, etc.) yet clearly length of day stands in no direct and obvious relation to the breeding seasons of birds under natural conditions. One is forced to the conclusion that light is only one of the factors concerned. Why, otherwise, should birds breed later in the boreal zone than in the temperate? After the March equinox the days are longer the further one goes north. The late arrival of migrants in the extreme north is no complete answer, for the phenomenon is also seen with resident species. It is difficult to exclude the possibility that temperature may be an important factor, despite the fact that under experimental conditions one can induce the growth of the testes of certain birds at extremely low temperatures by increasing the light-ration. An internal cause affecting (but not completely controlling) the onset of the breeding season is the internal rhythm, which is sometimes so strong as to cause a southern hemisphere bird to breed at the locally 'wrong' time of year, when introduced into the northern hemisphere (Baker and Ranson, 1938). Internal rhythm probably often plays an important part in determining the onset of the breeding season a considerable time before the external proximate causes stimulating reproduction are beginning to be effective."

Although there appears to be overwhelming evidence that migration and sexual periodicity in numerous species of temperate zone birds are somehow controlled by light and dark fluctuations, A. J. Marshall (1954) also strikes a note of caution. The majority of experiments have been carried out under conditions that have little in common with the normal lives of the birds involved. "Most of the experiments have been crude in the extreme, and have involved merely the photo-stimulation of caged males for various daily periods with different intensities and wavelengths ... It is one thing to stimulate a bird's neuro-hormonal apparatus by massive illumination but another to show that the small difference in daylength naturally occurring between 21st December and 8th January does the same thing in, for example, the British robin in the Midlands where the weather is so often very dull and foggy."

Nevertheless, the time-sense involved is the same order as that required for solar navigation and as in the case of diurnal changes, increase or decrease in light intensity are likely to give a far more reliable indication of seasonal change throughout the year than are alternations in any other physical factor of the environment.

Nevertheless, numerous published data indicate that the breeding season fluctuates according to the mildness or severity of the weeks preceding breeding and it is evident that several climatic factors are involved in the synchronisation of reproductive rhythms, in addition to the duration of daylight.

The interactions between these environmental factors and the internal rhythms of animals, similar to those between 'clues' and diurnal rhythms, are discussed by Aschoff (1958) who concludes his recent review of the influence of the *Zeitgeber* as follows:

"It is only in rare cases that the external factor which originally caused adaptation, for instance the relation between hunter and prey, will take over the function of a timegiver too. In some cases a succession of several timegivers may guarantee the controlled series of events. This particularly applies to the yearly periodicity. It is quite possible that, in the animal's environment, one timegiver more or less merges into the next in much the same manner in which, within the organism, in the anoestrous cycle of organs, one state of endocrine functions merges into the next and as one behaviour pattern is replaced by the following one. In animals breeding in spring the growth of the gonads is controlled by the increasing duration of the daily period of light, the anoestrous period being the shortened day-length of winter. It is hard to decide at what times the endogenous factor and at what times the timegiver is more effective in this interaction.

"The better the endogenous factor is developed the greater is its influence, under normal conditions, on the course of events and the more, correspondingly, the timegiver tends to function as a mere synchroniser determining the phases without using up much energy. Under these conditions the timegiver can be likened to what is called a *Steuerfrequenz* in technical terms. If the timegiver is altered—in the sense of a shifting of the phases, or a change of form of period or of frequency—an interaction develops between the pair of forces, the endogenous periodicity and the timegiver; in this case the behaviour of the animal is, within the limits of its plasticity, the resultant of these forces."

To summarise. The final timing of migration and the breeding season of most species of animals appears to be controlled not by a single factor such as photoperiodicity, but by a combination of external stimuli, including behavioural ones, which vary in different species but nevertheless operate through sense organs upon the internal rhythms of the individual. In the case of vertebrates, this mediation operates through the exteroceptors, the central nervous system, the hypothalamus and anterior pituitary which secretes the appropriate gonadotrophic hormones.

VERTEBRATE BREEDING RHYTHMS IN THE TROPICS

Parts of the tropics which experience almost uniform climatic conditions throughout the year are of extreme interest to students of seasonal rhythms. In such countries some animals can always be found breeding, but the majority of species maintain regular annual cycles and the question arises as to how these can maintain their synchronisation with the calendar.

The most important survey of breeding rhythms in the tropics is that of Baker and his co-workers (1936–47) describing the results of the Oxford University Expedition to the New Hebrides in 1933–4. At Hog Harbour on Espirito Santo, where the expedition was based, the mean temperature varies only 2°C between the warmest and coolest months, the longest day is only 1¾ hours longer than the shortest and there is no dry season.

Particularly interesting results were obtained with bats. In temperate regions these animals usually mate in autumn although ovulation and fertilisation by the stored sperms does not take place until the spring. In the New Hebrides, the fruit-bat, *Pteropus geddici*, usually copulates about February to March, and gives birth to young in August and September. The social habits of both sexes vary seasonally too, so there is a distinct breeding season, despite the small seasonal climatic change (Baker and Baker, 1936b).

Now Baker and Baker, (1936a) have argued that physiological mechanisms could never alone account for periodicity in seasonal breeding.

A thousand clocks set off ticking together would sooner or later get out of time and before long the differences would become larger. Yet the striking feature of breeding seasons in animals is that the whole population of a species matures together with little variability.

A hypothetical clock varying only 6 minutes per year could, since the last ice age, result in a spring-breeding animal reproducing at the opposite time of the year today. The internal 'clock' would need periodic adjustment.

Although the food of fruit-bats varies considerably during the year, certain foods are available at all times; and Baker and Bird (1936) do not consider that this is a factor of importance. Nor does it appear that temperature controls the onset of the mating season either. During the period when the testes are increasing in size, the length of the day and the hours of sunshine are increasing very slightly and the amount of ultra-violet light is increasing more markedly, so this may be the significant factor.

The insectivorous bat, *Miniopterus australis*, presents an even more sharply defined breeding cycle. Copulation occurs in that part of the year corresponding with the southern spring. Fertilisation and development of the embryo proceed without delay and there is no evidence of prolonged storage of sperms by the female (Baker and Bird, 1936).

That a cave-dwelling species in an almost unvarying climate should nevertheless possess a sharply defined breeding season is remarkable. It might be thought that the duration of twilight could influence the bats, but it has been shown that there is no regular change in the period of dusk and dawn in those regions, so this cannot be the explanation. As suggested in an earlier chapter, however, (p. 93) it may be that the lunar cycle imparts great accuracy to the timing of an internal rhythm with approximately a yearly periodicity (Bullough, 1951).

Baker (1939) has shown that there is a general tendency for birds in the tropics to reach the height of their main breeding seasons somewhat before the sun passes overhead. Two breeding seasons in the year are therefore quite common, but birds that breed only once select either the northward or southward swing of the sun. The Accipiters, Passeres and Coraciiformes are an example of the former, aquatic families such as the Charadriiformes, Grallae, Herodiones and Anseres of the latter.

Not only bats, but birds too, exhibit seasonal reproduction in unvarying tropical climates, as Baker, Marshall and Harrison (1940) have shown in their study of the Golden Whistler, *Pachycephala pectoralis*, in the New Hebrides. The onset of breeding is not so dramatically abrupt as in bats, but the seasonal change in the size of the testes is far greater. In this case, no suggestion was made as to the environmental change controlling the breeding-season. Certainly, increasing daylight does not stimulate the testes because these grew by regular monthly increments from January to June while the days were growing shorter and while they were increasing from October to December, the testes were shrinking to less than one fortieth. Baker (1947) concluded the series of papers by himself and his co-workers (1936–47) with the words: "It seems probable that the breeding seasons of the animals investigated are regulated by some altogether unsuspected cause or causes." I am unable to accept this conclusion and think it more probable that reproduction is associated directly or inversely with some factor such as length of day which does vary a few minutes in most places during the year.

In certain tropical species, however, the uniform climate does seem to have the effect of eliminating breeding seasons. A breeding season also tends to disappear in certain social species in temperate regions. Thus, certain penguins are almost unique among birds in having freed themselves from external influences. In this respect they are comparable to man and the domestic dog of which the male is capable of breeding at any time of year while the female experiences a regular sexual cycle which appears to occur independently of external stimulation. Black-footed and other penguins can breed several times a year in captivity and many sea birds appear to have a continuous breeding season.

On the other hand, the Sooty tern, *Sterna fuscata*, has a breeding season about every 9 months on Ascension Island. In consequence, the nesting season begins earlier each year, and the birds breed on the average four times within 3 years. "It would seem as if in this species breeding periodicity depended entirely upon an internal sexual rhythm unaffected by seasonal exteroceptive factors." (Marshall, 1936). Of course, the cycle for each individual tern need not be exactly on time, because courtship and mutual stimulation will ensure synchronisation. Nevertheless, one must admit that the birds' internal chronometers are exceptionally accurate over many months.

CHAPTER 6

Biological 'Clocks' in Crustacea and the Influence of Exogenous Factors

RHYTHMIC colour change in Crustacea has been investigated over a number of years, and the evidence obtained is discussed here in relation to one of the major problems postulated by the existence of periodic phenomena, viz. are rhythms due to physiological 'clocks', or do organisms act as cosmic receiving stations?

Environment-independent, or endogenous rhythms which persist under constant conditions at different temperatures have been reported for great numbers of animals and plants. Most of the observations have been made after placing the animals in darkness at some arbitrarily selected temperature and have therefore implied temperature-independence of the mechanisms responsible for maintaining the frequency of the cycles, at least over a few degrees of temperature. For example, Welsh (1941) found that the diurnal-pigment of the crayfish *Cambarus bartoni* persists at the same frequency in animals maintained in constant darkness at constant temperatures. The migration of the retinal pigments to the day position when the pseudopupil of the eye is small or absent is due to the release of a hormone from the sinus gland. Migration to the night position when the pseudopupil is large is due to a reduction in the amount of hormone released and a subsequent lowering of the amount in the blood stream. Nevertheless the only reported difference between two groups of animals, one of which was maintained at 6 to 8°C, the other at 21 to 23°C, was the length of time for which the rhythms persisted, the time being 4 months at the lower and 5 at the higher temperature.

The innervation of the sinus gland is complex: it is supplied by motor fibres from the oculomotor nerves, from the medulla terminalis and the supra-oesophageal ganglion. Welsh suggested that tonic inhibitory centres in the medulla terminalis or supra-oesophageal ganglion normally prevent the release of the retinal pigment hormone and that stimulation of the eye by light reduces or abolishes the activity of these inhibitory centres, thus permitting the release of the hormone. The evidence for this hypothesis, however, was largely indirect and based on the observed effects of anaesthesia, oxygen lack, low temperature and general inactivity and it was suggested that these factors tend to lower the activity of the nervous centres, thereby indirectly causing a migration of retinal pigments towards the positions characteristic of the light, even though the animals were maintained in darkness.

The diurnal colour change in the fiddler crab *Uca* has been shown to persist for as long as 30 days under conditions of constant darkness, constant temperature and under water (Brown and Webb, 1948). However, when all metabolic processes were greatly reduced in rate by temperatures in the neighbourhood of 0°C, the diurnal rhythm was delayed by an interval approximately that of the time of exposure to the low temperature. Thus a rhythm which had been delayed for approximately 6 hours appeared to continue in constant darkness as a 24-hour rhythm 6 hours out of phase and persisted unmodified for at least 6 days. From this it was concluded that the frequency of the rhythm must, at least in part, be metabolically determined and specific events in the rhythm are not controlled directly by specific external events.

More recently persistent rhythms of primary solar and primary lunar frequencies for oxygen-consumption have been described in two species of fiddler crab, *Uca pugnax* and *U. pugilator* and in the salamander *Triturus viridescens* by Brown, Webb, Bennett and Sandeen (1955). They claim these rhythms appear to be statistical rather than overt, for they become apparent only when the data of several days is averaged. The form of the daily variation in oxygen-consumption shows a monthly variation, the form of the rhythm for a 2-week period straddling a new moon being different from that straddling a full moon. In all three species, the rate of oxygen-consumption increases in direct relationship with the concurrent rate of barometric pressure fall and decreases in direct relationship with the rate of pressure rise, but there appears to be less correlation with the absolute barometric pressure. Indeed, the rhythm of barometric pressure changes includes a very large random component owing to storms, etc., and this, it is suggested, accounts for the fact that rhythms imposed upon the animals by such factors as this appear not to be overt, whereas the pattern of the daily changes in overt rhythms such as those of colour change and retinal pigment migration are usually quite different from the basic metabolic rhythms and also from each other. The overt rhythms are probably directly regulated by an internal 'clock' which can be reset by light and temperature but the imposed statistical rhythm seems to be unmodified when the internal 'clock' is reset.

In other words, the phases of the 24-hour rhythm of colour change could be reversed in relation to solar time by delaying the colour change for 12 hours with very low temperatures, while the phases of oxygen consumption were not affected. Therefore it is to be concluded that the 24-hour rhythms of different functions do not affect each other.

Brown, Webb, Bennett and Sandeen (1955) conclude as follows:

"Although we still know little or nothing about any functional inter-relations between the internal and imposed daily rhythms, it is tempting to speculate that the imposed one in some manner contributes to the observed temperature-independence of the internal clock, at least over extended periods. A reasonably accurate daily internal clock would seem also to be a necessity in the resolution of the phases of the external rhythms which become evident only when several days of data are averaged. The daily clocks of the animals may well be a consequence of the co-operation of these two rhythms. Suggesting this is the often-observed variation in the times that the animals go into the night phase in their overt daily rhythm of colour change. The variation about a mean may be more than a half hour from day to day, and yet there is no statistical drift in constant darkness even over months. This would find a reasonable explanation in terms of the internal clock being reset continuously by the rhythms of these factors which are responsible for the imposed clock."

It is obvious from the numerous publications on the subject by Brown and his co-workers that the problem of the temperature-independent metabolic clock system in the Crustacea is an extremely complex one. Superimposed upon the diurnal rhythm in *Uca pugnax* and the blue crab *Callinectes sapidus* is a tidal rhythm with a frequency of 12.4 hours (see p. 84). This rhythm is manifested by a supplementary dispersion of melanin which occurs about 50 minutes later each day. The tidal rhythm is most evident when the low or high tide occurs either in the morning or in late afternoon. Under these conditions the diurnal rhythm curve is skewed to the left or right or tends to be bimodal, depending upon the times of the tides, but there is no difference in the response to low or high tide. The tidal rhythm maintained under constant laboratory conditions persists even on days that the normal diurnal tidal cycle of their original habitat becomes semidiurnal (when there are two low and two high tides per lunar day†). This phenomenon occurs twice each lunar month in the Gulf of Mexico, when the moon is in the plane of the equator. Only once every 14.8 days are the diurnal and tidal rhythms in the same phase relative to one another. Thus these animals can be said to exhibit a semilunar rhythm also. When the phases of the diurnal rhythm were abruptly shifted by light changes so that they occurred about 5 hours earlier in the day, the phases of the tidal rhythm followed by approxi-mately the same number of hours in the same direction. The tidal rhythm during the shift thus maintained its temporal relations with

† 24.8 hours.

the diurnal. This means that the precise temperature-independent diurnal rhythmic mechanism participates in the endogenous mechanism of tidal rhythmicity (Brown, Fingerman, Sandeen and Webb, 1953; Fingerman, 1955).

The tidal rhythms of *Uca pugilator* and *U. speciosa* are similar, a tidal component moving across the diurnal rhythm as the tide becomes progressively later in the day. Again, no detectable difference in the character of the pigment migration was apparent at times of low and high tide (which occur 12.4 hours apart where these two species of *Uca* were collected). The tidal rhythm of *Uca speciosa* however was 6 hours behind that of *U. pugilator* which may be correlated with the fact that *U. pugilator* lives at a lower level of the beach (Fingerman, 1956).

The diurnal rhythm in fiddler crabs appears to be a very deeply seated physiological phenomenon. If its phases are altered experimentally, the altered condition persists for long periods with its characteristic frequency and the same applies to lunar rhythms. Like the former, to be of adaptive value to the organism, the tidal rhythm must have its frequency independent of temperature (otherwise it would be speeded up in summer and slowed down in winter) and this appears to be achieved by using the diurnal rhythm as a portion of the tidal-rhythm mechanism which is superimposed upon it. "It has been of some doubt to many biologists that the diurnal rhythm was actually of adaptive significance to the crabs inasmuch as field observations led to the conclusion the animals were as active by day as by night. As a regulator of normal rhythmic activity the diurnal rhythm could be highly significant if the mechanism were proven to be essential to the existence of a tidal rhythm. There is a clear tidal rhythm of feeding activity of *Uca* in their natural habitats.

"It is interesting to speculate that rhythms comparable to those in the fiddler crab are present in many other animals and plants to constitute a basis of persistent semilunar and lunar periods of activity and breeding. Lunar breeding cycles have been abundantly described for marine animals. As far as is known there is no published evidence that such lunar rhythms persist under constant laboratory conditions. While it is difficult to understand how direct lunar influences could become of such importance to organisms as to become responsible for the determination of such periodic breeding, it seems easier to understand how such diurnal and tidal cycles could, by natural selection, impose rhythms upon organisms. As this investigation has clearly shown, the simultaneous presence of persistent tidal and diurnal rhythms in the same organism produces, as a resultant, a persistent semilunar rhythm. The phases of the semilunar rhythm may obviously bear any relation to the phases of the moon simply by having differences of the phases of the tidal cycle with respect to the solar cycle for any given day. Once fixed in their inter-relations the tidal and solar cycles then repeat their detailed relation-ships with one another every half lunar period. Lunar periods could be physiologically demarked by having the organism require the induced events from two such cycles to complete breeding preparation.

"It is possible that such persisting rhythms may in some manner con-tribute to the production of longer biological cycles than lunar ones. Adaptive environmentally induced modifications of physiological expressions of the diurnal and tidal rhythms may co-operate with varying environmental factors even in the production of annual cycles.

"Finally, it is interesting to note that the diurnal and tidal rhythms possess another highly adaptive characteristic. They are readily brought into synchrony with external physically varying events. Since some factors, e.g. temperatures near freezing, can get them out of synchrony these rhythms would soon get the organism out of feeding and breeding harmony with their fellows and the physical environment, were not the phases capable of being efficiently reset" (Brown, Fingerman, Sandeen and Webb, 1953).

One of the chief problems posed by rhythmic phenomena is how a metabolic 'clock' can maintain such uncanny precision for so long and over such a wide temperature range.

"If it is postulated that the normal rhythm is maintained exclusively by a series of metabolic events proceeding at a relatively precise rate, one seeks in vain for descriptions of a biological mechanism which could reasonably be expected to maintain the rhythms in all the conditions under which they have been observed. Such a mechanism requires a process unaffected by temperature, a temperature-compensating mechanism, or a temperature-regulating mechanism. Such mechanisms for *Uca* are entirely hypothetical; but even with the existence of such a one, it is difficult to credit it with sufficient precision to account for the remarkable synchronisation of the rhythm of *Uca* for as long as a month in constant darkness at such a wide temperature range" (Brown and Webb, 1948).

This indeed is the crux of the problem. Furthermore, the possibility that some diurnally rhythmic factor in the external environment is operating cannot be entirely ruled out. But if such a rhythmical event acts as a pacemaker for a series of metabolic events within the organism, there is still a difficulty, although not an insuperable one, in explaining how an external diurnal varying event can maintain a 24-hour periodicity in an organism despite the fact that the latter is no longer in phase with it. It is possible, however, that experimental changes may not reset the basic 'clock', but rather shift specific behaviour patterns in relation to it.

Nevertheless, although it may be difficult to conceive how an environment-independent clock system can be as accurate as that observed in fiddler crabs, the only known environmental conditions not controlled during the experiments described above were barometric pressure, cosmic ray showers, geomagnetic forces, ionisation and humidity of the atmosphere (which presumably would not affect crabs in sea-water) and doubtless other still unrecognised factors which Pittendrigh (1958) terms 'residual periodic variables'. If there is some external varying force that regulates the daily rhythms of oxygen consumption and colour change in fiddler crabs, its nature is certainly by no means clear. It could be barometric pressure itself, but Guyselman (1957) has shown that in the crayfish, *Cambarus virilis* conditions of constant pressure do not obliterate 24.0 and 12.4 hour cycles, from which he concludes that pressure fluctuations exert no causal effect on activity.

On the other hand, there are a number of other factors which show some degree of correlation with barometric pressure changes and which cannot be dismissed without consideration. One of these is cosmic radiation, for when the barometric pressure drops, the screening effect of the atmosphere is reduced. It has been shown, moreover, by placing thin lead plates (which serve to increase the effect of the radiation) above them, that fiddler crabs exhibit a measurable response in the state of their pigmentary system to alterations in the intensity of cosmic ray showers (Brown, Bennett and Ralph, 1954). The correlation with barometric pressure leaves the effect of such radiation as a distinct possibility, but naturally does not provide any direct, positive evidence.

A widespread occurrence of a correlation between barometric pressure changes and biological activity has been described by Brown, Freeland and Ralph (1955) and Brown, Webb, Bennett and Sandeen (1955). These authors, who were investigating fluctuations of oxygen consumption in carrots, potatoes, the seaweed *Fucus*, fiddler crabs and salamanders, found correlations highly significantly different from zero between hourly rates of oxygen consumption and the concurrent rate and direction of barometric pressure change. Furthermore, the rate of change of pressure on any day between 14.00 and 18.00 hours is correlated with the mean daily barometric pressure 2 days later and these were reflected in the metabolism of the organisms. Again Brown, Bennett, Webb and Ralph (1956) found correlations between the opening of oysters, *Ostrea virginica*, and quahogs, *Venus mercenaria*, and barometric pressure changes. Both these molluscs, whilst appearing to possess no overt rhythm, were found to possess statistical rhythms of opening their shells. Study of the data to detect any possible lunar-day cycles revealed an unequivocal cycle with a characteristic pattern that was repeated at 27-day intervals. It was postulated that this rhythm might be induced by variations in the intensity of ionising radiations in some way related to the 27-day cycle of rotation of the sun on its axis. More recently, diurnal and annual rhythms in the oxygen consumption of potatoes and carrots have been related to an exogenous reference clock (Brown, 1958a).

The work described above is, however, open to the charge that a number of cycles or rhythms are postulated and these are correlated with more than one environmental periodicity. As Cole (1957) points out, the physiologist faces a major problem in recognising the rhythms in his data and in disentangling the components when several rhythms are present simultaneously. The principal difficulty in finding correlations between a series of observations at some environmental rhythms lies in the fact that time series sometimes show correlations in which no causal correlation is apparent, a point that has already been noted (p. 1). In addition, however, biologists commonly consider statistically significant any experimental result that has odds of 19 to 1 (p = 0.05) against its occurrence as a result of chance above. Consequently, any one who has experimental data and sufficient patience to compute different indices and to match these with several independent environmental fluctuations should have a reasonable expectation in 20 or so trials, of obtaining at least one 'statistically significant' result. Furthermore, most conventional tests of statistical significance involve assumptions that cannot strictly be assumed to hold when one is working with time series.

One way of smoothing complex time series is to 'smooth' the data by means of moving averages or comparable devices but this increases the prospect of finding rhythms. Indeed it has been shown by Slutzky (1937)[†] that such smoothing actually creates cycles in random data. A similar objection is applicable to analysis by means of correlelograms and periodograms, while the use of harmonic analysis produces results that are difficult to interpret.

For the sake of argument in the paper under discussion, Cole chose the mythical Unicorn, an organism totally insulated from all exogenous rhythms! He assigned to it an initial metabolic rate of 20 arbitrary units and then worked through the table of normal deviates to find the metabolic rate in subsequent hours. "In the first hour, for example, the rate was 20–1.276 or 18.724, in the second hour it was 18.724–1.218 or 17.505, and so on. One hundred and twenty consecutive observations of metabolic rate were made in this way. These were taken to correspond to hourly readings over five consecutive days. It seems to be standard procedure in analysing data on physiological rhythms to average the corresponding hourly data of several days. We did that in this case and the data seems to suggest underlying rhythms but no pattern was clearly apparent. While contemplating the data, it occurred to me that in

†Slutzky, E. (1937). *Econometrica*, **5**, 105.

summer at 40° latitude the hour of rise of the moon may be retarded by approximately 1 hour each night. Consequently to eliminate any such lunar rhythms, we 'slipped' the data 1 hour per day. Aligning "hour 1" of the first day with "hour 2" of the second day, with "hour 3" of the third day, and so on. This seems to be a standard procedure for analysing such data. Now, when the hourly figure for the 5 days was averaged, a daily rhythm came clearly into focus. This rhythm must have been obscured by the simultaneous presence of the lunar rhythm."

This example illustrates some of the possibilities for detecting cycles by means of relatively simple arithmetical procedures. As Cole concluded, a rhythm as definite as this "could easily be shown to be highly correlated with environmental fluctuations but the nature of the material employed in this experiment seems to preclude any such causal relationships." It is true that by the introduction of moving averages a periodicity will be introduced into random data, but Cole used unrealistic probabilities and it is not possible to dismiss in so cavalier a fashion the immense number of significant correlations that Brown and his co-workers have amassed during the past years.

An objection to the hypothesis that cosmic ray showers may serve as 'clues' to regulate activity rhythm is that Beling (1929) found that the time-sense of bees operated normally against a small background of radium emanation. Again, Pittendrigh (1957) found that the clock systems of *Drosophila pseudo-obscura* was not affected when the culture was maintained within a lead jug whose walls and lid $2\frac{1}{2}$ inches thick filtered off about 70 per cent of the cosmic radiations normally falling on the flies.

Furthermore recent experiments have given positive results which weaken the idea: Brown, Webb and Bennett (1955) transported 250 fiddler crabs 51° westward (from Woods Hole, Massachusetts, to Berkeley, California). When these animals were compared with the same number of controls kept in Woods Hole, there appeared to be no tendency for any drift in the cycles of the crabs in California from those of the controls in Massachusetts, the animals averaging relatively precise 24-hour cycles during a 6-day period in each of the two sites (Fig. 14). It seems probable, therefore, that the crabs were able accurately to maintain solar and lunar day lengths without any external rhythmic clue. In this experiment every environmental condition which normally shows a 24-hour cycle dependent upon the rotation of the earth had been delayed for the crabs by 3.3 hours; yet the rhythm of colour change in the animals remained unaltered.

In a similar way, Renner (1955) has demonstrated the existence of an endogenous clock in bees. Honeybees were trained in Paris to come to a feeding station at a particular time of day. They were then sealed in their hive and taken rapidly to New York. When the container was opened in a room exactly similar to that in which the bees had been trained, they then continued to feed at their original Paris time. A possible objection to this work is that constant light was used in the experiment. If the bees' behaviour is affected by light intensity, as occurs in mammals (M. S. Johnson, 1939), it is to be expected that their rhythms might be slowed down by the condition of the experiment, so that they responded

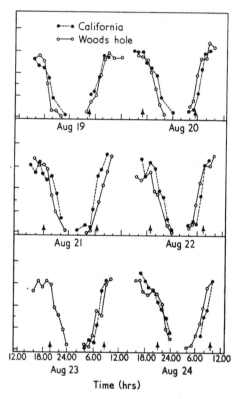

FIG. 14. The cycles of change in degree of dispersion of melanin in the melanophores of fiddler crabs, *Uca pugnax,* in Berkeley, California (122°W; 38°N), compared with similar cycles for control animals kept in Woods Hole, Massachusetts (71°W; 42°N). The cycles were determined under similar constant conditions. All the times are Eastern Standard. The arrows indicate the times of low tide in the place of collection of the crabs. (After Brown, Webb and Bennett, 1955)

in New York according to the same time schedule they had shown in Paris. Renner makes no reference to control insects in Paris whose rhythm might also have slowed down in relation to siderial time. On the other hand, of course, if they had been exposed to alternating light and darkness, this would naturally have acted as a clue to reset their internal 'clock' system.

The work of Brown, Webb and Bennett (1955) and of Renner (1955), could of course be interpreted by suggesting that a specific physiological and behaviour pattern was shifted relative to the phase of some internal chronometer, synchronised with residual periodic variables of unknown nature. It is difficult to see how such an hypothesis can entirely be disproved. On the other hand, the necessity for postulating residual periodic variables to maintain the rhythm is far from well established. Much more research will be required before any definite conclusion can be drawn.

Brown's view may be summarised as follows: the basic mechanism of temperature independence of the frequency of biological rhythms involves cyclic exogenous stimuli giving rise in all cells to systematic fluctuations containing all major natural periodisms of the external environment. These are used by the organism in timing its endogenous rhythm (Brown, 1957b). The evidence points to the possession by the organism, even in so-called 'constant' conditions, of environmentally imposed oscillations of the natural daily and annual periods. The fluctuations in the still unidentified external effective factor appear to be largely influenced by, and may possibly even in some measure determine meteorological changes of temperature and pressure (Brown, 1958a). Thus, potato tissue sealed in a respirometer is informed of barometric pressure changes as well as changes in the outdoor temperature. The higher the temperature rises, the greater the amplitude of the daily metabolic fluctuation (Brown, Freeland and Ralph, 1955).

The following suggestion has been made as to the nature of the unknown external factor (Brown, 1959). Solar day atmospheric tides express themselves in rhythms of barometric pressure. The atmospheric tide rises in the morning, reaching a peak about 10.00 hours and then falls during the afternoon. The daily rhythms of organisms, even when they are sealed off from subtle pressure changes are somehow associated with these daily tides of the atmosphere and their regular modification by lunar influence. Terrestrial magnetism is known to fluctuate rhythmically with the solar and lunar cycles and this influences cosmic ray fall out. Furthermore, the earth's magnetic axis, at an angle to its polar axis, wobbles as the earth rotates and produces movement of the magnetic field in relation to the polar axis. The mud snail, *Ilyanassa obsoleta*, when oriented geographically, displays solar and lunar day rhythms in its tendency to veer from a true south path, even in apparently unchanging conditions. Experiments with magnets further prove that the snails can perceive very weak magnetic fields. In addition, the response to bar magnets shows both solar and lunar rhythms. The snails are also able to distinguish the directions of magnetic fields and the magnetic receiver behaves like a compass geared in with the living 'clock' system (Brown, Webb and Brett, 1959).

To a rhythmic organism, light and temperature have most impact during the sensitive period of the 24-hour rhythm. The organism is adjusted to the day-night environment only when its sensitive phase falls in the darker, cooler, night-time. When the same organism is isolated from natural light and temperature changes and placed in controlled conditions, the sensitive period of its rhythm is interpreted as 'daytime' and the organism keeps re-setting its sensitive period in a futile search for the night and day periods of the normal environment. This process Brown calls "auto-phasing", and it would explain the speeding up and slowing down of rhythms under constant conditions, as described in Chapter 8.

It has so far proved impossible to devise an experiment that will differentiate between an innate 'clock' mechanism and one derived from exogenous sources since it is possible, by analogy, to alter the hands of the clock relative to the works. Brown's hypothesis is unassailable in terms of logic, and the critical experiment to prove or disprove it can probably only be carried out in outer space. At the very least, he has stimulated other workers to look more carefully at their own data. Just as it is difficult to conceive of a distance-judging mechanism independent of space, so a clock system presumably requires some fixed points of reference. These, however, need be fixed only relative to the organism and it may be that the end of one cycle serves as reference for the beginning of the next. Until further evidence becomes available, it will be wise to keep a fairly open mind upon the whole subject.

CHAPTER 7

Further Evidence for the Existence of Environment-Independent Chronometers in Animals

FROM the information given in the preceeding chapters it will be realised that living organisms may show several kinds of periodicity which are frequently quite unrelated, although simultaneously apparent in the same individual. In this chapter it will be seen that even when rhythms are synchronised on a 24-hour basis, they are not necessarily related directly to one another.

In many instances the extent to which a particular rhythm is dependent on the environment has not yet been determined; and even where this has been tested experimentally there is often considerable disagreement in the interpretation of results. The possibility that environment-independent rhythms may, in fact, be synchronised by cosmic ray showers, changes in barometric pressure, humidity or ionisation of the atmosphere and doubtless other still unrecognised factors, to which Pittendrigh (1958) applies the collective term 'residual periodic variables', has seldom been tested. Nevertheless it would appear more likely that most organisms can measure time: and even if they are aperiodic in one function, such as locomotion in the cave crayfish *Cambarus pellucidus* as measured by Park, Roberts and Harris (1941), in other types of activity a 24-hour periodicity may yet be present.

As Pittendrigh and Bruce (1957) point out, this generalisation is based on fairly recent developments, in spite of the fact that much of the pertinent evidence is comparatively old. It has long been remarked that both human beings and animals have a time sense. Lane (1948) gives instances of sheep, mules, cattle, cats and dogs, badgers, monkeys and birds that appeared to have a marked sense of time, but the evidence is largely anecdotal and in most instances has not been subjected to controlled experiment. The existence of persistent, endogenous or environment-independent rhythms has long been known too, but only during the last decade has much attention been focused upon such rhythms from the point of view of biological chronometry.

119

For many years it has been known that bees possess a sense of time and as long ago as 1935, V. Stein-Beling reviewed the subject of time-memory in animals with special reference to its centre of origin. Nevertheless, the modern outlook owes much to the work of Kramer (1952 etc.) and his associates and of Matthews (1955 etc.) on time-compensated sun-navigation in birds. More recently, Pittendrigh (1954, 1958 etc.), stimulated by the results of Kalmus (1935 etc.), has focused attention upon the 'clock' system controlling the time of emergence from the pupa of *Drosophila pseudo-obscura*, and emphasised the ubiquity of biological 'clocks' in animals and plants. These are apparent in functions as diverse as the photo-periodic responses to day-length which determine the onset of diapause in animals, of flowering and other seasonal changes in plants, seasonal reproductive cycles, solar navigation in birds, insects and Crustacea, the time of awakening from hibernation in hamsters or ground squirrels, and so on. Selected examples given below illustrate how widespread is independence of temperature and other environmental factors, indicating that many rhythms are indeed manifestations of innate biological chronometers.

Pupal Emergence Rhythms in Insects

Periodic phenomena connected with the pupal emergence of holometabolic insects have not been studied very intensively and the existing data are contradictory in some respects. Nevertheless they afford some of the clearest evidence of temperature-independent clock systems in invertebrate animals. The literature on the subject has been reviewed in detail by Palmén (1955) who investigated the diurnal periodicity of pupal emergence in their natural habitats of nine species of chironomid midges. In all of them a very definite peak of emergence was observed during the hours following sunset. Small numbers of individuals emerged at other times also in some of the species studied, but in others practically no emergence could be observed between 03.00 and 21.00 hours. There was a time difference of about 2 hours between the peaks of emergence in June and August, and Palmén concluded that the timing of the mechanism governing periodic emergence is achieved by the day to night change in illumination. But, as the intervals between successive peaks and their actual position remained unchanged in spite of considerable differences in temperature, he suggested that the timing mechanism synchronising the almost simultaneous emergence of all the individuals present at the appropriate stage of development is probably temperature-independent within ecological limits.

Caspers (1951) found that the emergence of the marine midge *Clunio marinus* on the Heligoland coast takes place exclusively between 16.30 and 19.00 hours in mid-August. By means of simultaneous recording of pupal emergence at Heligoland and at Varna on the coast of the Black Sea, it was established that in the two localities pupal emergence coincided according to local times. As the difference in longitude of these localities is about 20°, the Heligoland animals transferred to Varna emerged about 80 minutes earlier than they would have done if no adjustment to local time had taken place. Therefore they adjusted to local time, presumably using light as a 'clue'.

In 1936, Scott showed that cultures of the moth *Ephestia kuhniella* could be induced by fluctuating temperature in darkness to establish an emergence rhythm at periods of 16, 20 and 24 hours but not greater periods than 24 hours as many moths emerged 24 hours after the last fall in temperature. This suggests that there is something fundamental about the 24-hour periodicity. Again, although 18-hour rhythms can be set up in cockroaches (Cloudsley-Thompson, 1953b) in isolated migratory locusts, *Locusta migratoria migratorioides* (Cloudsley-Thompson, 1953c) and spiders of the genus *Amaurobius* (= *Ciniflo*) (Cloudsley-Thompson, 1957) these rhythms are largely environment-dependent and are less marked than are the normal 24-hour periodicities. Only in the spiders did the 18-hour rhythm persist when the animals were returned to constant conditions, and after three cycles it reverted to a 24-hour period.

In addition Scott (1936) found that *Ephestia* kept in a constant temperature room for three generations still continued to emerge chiefly in the evening. This apparently inborn rhythm could be overcome by external stimuli: when there was a diurnal cycle of temperature, emergence tended to occur when the temperature began to fall and if larvae or pupae were exposed to an artificial periodicity emergence could be induced at an abnormal time of day.

More precise experimental work by Pittendrigh (1954) and Brett (1955) has shown that in fruit-flies, *Drosophila pseudo-obscura* and *D. melanogaster* respectively, the periodicity of pupal emergence is independent of temperature. Under normal day-night conditions *Drosophila* has a definite peak of pupal emergence between about 06.00 to 09.00 hours. The adaptive significance of restricting emergence to the coldest and wettest hours of the day is that emerging flies lose water much more rapidly than mature flies and fail to expand their wings properly when the humidity is too low. Populations cultured in constant darkness show an aperiodic distribution of eclosion, but when reared under alternating light and darkness a marked 24-hour rhythm of pupal emergence is engendered. This persists in constant darkness at different temperatures—Pittendrigh carried out experiments at 16°, 21° and 26°C, Brett at room temperature and 21°C—and can be reset or inverted simply by subjecting the culture to a single experience of dark to light transition. Aperiodic cultures raised from eggs in constant darkness show no

E

emergence rhythm, but can be made to develop one by a single experience of light. Low temperature can also produce a 24-hour rhythm of emergence in aperiodic cultures, but cannot reset 'clocks' established under a regime of alternating light and darkness. (See Fig. 15).

In all the experimental cultures the eggs were laid within 2 days, yet emergence activity, commencing about 17 days later, was spread over a period of up to 8 days depending on various conditions, especially

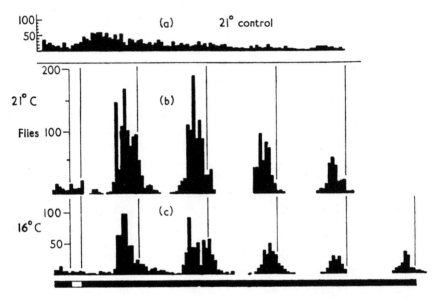

FIG. 15. Initiation of persistent eclosion rhythms in aperiodic *Drosophila pseudo-obscura* populations by single light stimulations. A. An aperiodic control population raised in constant darkness at 21 °C. B. Rhythm initiated by a single treatment with 4 hours of light in a population raised at 21 °C. C. Rhythm initiated by 4 hours of light in a population raised at 16 °C. (After Pittendrigh, 1954)

temperatures. Consequently the individual flies in a culture population could not have been synchronised in development throughout their lives even though they emerged in batches 24 hours apart. The precise shape of the daily emergence curve and the way this shape changes with the age of the culture strongly suggest that synchronisation of development is accomplished late in the history of the individual fly by the enforcement daily of a period that is forbidden for emergence itself or for the initiation of processes leading up to it (Pittendrigh, 1954).

"Suppose the 24-hour period to be partitioned, by means of information from the endogenous clock, into a relatively short period (the data suggests 6 hours or less) and a long (18-hour) forbidden period.

Flies that happen to be ready for emergence within the short allowed period emerge without further delay. However, flies becoming ready for emergence at random times within the forbidden period are required to wait onset of the next allowed period. Such a model, entirely formal as it is, explains three major facts: (1) it explains how effective synchronisation within daily periods of 6 hours is accomplished among individuals whose development rates show in other respects the variance of a nearly normal distribution spread over 8 days; (2) it explains the way the peak is skewed heavily to the right within each allowed period (this is due to the fact that at the beginning of the short allowed period the bulk of the emerging flies have long since been ready and emerge immediately on removal of restraint) and (3) most significantly, the model also predicts the way in which the shape of the daily peak is observed to change with culture age. Each emergence peak consists of two fractions: AP is the fraction composed of flies whose completed development falls by chance within the allowed period; FP is the fraction of flies whose completed development falls within the preceeding forbidden period and were required to wait. For each culture there will be only one day when AP/FP is large, viz. the first day of emergence, containing the fastest flies in the culture. In this case the emergence peak should be either normally distributed within the allowed period or even skewed to the left, and this is precisely what is observed. As the culture becomes older, AP/FP should become progressively smaller and the skew to the right should increase which, again, is what is observed." (Pittendrigh, 1954). Data on temperature effects suggest that the restraint exercised in the forbidden period is not on the act of eclosion itself, but rather on the initiation of special processes involved in the measurement of the last 24 hours prior to eclosion.

When cultures raised in alternating 12-hour periods of light and darkness are transferred without temperature change to constant darkness they show persisting rhythms with a periodicity of 24 hours, but when a culture maintained in alternating light and dark at 26° is transferred to constant darkness at 16°C, the periodicity is lengthened. Conversely transfer from low temperature cultures to constant darkness at higher temperatures elicits a much shortened periodicity: but for the first peak following the temperature change only. Kalmus (1940) who first observed this, came to the conclusion that the process invoved in the timing system was dependent on temperature in a way that could be explained according to van't Hoffs' rule. According to Pittendrigh, however, the transfer may result in the delay or acceleration of the first subsequent peak while the next peaks appear at the expected time or very near to it. "The whole system reverts immediately to a periodicity that is essentially 24 hours, and, what is more, a periodicity only 3 hours

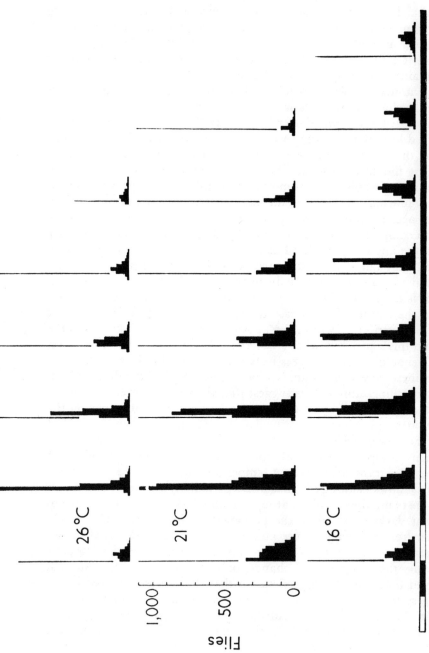

FIG. 16. Persistent rhythm in the eclosion of *Drosophila pseudo-obscura*, obtained in constant darkness at 26°C (top), 21°C (middle) and 16°C (lower). A light-dark cycle of 24-hour period established the phase of the rhythm. Vertical guide lines are 24 hours apart and ordinates represent numbers of flies eclosed per hour. (After Pittendrigh, 1954)

out of phase with that obtaining before the temperature shock." The same view was advanced by Brett (1955) who found that higher or lower temperatures may decrease or increase the length of the life-cycle predominantly by time units of 24 hours as a result of the temperature-independent periodicity of pupal emergence.

In attempting to explain these facts, Pittendrigh (1954) was forced to adopt a complicated and cumbersome hypothesis of a 'terminal clock' which was temperature-dependent. In a later paper, however, this explanation was completely withdrawn (Pittendrigh and Bruce, 1957). Instead, the departure from the natural period following temperature stimuli was regarded as a 'transient' imposed on the temperature-independent 'primary clock'; transients being defined as the arhythmic responses of an oscillator to non-periodic stimulation (Pittendrigh, Bruce and Kans, 1958).

Work along similar lines by Bateman (1955) has shown the existence of a diurnal periodicity of emergence in the Queensland fruit-fly *Dacus (Strumata) tryoni*. In these insects the rhythm can be induced and oriented by alteration of light and darkness during the larval stage or the

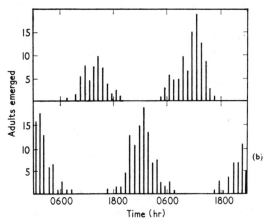

Fig. 17. Effect of light during the imaginal stage of the fruit-fly, *Dacus tryoni*, on the pupal ecdyses of the subsequent generation (larvae and pupae kept in constant darkness): (a) adults illuminated from 09.00 to 17.00 hrs.; (b) adults illuminated from 21.00 to 05.00 hrs. (After Bateman, 1955)

adult stage of the previous generation, but during the pupal stage it has no direct effect on the rhythm of pupal ecdysis. When pupae are exposed to a small daily fluctuation in temperature, the rhythm becomes more pronounced so that ecdyses are spread over fewer hours of the day. The fact that when larvae were reared in constant darkness, the periodic emergence of the adults was governed by the photoperiod experienced by the adults of the parental generation, would seem to be an important difference as compared with the results obtained with *Drosophila* where the periodicity of pupal emergence is not fixed at the prelarval stages.

Bateman did not carry his experiments beyond the second generation of flies, but Bünning (1935) claimed that even after 15 generations of *Drosophila* had been raised in constant light, a rhythm was still present. However, since such rhythms eventually fade away, it is apparent that they are not direct responses to environmental factors such as cosmic ray showers and other residual periodic variables.

The emergence rhythm of the Chironomid midge, *Pseudosmittia arenaria*, has been shown by Remmert (1955) to depend upon the length of day. In natural daylight and darkness a maximum is reached 6 to 8 hours after the beginning of the light period. In constant darkness, no imagos are formed and in constant light they are distributed evenly throughout the 24 hours. Light intensity is of no importance; the maximum emergence is related entirely to the beginning of the light period. With equal periods of light and dark, the shorter the artificial 'day', the closer is the peak of emergence to the onset of light. But in 'days' shorter than 18 hours, it appears at the beginning of the succeeding dark period, whilst in 'days' of 36 hours it appears just before the following light period. The arrival of an emergence maximum in a dark period causes a jump in the rhythm of emergence from once every other day to once every day.

Mori (1954) has shown that population size also affects the emergence rhythm of *Drosophila melanogaster*. The more the insects are crowded as larvae, the more the time of maximum emergence is delayed in the course of the day, probably as a result of lowered metabolism possibly induced by the accumulation of excretory products or by nutritional deficiencies. Thus again it can be seen that an inherent rhythm, normally influenced mainly by light may be secondarily affected by biotic influences.

In cases such as these, where periodic activity follows a single stimulus, the question arises whether this stimulus initiates rhythms in all individuals of a population, or whether it simply synchronises rhythms already present. These alternatives have not yet been resolved with certainty although I am inclined to favour the second hypothesis (Cloudsley-Thompson, 1958d). In either case the evidence in favour of there being an innate, hereditary, endogenous rhythm is strong. Even so, this does not disprove the views of Brown and his co-workers (Chapter 6).

THE TIME SENSE OF BEES AND OTHER ARTHROPODA

The discovery that worker honeybees possess a remarkably accurate time sense was made somewhat fortuitously by Forel (1906) who noticed that as he and his family often had their meals on a terrace in their garden, bees would appear at the table at meal times, whether or not food was present. He therefore suggested that bees could 'tell the time' by the sun, but did not carry out any experiments to determine whether this was so. Indeed, no further experiments were carried out until Beling (1929) repeated Forel's observations.

A considerable amount of research has since been carried out on the subject and is reviewed in detail by Ribbands (1953). Bees have been trained to visit the same feeding place not only once each day, but also at two or three different times, and the timing of such visits is apparently not affected by temperature and weather. Training was not disturbed

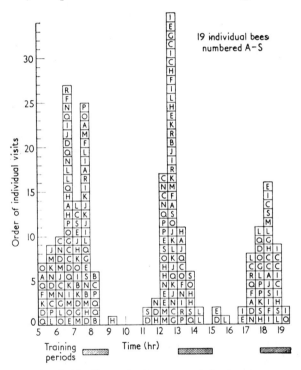

FIG. 18. Training of individually marked bees to seek food at the same place at three different times of the day. The bees were trained for 6 days and their visits were recorded on the 7th day when no food was provided. (After Beling, 1929)

when the insects were placed in an experimental room in continuous light, air humidity and temperature, nor when the air in this room was irradiated so that artificial ionization altered the periodicity of electrical conductivity of the atmosphere. Even down a salt mine, where external periodicity factors were eliminated, bees have been conditioned to time. Indeed, time perception appears to be inborn since bees have been trained which had hatched in a dark chamber and had never experienced the alternation of day and night (Beling, 1929). Now, as v. Frisch (1954) points out, this time perception cannot be associated with a feeding or hunger rhythm, since a bee does not come to the feeding dish in order to drink her fill as other insects do. She calls there, collects food for the colony and this is then stored inside the hive. Her foraging time is therefore not a "feeding-time" in the true sense of the word.

Wahl (1932) time-conditioned bees which were kept for 16 days in a dark room at 23°C. He then raised the temperature, both of the colony and of the room, by about 8°C, gave the bees two more days of training at these temperatures and found that on the third day they were still trained to the initial time interval. From this result he concluded that time perception was not dependent upon any internal metabolic rhythm, since such a rhythm would have been accelerated by the increased temperature. Admittedly a fairly constant temperature is normally maintained within the hive, but I do not think that this is an important factor in the bees' sense of time. Nor do I accept Wahl's conclusion, because compensation for temperature is by no means uncommon in the metabolic processes of poikelothermic animals as we shall see (p. 180). This work would have been more convincing if the training had not been continued after the temperature was altered.

Conclusive proof that the daily activities of bees do not depend entirely upon an endogenous rhythm, however, is offered by Newport (1837) in his unique observation during a total eclipse of the sun on 15th May, 1836. At 14.15 hours when the eclipse began and the sunlight was sensibly diminished, bees started flocking to the hive. At 15.15 hours when little light remained and the temperature dropped from 20° to 15°C the hive was quiet as in the evening: full activity was resumed at 16.00 hours when the eclipse was nearly over (see p. 186).

That the time memory of bees and wasps is the expression of an endogenous rhythm based on innate metabolic periodicity has been indicated by the experiments of Grabensberger (1934a) who trained these insects to visit their food places at a given time each day after which they were given food containing certain drugs and the effects upon subsequent visits noted. He claimed that after 0.015 per cent iodothyroglobulin (which is known to accelerate food metabolism) had been added and no food was subsequently supplied on the following 3 days, the bees returned successively about 5 hours, 2 hours and $1\frac{1}{2}$ hours too early. In a parallel experiment 0.015 per cent euquinine (which retards many vital cell processes in insects as in humans) was added and on the following 3 days the bees were about 4 hours, 3 hours and $2\frac{1}{2}$ hours late, successively. The influence of the drugs was somewhat less marked in the case of wasps than in bees.

Further experiments with honeybees were undertaken by Kalmus

(1934) who confirmed the effect of euquinine and found that anaesthesia for several hours or feeding with desiccated thyroid gland had no effect upon time perception; but that long and severe cooling (5° to 7°C for 11 hours) led to delay as did narcosis with self-produced carbon dioxide.

Whereas bees which have a marked diurnal rhythm and are normally active only in the daytime cannot be trained on other than a 24-hour basis, ants which may be non-rhythmic are said to have been trained to

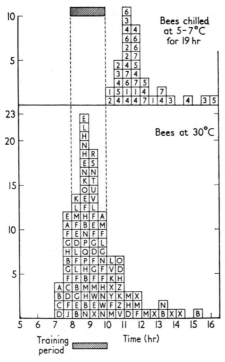

FIG. 19. Time perception in bees. Delayed visits by chilled time-trained bees; normal visits by time-trained bees kept at 30°C. No food provided on this day. (After Kalmus, 1934).

feed at several time intervals. Experiments carried out by Grabensberger (1933) have been claimed to show that in termites and ants, time perception is bound up with food metabolism. Members of experimental colonies of *Myrmica laevinodis, Lasius niger, Formica fusca* and other species were trained within 3 days of feeding to visit a certain place at fixed times daily. Various colonies were trained to different hours, not only according to a rhythm of 24 hours but to periodicities of 3, 22 and 27 hours as well. Frequently such rhythms, once established persisted from 6 to 9 days after experimental feeding had been discontinued. (Somewhat similar results were also obtained with *Termes lucifugus*.) Experimental increases in metabolic rate through feeding 0.05 per cent thyroglobulin or raising nest temperature caused the feeding visits of ants in treated colonies to be made somewhat in advance of training time. In contrast, reduction of metabolic rate through feeding 0.08 per cent euquinine or lowering nest temperature delayed the time of the maximum number of feeding visits. This again shows that the temporal memory has an endogenous basis: but since the application of chloroform and ether over periods of hours had no apparent effect upon any learned rhythm it was concluded that the factors underlying the phenomenon must be non-nervous in nature.

In a further series of experiments Grabensberger (1934b) obtained results which he believed to reinforce his previous conclusion. Ants in experimental colonies of *Myrmica rubida* and *Lasius niger* were given food containing 0.008 per cent salicylic acid which also has the property of accelerating metabolism. This caused them to visit a food place at an earlier time of day than that for which they had been trained. Feeding with 0.001 per cent yellow phosphorus caused the average number of visits to come 6½ hours earlier than the training time, while the effects of arsenic trioxide depended upon the dosage received. With 0.0001 per cent the ants came at the correct time, after 0.0005 per cent they were about 3½ hours late, after 0.00075 per cent they again came at the correct time, after 0.001 per cent they were 3½ hours too early and after 0.002 per cent they came 6½ hours too soon. These results were attributed to the oxidation-inhibiting effect of the drugs which, at different dosage strengths may produce anabolism, catabolism or metabolic equilibrium, thereby influencing nervous conduction and exerting different effects upon temporal memory (Grabensberger, 1934b).

As Ribbands (1953) points out: "A conflicting feature of the experiments on time perception is that Beling did not succeed in her attempt to condition honeybees to a 19-hour feeding rhythm, yet Grabensberger (1933) succeeded in conditioning ants to 3, 5, 21, 22, 26 and 27-hour feeding rhythms and termites to a 21-hour rhythm. Grabensberger (1933) emphasized that the food metabolism of ants did *not* take place in a 24-hour rhythm, but that if external influences were not materially altered it went on at a fairly constant rate. As ants and bees responded in a similar way to euquinine and iodothyroglobulin, it is likely that the physiological basis of time perception is identical in both groups. Beling's conclusion therefore requires confirmation".

On the other hand it may be that Beling is not at fault. Not only was Reichle (1943) unable to repeat Grabensberger's results, but these imply a closer relationship between the biological 'clock' and general metabolic rate than normally appears to be the case. Furthermore, they provide one of the few examples in which abnormal time intervals have been learned. The difference between ants and bees in this respect has been only partially explained by suggesting that ants may be non-rhythmic in nature whereas bees have a marked diurnal rhythm of activity and rest and consequently cannot be trained on periodicities of other than 24 hours.

Grabensberger's results are certainly exceptional. Pittendrigh and Bruce (1957), however, claim that they provide the only known case among animals in which an atypical period of time has been learned and

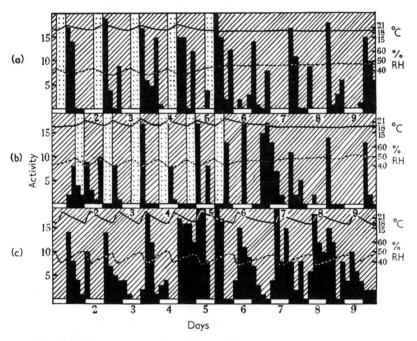

FIG. 20. Effect of alternating artificial light and fluctuating temperature on the diurnal rhythm of movement and rest in the spider, *Amaurobius ferox*.
(a) Effect of 6 hours of light alternating with 18 hours of darkness (a 24-hour cycle) followed by constant darkness.
(b) Effect of 6 hours of light alternating with 12 hours of darkness (an 18-hour cycle) followed by constant darkness.
(c) Effect of 18 and 24-hour temperature cycles. (After Cloudsley-Thompson, 1957a)

thereafter persisted under constant conditions. (They cite two other examples, óne of spore discharge in a fungus, the other of a rhythm of growth and photosynthesis in an alga). This is an exaggeration: 18-hour rhythms have been shown to persist for a few cycles in the cockroach *Periplaneta americana*, in the spider *Amaurobius ferox* and in the desert beetle *Anthia venator* (Cloudsley-Thompson, 1953d; 1956b; 1957a; see p. 121) while Kleitman (1940) found that the littoral woodlouse *Ligia baudiniana* would take up a pigmentary rhythm when in a cycle of 10-hours of light following 8 hours of darkness, but the pigment dispersal occurred during darkness and not in the light phase as it does in nature. (For other examples, see Harker, 1958a).

In view of these facts, it may be wise to withhold judgement upon the significance of Grabensberger's results until these have been properly confirmed by others.

A surprising example of time perception and memory in bees has recently been recorded by v. Frisch (1950, 1952). The dances of bees on a horizontal comb lit from a completely cloudy sky are normally disoriented because clouds depolarise sunlight. When, however, the comb was covered by a polaroid sheet transmitting polarised light only in a certain direction and the bees under it saw a pattern which they would have seen at that time at one point in the sky on a clear day, they aligned their dances according to this pattern. But if the pattern they saw differed from what they could have observed in the sky had the day been clear, they would not respond to the polarised light transmitted by the polaroid sheet. Presumably the bees were associating their perception of time with memory of the pattern which would have appeared in a blue sky at that time and were orienting their dances in relation to the remembered pattern. In another experiment 29 marked bees were fed at a feeding place 220 yards west of their hive which was moved during the night to a new site 3 miles away. The following morning 20 of the bees flew to a new feeding site where they were captured, 220 yards west of the hive in its new position. Only seven bees visited sites in other directions. At this time the sun was in the south-east while during the training flights on the preceeding evening it had been setting towards the west. Visual landmarks had been eliminated by the overnight move of the colony so the bees must have been searching in relation to the remembered pattern of light polarisation, adjusting their direction to allow for the time of day at which they were foraging.

The question of the allowance made by bees for the passage of time has been taken up recently by Kalmus (1956) in experiments carried out (in Brazil) in the southern hemisphere where the sun's daily movement is anti-clockwise instead of clockwise.† Foraging bees from a strain long established in the region were fed in the evening on a dish in a particular geographical direction and transferred overnight to a new locality unknown to them. During the next day the majority of bees were at all

† To an observer in the northern hemisphere facing south, the sun rises on the left and sets on the right: but to an observer in the southern hemisphere, who must face northwards to see the sun, it will appear to rise on the right, and set on the left hand.

hours searching in the direction of their previous training. On the other hand foragers which were the offspring of queens recently imported in an inseminated condition from the northern hemisphere showed, after similar training, systematically false orientation on the day of observation as they tended to make a reverse allowance for the sun's movements as if it were in the northern hemisphere. Bees of hybrid origin, reared locally and partly descended from "Italian Queens" imported within the past 10 years, also showed false orientation. Kalmus therefore postulated the existence of innate mechanisms compensating in northern bees for the sun's clockwise movements and in Brazilian bees for its anti-clockwise motion. The change in the direction of compensation must have occurred during the last 425 years since the first honeybees were shipped from Portugal to Brazil in 1530 A.D.

Foraging under natural conditions is more or less continuous. Between one sortie and the next the change in the sun's direction is small: hence the ability to recognise direction and communicate it can operate independently of time sense and allowance for the sun's movement. Local bee-keepers agreed that recently imported Italian-Californian bees were as successful as foragers as the old Brazilians, so one might infer that sun-navigation does not play an important role in the foraging of workers. Kalmus suggests tentatively that the biological advantage may lie in swarming and may have been brought about by selection of the sexual forms.

A similar type of false orientation has been shown to occur in individuals of the sand-hopper, *Talitrus saltator*, which Papi (1955a) transported from Italy to the Argentine. These animals normally have an

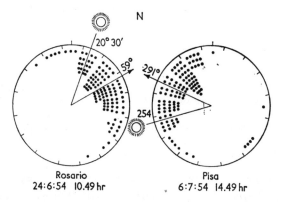

FIG. 21. A. Distribution of 117 position records in relation to the sun, of 13 sand-hoppers *Talitrus saltator*, in Rosario de Santa Fé, Argentina at 10.49 hr. on June 24th after being kept in darkness since their collection in Italy on June 10th, 1955. B. Control test at Pisa with the same number of specimens at the corresponding Italian local time. Arrows indicate the resulting mean direction of escape. (After Papi, 1955a)

orientation mechanism based on the position of the sun, which enables them to maintain a constant direction of escape towards the sea. The oriented escape reaction is released when animals living on the damp sand of the beach are transferred to a dry place: whereupon they attempt to return to the sea, following a line approximately at right angles to the coast. A constant escape direction is maintained by assuming an angle with the sun which varies during the course of the day, probably according to an endogenous physiological chronometer. Individuals taken to the southern hemisphere orientated themselves in relation to the sun in exactly the same manner as control animals from the same population did in Italy. In another experiment animals transferred to a different longitude adjusted their orientation angle with the sun according to the time and place of origin and not according to local time, thus demonstrating the existence of an endogenous time sense.

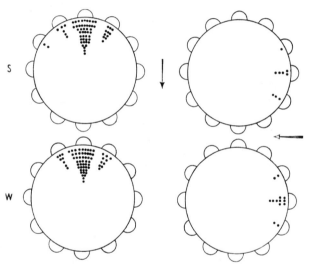

FIG. 22. The effect of the state of the internal 'clock' on the sense of direction of two starlings. The black arrow indicates the direction of training (26 Feb.-31 Mar.), the white arrow the expected choice of direction (13-19 June) after the internal 'clock' of the bird had been experimentally advanced by 6 hours. Each point within the circles indicates a single experimental choice, whilst the empty boxes around the circles represent food containers. (After Hoffmann, 1954)

By means of similar experiments, Papi (1955b, c) has shown that wolf-spiders, *Arctosa perita*, when placed on the surface of water, return to the ground in a direction perpendicular to the line of the shore. They orientate themselves visually by means of objects in their surroundings when the sky is covered by cloud, but under a clear sky orientation is astronomical, based on the capacity to find an azimuthal direction determined by the position of the sun and the direction of polarised light vibrations from the sky. The spiders can orientate themselves correctly under a clear sky even when they are placed in such a position that they are unable to see the sun. Specimens kept in the dark for several days still orientated correctly at whatever hour the experiment was made, indicating that they must make allowance for the movement of the sun. Analagous experiments with individuals of different populations showed that every one of these has its own direction of flight which corresponds to the lie of the shore which it inhabits. (See also Papi and Serretti, 1955).

No doubt the phenomenon of time-compensated sun-navigation is far more widespread than has previously been realised and future work will show that it occurs in a wide variety of animals, both terrestrial and aquatic.

ENDOGENOUS RHYTHMS IN PLANTS

Pupal emergence and the time sense of social insects provide some of the most convincing demonstrations of inherent endogenous rhythms.

An interesting parallel from the realm of botany is afforded by the work of Ball and Dyke (1954) who have shown that when *Avena* seedlings are germinated in red light and subsequently transferred to darkness a growth rhythm is established in the coleoptile in which the first peak occurs about 16 to 17 hours after the transfer and a second peak 24 hours later. When the transfer is made sufficiently early, three peaks occur before growth ceases. Alteration of the point in the life history at which the seedlings are transferred from light to darkness changes the times of occurrence of the peaks, but does not affect the period of the rhythm whose incidence shows no correlation with time of day and is therefore not due to diurnal changes in external conditions. Between 16° and 28°C temperature has little or no effect on the period of the rhythm.

Again, Leinweber (1956) has shown that under constant conditions the primary leaves of *Phaseolus multiflorus* show no diurnal movements†, but 28-hour periods can be initiated by a single light stimulus. The time of transfer to light from darkness, and to a lesser extent to darkness from light, determine the phase of these movements. Compensation for retardation due to cooling is brought about by an acceleration subsequently—in other words, the periodicity after cooling is shorter than the 28-hour period previously recorded. There is thus something of a parallel with the work of Pittendrigh (1954) on *Drosophila* which has already been discussed. In *Phaseolus* the period is comparatively independent of temperature between 15° and 25°C, but below 15° there is marked temperature dependence.

In a review of endogenous rhythms in plants (Bünning, 1956a) it has

† In normal daylight and darkness, the leaves bend downwards at night.

been shown that these are widely distributed. Some do not show any correlation with environmental changes, but others have a periodicity corresponding to annual, diurnal or tidal rhythms. Endogenous diurnal and annual rhythms, in particular, play a decisive role in several extremely important physiological processes and in these cases must have a high selective value. "Therefore, the marked predominance of endogenous rhythms showing similarities to external rhythms is readily explainable on the basis of the generally accepted principles of phylogenetic evolution".

Physiological relationship between the phenomena in plants and animals is shown by temperature independence, or to be more exact, by only slight temperature dependence. Experiments on the effects of temperature on the length of the period have shown that several components are concerned. Thus leaves of *Phaseolus multiflorus* have an endogenous rhythm with a period of 25.0 ± 0.2 hours. The rhythm is exceptionally temperature-resistant and operates in cells heated almost to lethal temperature. It is only suppressed by 2:4-dinitrophenol and high or low pH values when these cause visible damage to the leaves. On the other hand, colchicine, phenylurethane and urethane produce irregularities. Concentrations not large enough to suppress the rhythm altogether may prolong the period; to 28 hours in the case of colchicine and up to 36 hours with 1 per cent urethane. Trypaflavin and acid-inorange cause injury but do not affect the period, while ether causes disturbances similar to those caused by colchicine and urethane, but again without modification of the period. Bünning (1956b) concludes that the primary phenomenon of the endogenous diurnal rhythm consists of periodic structural changes in the protoplasm. In his opinion, the structures concerned must be related to, or identical with those which participate in the division of the cytoplasm during mitosis. Here again we see a reflection of the fundamental nature of endogenous rhythm.

In a third paper (1956c) Bünning discusses the evidence in favour of physico-chemical mechanisms involved in the 'clock' systems. In physical processes temperature dependence is often slight, but it is by no means impossible to imagine a chemical mechanism that also has no temperature dependence. For example, if part of the mechanism were concerned with supplying a particular substance while a second partial process destroyed it and both processes were equally temperature-dependent, then the substance would accumulate at the same rate irrespective of temperature. No doubt in the organism there is some kind of interaction between several such processes. Hence, if the 'clock' has not time to adjust itself to a definite temperature, a considerable error may be observed under certain conditions: for example when a plant kept at one temperature from germination is suddenly transferred to a different temperature.

After a few days, however, a regulatory process intervenes which diminishes the temperature error and restores normal periodicity. Temperature-independence in animals is further discussed in Chapter 10.

The fact that colchicine can affect the rhythm is interesting since this mitotic poison hinders the orientation of polypeptide chains which cause the formation of the spindle in nuclear division. This supports the assumption that periodic structural changes in the range of macro-molecular dimensions are definitely connected with the mechanism of the physiological 'clock': other mitotic poisons such as phenyl urethane also upset the endogenous rhythm markedly. But since periodicity persists in cells that are no longer able to divide, it is suggested that the periodic structural changes in the proteins which form the spindle in young cells must continue after nuclear divisions have ceased. At the same time such periodical structural changes may become apparent in the periodic volume changes of the cell nucleus. (See p. 193).

The fact that a short light stimulus which is not sufficient to cause a complete change in the phase of an endogenous rhythm may, never-theless, cause a slight effect which is repeated at the same time on sub-sequent days, may be explained by supposing that in this case, single cells of the individual are displaced in phase in relation to the endogenous rhythm of other cells. This in turn suggests that a single stimulus may initiate a rhythm by synchronising many separate 'chronometers' in the cells of an organism. Just as animals can have an inborn concept of *spatial* configuration, so both animals and plants may carry within them an inherited appreciation of the *temporal* configuration of the environment (Bünning, 1956c).

Sun Navigation in Birds

The existence of navigational ability in birds has long been known. In recent years attempts have been made to discover what physical features of the environment are involved and the sensory physiology needed for a bird to react to such stimuli. This work has been reviewed by Griffin (1952) and Matthews (1955) and will not, therefore, be con-sidered in great detail here. As a result of the experiments of Matthews (1955), Kramer and his colleagues (1952 etc.), Hoffmann (1954) and others, the existence of some kind of navigation, depending upon the position of an endogenous chronometer, has been established almost beyond doubt, although there is considerable disagreement as to the method (Hoffmann, 1958).

Furthermore, neither spontaneous nor conditioned responses to arti-ficial radiation have been obtained. At the same time it has been shown that nocturnal migrants are not influenced by the moon and trapping records of the *Vogelwarte* "Heligoland" show that night migrations occur to the same extent on moonless and moonlit nights.

The subject of bird-navigation has been discussed in considerable detail by Matthews (1955) who concludes: "The function of the day/night alternation as a pace-maker is clear, but the nature of the basic rhythmic processes which can keep the chronometers running for many days when the external rhythm is removed remains quite obscure. We need information on the nature and accuracy of these chronometers independently of their function in orientation".

Hoffmann (1954) trained three starlings to compass directions and then exposed them to an artificial day in which the periods of light and darkness were shifted, although of the same duration as in natural conditions. The birds, when tested, chose a direction which was altered to an extent corresponding with the artificial manipulation of night and day. When the artificial day was postponed by 6 hours, the birds chose a direction about 90° to the right of that to which they had been trained; when the artificial day-light changes took place 6 hours earlier, the direction chosen was about 90° to the left of the original direction; and when the natural conditions were restored, the original training direction became apparent.

Recently experiments have been carried out at Freiburg (Sauer and Sauer, 1955; Sauer, 1958) into the nocturnal migration of warblers, *Sylvia borin* and *S. atricapella*. Even when these birds were hatched in completely enclosed, sound-proof chambers in constant light, so that there were no outward clues of the yearly seasonal rhythm, nevertheless in the autumn at the time of migration, they would fly restlessly from perch to perch. In the spring they underwent another spell of restless, wakeful nights. When placed in a cage with a glass top, the birds orientated themselves by the stars and fluttered in the normal direction of migration. Warblers were now tested for the ability to orientate themselves in a planetarium. "By changing the north south declination (height) of the stars we could change the apparent geographical latitude, making the birds believe that they were farther south or north than they actually were. Similarly by shifting the sky in the east west direction we might mislead the birds about their position in longitude." (Sauer, 1958). In either case the warblers responded in a manner indicating a remarkable hereditary mechanism for astral orientation coupled with a precise time-sense. At the very first glimpse of the sky the birds automatically 'know' the right direction but on dark nights with thick cloud they get lost.

Recognition of the existence of biological 'clock' systems in birds certainly clarifies the situation and will inevitably provide a stimulus to further research that must be intimately connected with biological rhythms. It must be remembered, however, that field tests are likely to produce complications. As Arnould-Taylor and Malewski (1955) point out, in many experiments the seemingly positive results obtained may have been due, at least partly, to the influence of topographical clues which were not taken into account in the evaluation of experimental data. Thus it may come about that experiments to determine the nature of the physiological 'clock' mechanism in birds may shed greater light on the problem of navigation than field observations of migration, though naturally a combination of field experiment with laboratory research is likely to be the most fruitful line of approach of all. Furthermore, as we have seen (p. 103) the ability to measure increasing or decreasing lengths of daylight, are involved in the seasonal regulation of migratory and reproductive behaviour.

The most detailed experiments on diurnal rhythms in birds have been carried out on chickens. For example, Fraps (1954) found that intramuscular injections of 1.0 to 2.5 mg estradiol benzoate into regularly ovulating hens suppressed ovulation for several hours. The following day, however, ovulation took place at the usual time. In other words, egg-laying could not take place until the normal time next day, irrespective of the time at which the inhibitory factor was removed. From this, Fraps concluded that the neural mechanism thought to control the release of the ovulation-inducing hormone from the anterior pituitary body follows a 24-hour rhythm in its response to other excitatory hormones.

CHAPTER 8

Activity Rhythms in Mammals and the Search for their Control Centre

TWENTY-FOUR hour rhythms of activity have frequently been recorded in mammals (Aschoff, 1955b; Calhoun, 1945; Harker, 1958a; Kleitman, 1949 etc.). Animals such as white mice, rats and golden hamsters, for example are most active at night, but of these only the hamster remains inactive in light. Golden hamsters are also exceptional in possessing but one peak of activity which lies in the first few hours of darkness. Rats and mice, like most other creatures, show two distinct peaks (Aschoff and Meyer-Lohmann, 1954a, b).

Mammalian rhythms are usually remarkable for their persistence. For example M. S. Johnson (1939) found that the daily activity rhythm of the nocturnal deer mouse *Peromyscus leucopus* persists up to 18 months in the absence of exposure to daylight or daily change in light or dark, but in continuous light it is modified by the amount of illumination. The time of the daily active period becomes progressively later on successive days and may be shifted steadily round the clock with no tendency to be fixed at any particular time of solar day or night. The trend in the rate of shift in time of the daily active period typically remains constant while the light is constant, but varies with change in light intensity. These findings are consistent with the interpretation of an inhibiting action of light on activity in the deer mouse, but no procedure was found which would consistently or dependably move the regulator of the internal 'clock' system to the 'fast side'.

Similar results have been obtained by Folk (1959) with white rats. The well-known diurnal rhythm of running activity in the rat originates from a light-cycle and can be reversed by illuminating at night rather than by day. In continuous light, the activity phase of the rhythm remains about 12 hours in length, but shows a regular, constant and definite amount of alteration of the time of starting so that the activity block travels around the clock. Furthermore, the rate of change of time of activity is faster with an increase in the intensity of the light. In continuous light (5.1 ft.-candles) the delay was found to be 3 to 4 hours per day and the time of activity travelled round the clock in 16 days.

With a somewhat different approach, Brown, Shriner and Ralph (1956) have described persisting effects of exogenous factors superimposed upon a changing or moving endogenous rhythm in the white rat. The spontaneous activity of one male rat under constant conditions was recorded for 120 consecutive days. During the first 70 days in constant illumination of 1 ft.-candle the 12-hour daily period of activity occurred regularly about 1¼ hours later each day, with the period scanning the solar day about four times during the 70 day period. During the succeeding 25 days in darkness, the daily cycles averaged exactly 24 hours with the time of day activity that of the last day in constant light. This was followed by 8 days in constant light and 18 days in constant darkness with comparable results.

The daily running cycle, randomised relative to the hours of solar day, exhibited a daily cycle of amount of activity at each hour of the solar day; and randomising of both the daily activity period and the solar day basic cycle revealed a cycle of lunar day length, with minimum of lunar zenith and a maximum at nadir. There were also strong suggestions in the mean daily activities of 27-day and synodic monthly cycles. Thus, in addition to the well known overt daily rhythm which is capable of being reset but persists indefinitely in darkness as a rather precise 24-hour cycle, Brown, Shriner and Ralph claim to have found a complex of other rhythms. It is not impossible, however, that some of these may result from the method in which the data was manipulated (see discussion on p. 114).

Halberg, French and Gully (1958) found that the blood eosinophil and rectal temperature rhythms persisted in man after sub-total removal of a cerebral hemisphere (in the treatment of medically intractable epilepsy with co-existing infantile hemiplegia). The eosinophil rhythm also persisted in blind mice (Halberg, Visscher and Bittner, 1954). Although it was shown that visual stimulation appears to be the usual dominant synchroniser of the adrenal and other cycles (Halberg, Barnum, Silber and Bittner, 1958) non-photic stimuli must replace them in congenitally eyeless male mice in which these cycles are in no way abnormal.

Once the principle has been accepted that mammals, like other animals may have internal chronometer systems which regulate their physiological activities, it is reasonable to expect accompanying rhythms of heart rate, metabolism, blood sugar, blood cell count, mitosis, body temperature, excretion rate and so on. Many of these have been described in detail in man and other mammals and are reviewed by Halberg (1953), Halberg et al. (1959), Kleitman (1949) and others.

The search for hypothetical 'clock' mechanisms has not yet been successful and on account of the complexity of the problems involved, may well proceed for many years before success is achieved,

Nevertheless, certain lines of investigation have not proved unproductive.

As Folk (1957) points out, investigators using rodents have recently stressed two approaches (a) modifying rhythms or (b) describing them in quantitative terms. For example, Hemmingsen and Krarup (1937) found that if the rhythm of the white rat was reversed in 'reversed' light and darkness, it would persist in this form under constant conditions, but there were signs of the normal rhythm being present as well.

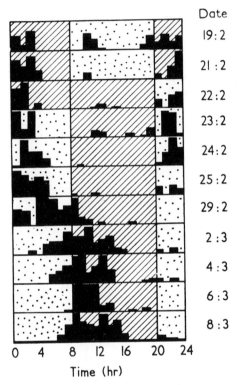

FIG. 23. Distribution of activity of an individual white rat in an experiment with a rapid change in the position of the light period. (After Holmgren and Swensson, 1953)

More recently, Holmgren and Swensson (1953) have studied the effect of 'reversed' light cycles on activity, body temperature and glycogen in the liver, and shown how activity is delayed in light so that the animals' rhythm gradually becomes reversed and in phase with the reversed environmental conditions.

Attempts have been made using white rats, mice and Japanese dancing mice, to discover whether the rhythm is present even when the animals have been in constant darkness from birth. The Japanese dancing mouse is believed to be a mutant form of the Central Asiatic group of *Mus wagneri* which has been raised in captivity for centuries, on account of its habit of continually whirling around in circles due to an hereditary defect of the semi-circular canals. Wolf (1930) recorded the spontaneous activity of these animals as well as activity associated with obtaining food and water. He found that activity was always so intense that it could only be judged by the length of the period of locomotion, since the marks of the stylus upon the kymograph drum always overlapped.

Under normal day-night changes of light intensity the short activity periods of the Japanese mouse were so grouped as to form a major peak of activity from shortly before dusk to midnight. After an interval of reduced activity, there followed a second period of great activity which lasted from about 01.00 or 03.00 hours until shortly after dawn. During the day the mice were relatively inactive. Wolf attributed this diurnal rhythm of activity to a direct effect of the diurnal cycle of light and darkness; but when the mice were placed in continuous darkness, they

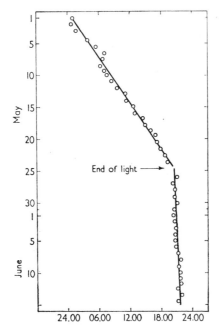

Fig. 24. Time of active period of an individual deer mouse, *Peromyscus leucopus*, in continuous illumination of 6.8 ft.-candles, followed by continuous darkness. Weighted mid-points of active periods are given, showing constant trend of rate of shift with constant light intensity, and abrupt end of shift with end of light. (After M. S. Johnson, 1939)

maintained the bimodal rhythm that they had expressed under a normal light cycle.

In continuous darkness, however, there was an irregular shifting of the cycle to make the major peak of activity occur approximately half an hour earlier each day. This shifting occurred regardless of whether the mice were subjected to a normal 24-hour temperature cycle or to constant temperature. Dancing mice held their bimodal nocturnal pattern of activity in continuous light also, but Wolf makes no mention of a shift in the cycle. In continuous darkness the total amount of activity in the diurnal cycle exceeded that under a normal light cycle, whereas under continuous light stimulation, the gross amount of activity decreased.

Wolf now raised *Mus wagneri* in continuous darkness. After reaching maturity two individuals from each of two litters were placed in recording apparatus while still in continuous darkness. In each case there was a bimodal 24-hour rhythm of activity, but both peaks were equal in duration and intensity. Furthermore, the shift in the time of inception of the first period of activity was greater than in animals which had been exposed to a normal cycle of light and darkness, sometimes by as much as 2 hours.

By raising white rats with no cycle of nursing or other environmental influences, Folk (1959) has also obtained evidence which strongly suggests that the 24-hour rhythm of activity and rest is inherited (see p. 146). When these rats were subjected to continuous light, rhythms of 25, 26 or 27 hours could be demonstrated with the activity phase still remaining about 12 hours in length and only the inactive phase increasing. Further experiments indicated that activity patterns could be altered by changing the feeding cycles as well as by changing a light cycle. If rats were kept for weeks in darkness and fed at midnight, the activity peak came shortly before the feeding period; and when feeding was changed to noon the activity peak shifted accordingly.

Aschoff (1952 etc.) has also investigated the effect of environmental influences on the activity rhythms of mice which were kept in cages completely shielded from external influences that might provide a clue (*Zeitgeber*) as to the time of day, food being supplied for a fortnight at a time. Activity was recorded over successive 20 minute periods. In normal illumination, consisting of artificial or natural light from 06.00 to 19.00 hours, a maximum of motor activity occurred about 20.00 hours with a subsidiary peak about 12 hours later. This rhythm persisted in constant darkness but the frequency was reduced to 23.0 to 23.5 hours so that, after 30 days, the peak occurred at 06.00 hours. Aschoff concluded that the 'biological day' or 'natural period' for mice is 23.2 hours' duration, but is easily influenced by external factors, especially the normal alteration of day and night. There was no change in the total amount of activity that took place over 24 hours when the mice were kept in constant darkness.

In constant light, on the other hand, the length of the period increased up to 26 hours or more, again depending upon intensity. On transfer to darkness the natural periodicity of just under 24 hours reappeared (Aschoff, 1952b).† As usual, the total amount of locomotory activity was not affected by the experimental conditions.

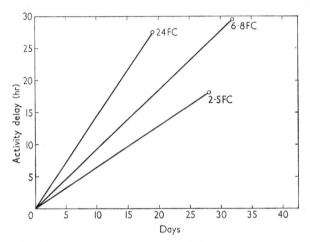

Fig. 25. Activity delay in *Peromyscus leucopus* at different light intensities. This figure shows increased rate of shift of active period with increased light intensity, indicated in ft.-candles. Lengths of lines indicate duration of exposure to light. The same mouse was used throughout. (After M. S. Johnson, 1939)

In a later experiment (Aschoff, 1955a), different strains of mice were maintained under constant environmental conditions, some in light others in darkness. The second and third generations were then examined for periodicity. Within each litter, the periodicities of individual mice were found to be very similar, but the frequencies of the rhythms of animals from different litters varied. Aschoff interpreted his results as proving the genetic origin of a natural period on the grounds that if the rhythm were learned there would be an accumulative error which would cause the third generation to have a frequency of other than 23.5 hours. But, of course, it might still be argued that the experiment merely proves the susceptibility of young mice to imprinting by the adults of a rhythm of nearly 24 hours. Mother rats not only nurse their young nearly continuously in daylight, but are away from the litter feeding and

† Naturally if the periodicity of exactly 24 hours is maintained under constant conditions the possibility of a *Zeitgeber* effect cannot be excluded.

carrying out other activities most of the night. The cooling of the litter caused by the regular departure of the mother might well serve as a 'time-giver' to the young inmates.

This problem, however, was found to have a solution: Folk (1957) as mentioned above, raised a litter of rats under constant conditions with a foster mother in addition to the natural mother. These females were changed at random times each day and it was observed that the young suckled from both mothers equally over each 24-hours: the mean weight at weaning was above average. After 93 days, some of the animals were studied in running recorders in a sub-basement room and found to have a periodicity of activity of approximately 24 hours.

This proves that the behaviour of the mother during the period of nursing is not necessary for the development of the periodicity. It is still possible that some periodic factor from the mother may have acted through the placental circulation and thereby influenced the embryos, but I do not think that this can be the case because chickens hatched and maintained in constant conditions also show persistent rhythms with a natural period of 24 hours (Aschoff and Meyer-Lohmann, 1954b).

Browman (1952) showed that even in white rats that had been inbred for 42 generations, the last 25 of which had been raised in an inside room under constant light, a clear 24-hour rhythm of voluntary activity was apparent in 11 of 16 animals tested. (Voluntary activity was again recorded by cyclometers attached to revolving wire drums.) No rat had a peak of activity coinciding with the feeding period. When subjected to an artificial 16-hour day, during which the temperature was 15° to 16°C in the dark period and 25° to 26°C during the 8 hours of light, 12 of the 16 rats settled into the new pattern within 5 days and continued in this rhythm for the duration of the 45-day period of observation. The other four rats were on a 16-hour day pattern 70 to 85 per cent of the time but did have short periods of irregularity, particularly during the oestrus period. Of the 11 rats with 24-hour rhythms in continuous light, all but one established a clear-cut 16-hour rhythm when subjected to artificial day lengths. Apparently no attempt was made to see if the induced 16-hour rhythm would persist under constant light conditions.

Of the innumerable 24-hour rhythms of physiological change that have been observed in man and other mammals, rhythms of change in the composition of the blood are among the best known. For example, Halberg and his co-workers (1953, 1956 etc.) have described quantitatively eosinophil rhythms and other rhythms in terms of a peak in the morning and a low level at night which continues in the absence of all external fluctuations but is critically dependent on the light sequence used. Reversal of the lighting regime completely reverses the eosinophil rhythm over a period of 9 days and when the diet is restricted, the time of feeding assumes a more critical role than lighting. Rhythms in the numbers of thrombocytes, leucocytes and red blood-corpuscles, in the time taken for a clot of blood to retract in a firm mass from which the plasma may be separated and in chloresterol and blood-sugar content have been described. The blood chloride curve also follows a rhythm, as does that of the pulse rate and blood pressure (for references, see Harker, 1958a).

Pitts (1943) described a diurnal rhythm in the blood sugar of the white rat, the difference between noon and midnight values being approximately 10 per cent. This rhythm persisted during 48 hours of starvation, but disappeared during longer fasts. By training animals to feed during the day, it was possible to dissociate the feeding and activity cycles. In such a situation, the blood sugar cycle was found to accompany the feeding rather than the activity rhythm. However, a period of between 5 and 14 days was involved before the change in the blood sugar cycle was completed.

Diurnal fluctuations of temperature and of sleepiness and wakefulness have been extensively studied in man (Kleitman, 1939) and have been shown to persist independently of any external rhythm for some time. The remarkable persistence of normal temperature and urinary rhythms in night workers in civilised communities has long been recognised. The persistence of an endogenous 24-hour rhythm in urinary volume, despite the suspension of the normal diurnal cycle of habits, has been demonstrated by Mills (1951) in six subjects who lived in a remote shepherd's cottage on the island of Arran about midsummer. It was suggested that the regular variations in sleepiness, temperature and urinary flow might be ascribed "to an habitual hypothalamic rhythm, autochthonous for a week at least but ultimately derived from external rhythms."

Numerous attempts have been made to relate rhythms of locomotory activity to various known physiological rhythms and to hypothetical basic 'clocks'. For example, Holmgren (1936, 1938) made biochemical assays and histological studies of the secretions of the pancreas, the absorption of fat through the intestine and the glycogen and lipoid content of the liver of the rat. These investigations were made on several rats killed at intervals of 2 hours over a 24-hour period. During the day, zymogen granules accumulated in the pancreas where they reached a peak of abundance at about 14.00 hours. At dusk they began to be released and this process continued until about 02.00 to 04.00 hours when the pancreas became nearly devoid of secretory granules. The absorption of fat through the intestinal wall followed a similar curve: during the night when the rats fed and were most active the lipoid content of the liver increased and the glycogen content decreased, whilst the reverse occurred during the day. Unlike the activity rhythm, which persisted during periods of starvation, the periodic secretion of the pancreas ceased when food was withheld from the rats and maximum zymogen content was maintained. On the other hand, when the rats were fed, the pancreatic rhythm persisted in that secretion did not take place if the animals were given food in the wrong phase of the 24-hour cycle. Thus, when rats were starved from 14.00 to 11.00 hours and fed for 3 hours before being killed, it was found that no zymogen granules had been released from the pancreas despite the presence of food. When rats were starved from 02.00 to 23.00 hours, however, and then fed for 3 hours, the pancreas was found to be devoid of zymogen granules when they were killed.

In a study of maze and running activity of seven rats from which the stomachs had been removed, no alteration in activity due to the operation was detected (Tsang, 1938). The adrenal may have a diurnal periodicity in its secretions for, in it as in the liver, the number of red blood corpuscles is highest during the night hours (Engstrom, Holmgren and Walhfart, 1938). Glycogen accumulates at night in the liver of rats, mice and rabbits and disappears again in the morning. This occurs to some extent in the muscles too. Consequently, as might be expected, mice show an increased resistence to insulin in the afternoon and particularly during the night. In rabbits, where these periodic changes are particularly striking, the urinary nitrogen output is increased during the night: this indicates that increased deamination of amino-acids occurs at night and that the formation of glycogen takes place partly at the expense of body proteins. This glycogen rhythm, which appears to be independent of food intake and occurs even in fasting animals, is destroyed when the adrenal is removed (Agren, Wilander and Jorpes, 1931).

On the other hand, Bacq (1931) found that abdominal sympathectomy did not affect spontaneous activity in the albino rats and combined with adrenal inactivation, it did not affect for more than 10 days the voluntary activity, which was slightly below that of controls, in 13 rats. Subsequent removal of one or both stellate ganglia with the upper part of the thoracic sympathetic chains had no significant effect on spontaneous activity either. It was concluded, therefore, that removal of the sympathetic nerve supply to the genital organs and adrenals does not affect the normal secretion of the endocrine products which are known to affect the spontaneous activity of the rat. Furthermore, the oestrus cycle, maternal behaviour, fecundation and gestation were not affected by abdominal sympathectomy although the young were born in two batches a few days apart and normal milk secretion did not occur after parturition (Bacq, 1932).

A number of other endocrine organs have also been investigated in attempts to find a centre controlling the diurnal rhythm. Neither hypophysectomy nor removal of the thyroid, however, appear to eliminate all traces of periodicity. Richter (1933) found that removal of the thyroid, whilst disturbing the rhythm did not eliminate all trace of it. Animals in which a very small piece of thyroid tissue remained, showed no change in activity, food and water intake, whilst rats from which all or nearly all the thyroid had been removed showed reduced and fluctuating activity and reduced food intake. Water intake was unaffected. Furthermore, the reproductive cycle became irregular; but all these symptons were corrected by giving small extracts of thyroid with the food, so it is evident that the affects were due to simple thyroid deficiency rather than the absence of cyclic production of the hormone.

Richter and Wislocki (1930) completely removed the pituitary hypophysis from ten adult rats and partially from fifteen others, leaving intact either part of the anterior lobe or parts of both anterior and posterior lobes. Running activity was measured in the usual way by means of revolving drums and it was found that the ten rats with total removal were very inactive but spontaneous activity was not affected by partial removal of the gland, although body weight and food intake decreased to a low level and then remained constant. The 4-day sex cycles were absent in the hypophysectomised animals, but were normal in the rats with only the anterior lobe of the pituitary remaining. On the other hand in three animals with parts of both anterior and posterior lobe tissue present, the sex cycles were markedly disturbed. It was suggested that the low level of activity of hypophysectomised rats might result from altered activity of the adrenals and sex glands rather than on removal of the pituitary itself.

Levinson, Welsh and Abramowitz (1941), also found that rats exhibited little activity and no diurnal rhythm in darkness at constant temperature (22.8°C), during the first two days after removal of the hypophysis; but in the next ten the amount of activity (measured with a running-wheel equipped with an automatic recording system) showed a gradual increase and the rhythm reappeared. After a second week there was a further increase in total activity, to a third or half that of the preoperative level, and complete restoration of the diurnal rhythm. Two hypophysectomised animals, 41 days after the operation, were exposed to periods of illumination corresponding to solar day and night for 6 days. The periods of illumination were reversed, resulting in a corresponding reversal of the diurnal activity rhythm of the animals, as would have occurred with intact rats. It is significant that although the pituitary was involved in the maintenance of the day-to-day level of spontaneous activity, the diurnal rhythm of spontaneous activity became re-established at the time when the gonads, adrenals, thyroid and other endocrine organs dependent upon the pituitary for their maintenance had become atretic.

Removal of parts of the brain has given somewhat contradictory results. Kleitman (1939) has suggested that the cortex may be responsible for the sleep rhythm while the wakeful state is maintained by the hypothalamus, for he found that decorticated dogs had no rhythm of activity or temperature; but these dogs were blinded by the operation. Furthermore, Rothmann (1923) did not find a loss of rhythm in decorticated dogs while Beach (1941) obtained loss of rhythm in some rats with lesions in the frontal tissue and corpus striatum, but not in all. Lesions to the posterior parts of the brain tended to result in increased activity, but this result was not always obtained. Anterior brain lesions tended to produce more pronounced increase in activity than did lesions confined to the posterior brain region. Changes in emotional behaviour tended to be temporary and to consist only of increased reflex excitability. On the other hand, Ranson (1939) found that somnolence was caused by hypothalamic lesions in monkeys.

It is worth remembering that in all these experiments employing surgical operations, probably the most important results are those in which rhythms persist after operation. The disappearance of a rhythm from a damaged animal is not necessarily significant.

Numerous reports on 24-hour physiological periodicities describe variables affected by, or dependent upon adrenal regulation, cortical as well as medullary (for references, see Halberg, Visscher and Bittner, 1953). Furthermore, adrenal periodicity, whilst it is responsive to changes in the external environment as well as in the internal physiology of the animal, nevertheless persists in the absence of such changes. For this reason, Halberg, Halberg, Barnum and Bittner (1959) have suggested that the 24-hour adrenal cycle may deserve consideration as a critical mechanism under-lying adaptation to diurnal activities. Of course, this view is at variance with the unqualified assumption that diurnal changes of adrenocortical secretion constitute responses to the stresses of daily life. Nevertheless, the peak of the mitotic rhythm in the adrenal cortical parenchyma and stroma of the mouse precedes the peak of corticosterone in the blood and also the major daily bursts of locomotory activity. This agrees with the suggestion (Halberg, 1953) that the adrenal cycle describes processes occurring, at least in part, in preparation for daily activities, rather than solely as intermediate reactions to them.

As a result of experiments using injections of drugs, Everett and Sawyer (1950) have postulated that a neural mechanism exhibiting a 24-hour periodicity of sensitivity may control the release of ovulation-inducing hormone in rats, as has been described in birds. They found that

Nembutal (phenobarbital sodium—standard dose: 30 mg./kg. intraperit.) prevented the ovulatory activation of the hypophysis when administered at 14.00 hours during proestrus. Persistence of Graafian follicles for 2 or 3 days resulted from Nembutal treatment on successive afternoons at the same critical hours. On the second and third days, a supplementary injection was required at 15.30 to 14.00 hours. If, on any of these 3 days, treatment was omitted or postponed until after 14.00 hours, pituitary activation promptly occurred and ovulation followed during the night. Similar results were obtained with amytal dial, barbital and phenobarbital. Blockade of luteinising hormone release by treatment with the barbiturates on successive days disclosed a follicular cycle which terminated in atresid about 2 days before the onset of the next proestrus. Everett and Sawyer concluded that the 24-hour rhythm, although possibly a property of the luteinising hormone release-mechanism in other spontaneously ovulating forms as well as the rat, cannot be considered as a universal characteristic unit until a variety of animals has been investigated.

In order to determine whether the various physiological rhythms of mammals are in fact under the control of a single central 'clock', or whether there may be separate controlling mechanisms for each, Folk (1957) has attempted to separate various biological rhythms in hamsters, ground squirrels and bats. His experimental work includes attempts to separate the rhythm of heart-rate and body temperature by exercise, to extinguish or modify the body temperature rhythm by cold exposure, to separate or extinguish by exposure to cold the rhythms of activity and bladder function, and finally to record rhythms during hibernation or dormancy.

It was found that a mammal at midnight in a condition of partial muscular warm-up with a body temperature of 37°C at a heart-rate of 400 beats/min. showed, after exercise, a heart-rate of 450 beats/min. and a body temperature of 38°C. On the other hand at noon in a condition of muscular 'coldness', the body temperature was 36°C and heart-rate 350 beats/min., but after the temperature increased to 37°C and the heart-rate to 400 beats/min. This means that the two rhythms persist after exercise and may be closely linked. If the heart-rate after exercise were found to be the same at noon and at midnight, this rhythm would be said to be extinguished.

Body temperature rhythms were measured during 3 days at 21°C, 3 at 5°C followed by a return to 3 days of the warm temperature. The results obtained showed little change in the rhythm as a result of the temperature change in rabbits, raccoons and skunks. In hamsters (Folk and Schellinger, 1954) there was no appreciable effect of exposure to cold on the rhythm of body-temperature either, but in ground squirrels the rhythm not only had much larger amplitude in the cold and was at a lower level, but in addition was modified in time. The control periods showed a major peak of temperature in the early morning and a minor midnight peak. These peaks were shifted 6 to 10 hours by exposure to cold, an effect not demonstrated with any of the other animals investigated, except bats.

"On the whole this cold-exposure test divides these animals into two groups, as far as non-hibernating body temperature rhythms are concerned; these are a temperature-labile group and a temperature-stable group. The first includes the bat and ground squirrel and the second the hamster and remaining mammals. These groupings are used in spite of the fact that about 40 per cent of a colony of cold-exposed hamsters will take the "cold-vacation" path of hibernation. In contrast the ground squirrel and bat, although different in some important respects, are alike in that they have non-hibernating temperature lability and nearly 100 per cent hibernation after short exposure to cold. Also from the temperature rhythms was obtained evidence that the ground squirrel is predominately day-active, although it can be active at night." (Folk, 1957; see also Menaker, 1959, p. 179).

Attention was paid to a possible rhythm of bladder function, since little consideration has been given to the possibility that this organ and the kidney might act as a biological 'clock'. Bladder function and total activity in hamsters were studied simultaneously with eight recording devices for 178 days, under control conditions, in darkness and in cold. A distinct nocturnal rhythm of bladder function, which persisted in darkness, was observed. This was closely linked to the rhythm of muscular activity and at no time could the two be separated by experimental modifications.

An attempt was also made to determine whether a 24-hour rhythm would be extinguished, persist, or be prolonged in hibernating ground squirrels and bats kept at low temperature. Some evidence was obtained for regularity in the time of awakening of the dormant animals. The ground squirrels awoke on 17 occasions from 21.00 to 09.00 hours, in 19 cases from 17.00 to 21.00 hours, and in 25 cases from 09.00 to 17.00 hours. Predicted awakening at random at the same times would be 32, 11 and 22. The data therefore provide evidence that a biological 'clock' or mechanism has influenced the awakening process so that the animals awake in daylight which is their usual time of activity. Furthermore, the fact that ground squirrels and hamsters tended to wake at somewhat different times suggests that unknown exteroceptive factors did not influence the experiment.

In bats five stages of hibernation were apparent, varying from deep hibernation to a state in which movement of its feet or wings, or of its body from a vertical to horizontal position would result from a stimulus. The data obtained showed an equal amount of activity in solar day and solar night, but when graphed separately by the day there appeared to be some evidence of a 48-hour rhythm (Folk, 1957).

The remarkable fixity and non-modifiability of most rodent rhythms and the close linkage between rhythms of bladder function and muscular activity and of heart rate and body temperature are clearly demonstrated by the above results. On the other hand, if rats are illuminated from 06.00 to 18.00 hours, the feeding period is changed from midnight to noon but the pattern of running activity does not change, although light inhibits running activity induced by hunger (Folk, 1959). Therefore certain mammalian rhythms can be separated experimentally, which implies that there is no *single* controlling 'clock' system.

In this connection the work of Kleitman and Kleitman (1953) is of particular interest. It has been known for a long time that there is some relation between heart-rate and body temperature in man—indeed in pre-thermometer days, physicians often judged the degree of fever by the rapidity of the pulse. More recently it has been found that diurnal fluctuations of heart-rate and body temperature are correlated and that thyroid medication raises both of these variables concomitantly. Also, a shift in or inversion of the diurnal body temperature range is accompanied by a similar change in heart-rate variation.

In order to test whether the rhythm of body temperature is coupled with the parallel heart-rate curve, Dr. and Mrs. N. Kleitman and their two young adult daughters lived at Tromsö, Norway, from 21st May to 23rd July 1951, during which period the sun never set below the horizon. It was found that adherence to 18-hour and 28-hour sleep-meal-activity schedules, each for 3 weeks under conditions of continuous daylight in the arctic summer, led to a disruption of the usual 24-hour oral temperature rhythm in the two young women, but not in the middle-aged man. In contrast the heart-rates observed in Miss E. and Dr. N. Kleitman (whose diurnal temperature rhythm had been unaffected by the conditions of the experiment) promptly conformed to the two non-24-hour routines by acquiring 18-hour and 28-hour periodicities. Thus in certain circumstances the rhythms of temperature and heart-rate can be dissociated.

Kleitman suggests that heart-rate rhythm can be separated from that of body temperature by activity, but this is not always so, since Folk (1959) has shown in ten human subjects that the heart rhythm may be independent of activity.

Again Lewis and Lobban (1957a, b) studied twelve human subjects who lived as two isolated communities on Spitzbergen (79°N, 16°E) for 7 weeks during the summer when perpetual daylight was experienced. Indeed the external environmental conditions showed little variation in

F

either light or temperature so that it was possible to impose abnormal time routines on the subjects without their being aware of the real time of day. Seven subjects (four male and three female) carried out their normal activities within the abnormal time scale of a 21-hour day, while the remaining five subjects (three male and two female) lived on a 27-hour day. Six experimental cycles (48 experimental days = 42 real days) were carried out on the 21-hour routine, while five experimental cycles (40 experimental days = 45 real days) were completed on the 27-hour routine. The diurnal rhythms of excretion and body temperature were followed throughout and on two control days on 24-hour time at the beginning of the experiment.

Specially adjusted 21-hour and 27-hour wrist-watches were worn, so that in the periods between recording cycles, when the subjects were free to pursue their own interests, they would always live on the experimental time routines.

The rhythm of body temperature became adapted almost immediately to the abnormal time routines in 11 of the 12 subjects, in marked contrast to the excretory rhythms which adapted immediately in only three subjects. Fourier analysis of the data obtained, confirmed that, when living on a normal 24-hour routine, the excretory rhythm for water, chloride and potassium were extremely similar, both in amplitude and timing. On the abnormal routines, however, small but statistically significant differences between the three rhythms were very common and marked dissociations not uncommon.

The usual type of marked dissociation was that in which the rhythm of potassium excretion was out of phase with those of chloride and water, the potassium excretory rhythm showing more evidence of the persistance of an endogenous 24-hour component. Examples of marked dissociation between the excretory rhythms of water and chloride were rare. Thus, of the four rhythms studied, that of body temperature appeared to be the most determined by the environment, that of potassium excretion the most determined by some intrinsic mechanism with a 24-hour periodicity.

It is therefore clearly impossible to assume that all diurnal rhythms in man are controlled by a single mechanism: at least two mechanisms must be involved to produce the observed independence of response. Inherent 24-hour excretory periodicities were persistent in many of the subjects, while the sleep rhythm showed rapid adaptation to abnormal routines in almost all subjects (Lewis and Lobban, 1957a, b)†. Nevertheless, the sleep/wakefulness ratio appears to be constant for individual subjects, regardless of the time occupied by the complete daily routine (Lewis and

† This work has been criticised by Halberg *et al* (1959) on the ground that the subjects may have been subconsciously aware of the real time.

Masterton, 1957) and it is not unlikely that the sleep rhythms may affect the rhythm of body temperature which adapts equally rapidly in most subjects. (Kleitman and Kleitman, 1953).

In conclusion, Lewis and Lobban (1957a, b) suggested that it is now generally accepted that the sleep rhythm is controlled by a centre or centres in the hypothalamus (as we have seen above). Other bodily functions which show regular diurnal fluctuations and which may therefore be controlled by the hypothalamus are retention of water, chlorides and the regulation of body temperature, whilst the diurnal rhythms of potassium excretion may be controlled by the adrenal cortex.

To summarise. When nocturnal mammals such as white rats and mice are maintained in continuous light the activity phase of the 24-hour locomotory rhythm continues to be about 9 to 12 hours in length, but shows a constant definite delay in the time of starting so that the activity block travels around the clock. The rate of change of time of activity is faster with increased light intensity, but in constant darkness the daily delay in time of starting ceases. Day-active rodents have not been satisfactorily tested for their type of response to continuous light, but, with day-active greenfinches, *Chloris chloris,* Aschoff and Meyer-Lohmann (1955a) found an acceleration in the time of starting activity which increased with intensity of light. Since the frequency of the period depends upon the intensity of light stimulus, it cannot represent the 'natural period' of the animal. With nocturnal animals this must be ascertained in darkness where the rhythm usually persists, since darkness is not a positive environmental factor.

Continuous darkness, however, cannot be used to investigate the natural period of a day-active mammal since it will alter the animal's activity. For example, ground squirrels showing a distinct running pattern of 7 miles daily, cease running completely in total darkness. According to Aschoff, the solution is to use continuous dim light, which has little effect upon the normal activity pattern of day-active animals.

The ecological significance of these automatic accelerations or retardations in the time at which the activity period begins, which depend upon light intensity, probably lies in the fact that they result in a compensation for the fact that in the spring the days get longer. Consequently a day-active animal must awake increasingly earlier as the spring advances and the intensity of daylight increases. At the same time the activity of a night-active animal must begin later. Conversely in the autumn as the intensity of daylight decreases, day-active animals awake progressively later, night-active species progressively earlier. Synchronisation is achieved in a similar way in invertebrates (Cloudsley-Thompson, 1959c, d).

The difficulty in engendering 16-hour rhythms in rats may be due to the fact that if the animals are exposed to 8 hours of light followed by 8 hours of darkness, it is inevitable that at least 4 hours of the rats' normal 12-hour period of activity will be illuminated and therefore delayed.

Diurnal animals show a peak of activity at the beginning of the light period, nocturnal animals at the beginning of the dark period. Subsidiary peaks follow about the middle of the 24-hour period. The distance between both peaks is not strongly fixed. In the course of a year the periodicity will change as sunrise and sunset times alter (Aschoff and Meyer-Lohmann, 1954a).

The duration of daylight varies greatly throughout the year in temperate regions. In southern England, for example, it increases seasonally from about 8 hours in winter to 16 in the summer. At first sight it might appear difficult to understand how any animal could, in such a changing environment, maintain a regular 24-hour periodicity of activity. It must be remembered, however, that the period of the activity pattern is synchronised each day, usually by dawn or sunset. Thus light reversal experiments are not really unbiological; they merely accelerate a natural process. The diurnal activity pattern varies from one species to another—the hamster has one long main period of activity, the guinea-pig has two peaks one at dusk, the other nearer dawn.

The search for the location of a hypothetical biological 'clock' is difficult in mammals and better results have been obtained with invertebrates as we shall see in the following chapter. Nevertheless, it is abundantly clear that central control is extremely deep-seated and complicated since it persists after the removal of major organs. Furthermore, there is no single 'clock' system, since various rhythms can be dissociated experimentally.

Further work on endocrinology may be facilitated by information regarding the diurnal cycle of physiological activity, for the threshold of drug action may well depend upon the time of day at which it is administered.

CHAPTER 9

Some Aspects of the Physiological Mechanisms of Rhythmic Activity

In the previous chapter a number of preliminary speculations were made regarding the physiological nature of biological chronometers in animals. These will now be considered in greater detail, and in the light of further evidence.

INHERITANCE OR LEARNING OF PERIODICITY

A fundamental problem touched on in the previous chapters can be expressed as follows: is the running 'clock' inherited, or merely the 'clock' mechanism? In other words, are rhythms due to inherited memory or acquired learning?

Many attempts have been made, by means of alternating light and darkness or fluctuating temperatures having a period of other than 24 hours, to force rhythms which normally follow 24-hour cycles to run in cycles of a different frequency. As Harker (1958a) points out, if the 24-hour clock could be altered to run for other periods, this would add considerable weight to an opinion that 24-hour cycles are not inherited. The points on which information is required include the persistence of experimental rhythms under constant conditions, the effect of such constant conditions on the new rhythms and the old and whether the new conditions are not such that they are, in fact, merely reinforcing the 24-hour rhythm from time to time.

One supporting fact in favour of the inheritance of 24-hour periodicity is the variability of natural periods from 23 to 25 hours in different species (Pittendrigh, 1957). If species at opposite ends of the 2-hour range were 'tuned-in' to environmental synchronisers, these would have to be completely different 'residual periodic variables' which were out of phase with one another. Secondly, the natural period tends to vary within a species which makes more plausible an interpretation which accepts these rhythms as having natural periods rather than having cosmic synchronisers.

On the other hand, M. S. Johnson (1939) has described rhythms with a period of 24-hours and others which vary in a pendulum fashion on both sides of 24-hours. Harker (1958a) summarises such observations by saying that the drifting of rhythms in darkness may cease when the peaks have arrived at the time at which they normally occur in nature and it is possible that some unknown 'clue' was controlling the time of activity, for it would be unlikely for an inherited rhythm to have a frequency of exactly 24 hours. As we have seen, however, the evidence in favour of the hypothesis that animals use cosmic-rays, barometric pressure or other 'residual periodic variables' as time-markers is slight. The extension or shortening of the frequency of a rhythm in constant conditions is more likely to be a mechanism that allows for synchronisation of the rhythm of an organism with that of the environment.

Pittendrigh and Bruce (1957) have stressed the ubiquity of biological 'clocks'. They regard the widespread phenomenon of temperature-independent persistent (endogenous) daily rhythms as a manifestation of the same basic time-measuring ability that underlies the elaborate chronometry of birds and other Metazoa. Indeed, they maintain that temperature-independent time measurement is an almost universal feature of living systems. Thus they suggest that Calhoun's (1944) statement, quoted by Thorpe (1956) that we do not know of a single case of an inherited rhythm, to be in need of complete inversion. They claim that there is no evidence that atypical periods can be learned any more than that the typical natural period is learned.

Now it is possible, of course, that the difficulty usually experienced in setting up rhythms with periodicities of other than 24-hours (Cloudsley-Thompson 1953d; 1956c; 1957a, etc.) may be due to 'imprinting' of the 24-hour period at an early age. There can be no doubt that some periodicities, such as the 18-hour rhythms described in insects and spiders are actually learned, but when, as frequently seems to happen, these revert to a 24-hour periodicity under constant conditions, the implication that the 'clock' cannot be altered to a periodicity of other than 24 hours is strong. Indeed, it may be that the apparent 18-hour rhythms that have been obtained are merely the result of an 18-hour environmental cycle reinforcing parts of a bimodal 24-hour rhythm.

The interaction between environmental and inherent rhythm in the sea-pen, *Cavernularia obesa*, has been investigated by Mori and Ondô (1957) who found that synchronisation occurs only when a cycle of environmental light periodicity falls between 18 and 30 hours. Outside this range, the 'normal' 24-hour periodicity tends to return.

For example, it has been found that the field cricket, *Gryllus campestris*, is normally active during the daytime, the rhythm being endogenous and its frequency temperature-independent. When the 24-hour rhythm has died away after weeks in constant conditions it can be re-established by a single exposure to light or by a return to higher temperatures after a period at 5°C. (Cloudsley-Thompson 1958d). There is a parallel here with the observations of Bünning (1935), Pittendrigh (1954) and others who have found that a rhythm of emergence of adult fruit-flies and other insects from the pupa can be induced by a single short exposure to light (see discussion in Chapter 7).

A simpler, and therefore more acceptable hypothesis than learning, in this case, may be that there are a number of internal 'clocks' in the cricket, each possessing an inherited 24-hour periodicity. These are normally synchronised by alternating light and darkness reinforced by fluctuating temperature and humidity.

Since 24-hour rhythms are known even in Protozoa and unicellular algae (see p. 42), it is probable that all living cells possess an inherent 24-hour periodicity, synchronised either directly by fluctuations of some factor of the environment, or by a 'master clock' which engenders a behaviour pattern that is, in turn, synchronised with the environment.

Indeed, one might go further and take the line that there is no such thing as a true exogenous rhythm! Certainly environment-dependent rhythms seem to be rare in nature and there are probably few rhythms which do not persist, at any rate for a short while, under constant conditions. The basic difference between exogenous and endogenous periodicities probably lies in the fact that the cellular 'clocks' involved in the former get out of phase with one another very soon after the removal of an environmental 'clue'. In the case of endogenous rhythms, synchronisation is maintained for longer in the absence of such a synchroniser or 'clue'.

INDEPENDENCE OF RHYTHMS WITHIN THE ORGANISM

Brown and Stephens (1951) have postulated that when the problem of the control of the magnitude of the periodic dispersion of black melanophores in the fiddler crab, *Uca pugnax*, are considered, several lines of reasoning suggest that there must be two more or less independent controlling centres. The first of these manifests a persistent 24-hour periodicity in the secretion of a black-dispersing hormone and the extent of this activity is modified only by changes in the length of the daily photoperiod to which the animal is exposed. In addition, this secretion, or another from the same centre, exerts a controlling influence on the rhythmic activity of the second centre. Total darkness or a daily photoperiod below some threshold length is not effective as a stimulus in changing the activity of the centre.

The second centre exhibits a more labile and less persistent 24-hour periodicity than the first. It becomes completely synchronised with the first when the environmental stimuli which normally influence it are absent. Both black-dispersing and black-concentrating substances are produced, the latter being secreted in darkness, the former in light. Thus, while the first centre is influenced only by the length of the photoperiod to which the animal is exposed, the second is affected by the duration and intensity of light, the duration of the dark period and by the activity of the first centre.

This hypothesis is in no way incompatible with that postulated by Brown and Webb (1949) to account for other responses of the rhythmic

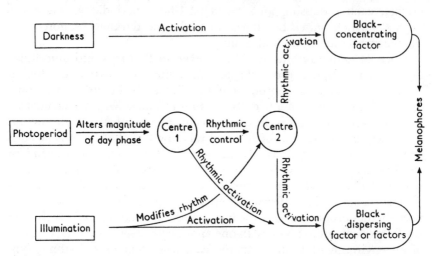

FIG. 26. A diagrammatic representation of the postulated control mechanism of the black chromatophore rhythm of *Uca pugnax*. (After Brown and Stephens, 1951)

mechanisms of *Uca*: in fact they both exhibit the same intrinsic characteristics, viz. the presence of two centres of rhythmicity within the animal, each one capable of having its rhythm altered independently of the other and with one of the centres, that having a more persistent rhythmicity influencing the other.

Again, Fingerman and Lago (1957) have studied the 24-hour rhythm of distal retinal pigment migration in the American dwarf crawfish, *Cambarellus shufeldti*, and found differences in the rate of dark and light adaptation at different times throughout the day and night. They have interpreted this rhythm as being due to changes throughout the day in the quantity of light-adapting hormone present in the blood.

When spontaneous locomotor activity and oxygen consumption of the crawfish, *Orconectes clypeatus*, were recorded continuously analysis of the data revealed 24-hour periodicities in both functions (Fingerman and Lago, 1957). The population appeared to consist of two types of individual with different times of maximum activity. Fingerman and Lago attempted to explain their results by an hypothesis based on the existence of two centres of rhythmicity, one having an excitatory effect on locomotory activity, the second an inhibitory effect.

Brown and his associates have pointed out in a series of papers already discussed, that both 24-hour and tidal rhythms appear to be very deep-seated phenomena and that the normally rhythmic environment, rather than inducing rhythm, appears to act as a suppressing factor upon an endogenous mechanism. They divide rhythms into two types, overt and statistical, and show that overt rhythms may be out of phase with each other within the same animal. On the other hand, the only known statistically apparent rhythm, that of oxygen consumption, is similar in all the cases recorded. They suggest that overt rhythms are controlled by an 'internal clock' whilst statistical rhythms are purely exogenous depending upon variations in cosmic ray intensity.

Hoffmann (1954) found that the choice of compass direction to which starlings had been trained (see p. 134) did not vary throughout a period of 28 days with constant light and approximately constant temperature although the activity rhythm seemed to be greatly upset. This suggests that the endogenous 'clock' system persists even though the diurnal activity rhythm has been altered.

The experimental dissociation of mammalian rhythms has already been discussed in the previous chapter so I will not refer to it again. Evidence of a completely different nature has recently been provided by Perttunen and Lagerspetz (1957). These authors have shown that a dissociation of the pulsation rhythm in the anterior and posterior parts of the heart occurs at high and low temperatures in the larva of the gnat, *Corethra plumicornis*. Over a wide temperature range (7° to 37°C) the rates of the anterior and posterior parts of the heart are equal. But if the temperature is lowered beyond this range, the anterior part of the heart starts to beat about half as fast as the posterior part, whilst above the normal temperature range the anterior part again beats more slowly than the posterior part.

It is quite obvious, therefore, that the various rhythmic phenomena within an animal are often basically independent and can be dissociated experimentally. Nevertheless, under natural conditions, most rhythms are no doubt synchronised or otherwise co-ordinated, while others interact, thereby engendering further endogenous periodicities within the organism.

Synchronisation of Internal Chronometers by Environmental 'Clues'

The phases of a diurnal rhythm can be inverted by a few days of 'reversed' illumination during the night with darkness during the day. Endogenous 'clocks' can also be reset by illumination changes at sensitive times of the daily cycle. For example, fiddler crabs which have been kept in very bright continuous illumination for about 10 days remain continuously black. If these rhythm-inhibited animals are placed in a darkroom, either at 12.00 or at 18.00 hours, a normal rhythm of colour change commences at once. If, however, they are placed in the darkroom at 06.00 hours, the rhythm which now reappears in darkness is set forwards by about a quarter of a cycle, or about 6 hours (Brown and Webb, 1949). See also Bünning (1958b), quoted below (p. 180).

On the other hand, if fiddler crabs having a normal rhythm in darkness are illuminated on three consecutive days from midnight to 06.00 hours, the phases of the cycles are set backwards about a quarter of a cycle (Webb, 1950). In those cases of alteration in which a clear answer has been obtained, the evidence seems to suggest that when a rhythm is altered, it is altered abruptly by a single light change, or by a single period of illumination. Brown and Webb (1949) have suggested that there may be two centres of rhythmicity within an animal, each one capable of having its rhythm altered independently of the other but that one which has a more persistent rhythm may influence the other.

Folk, Meltzer and Grindeland (1958) have shown that when hamsters and ground squirrels were maintained at controlled temperatures with a daily cycle of 12 hours of artificial light and 12 hours of darkness before hibernating for 4 months in a cold chamber ($6 \pm 1°C$) with a light cycle (7 ft.-candles), the awakenings of the hamsters were at random but the ground squirrels awoke 72 per cent of the time during the periods corresponding to the original light cycle. Mammals in hibernation appear to be blind, and once ground squirrels begin to awaken from hibernation, they do not interrupt the process and return to the dormant condition until they have remained fully active for at least 12 hours. It is probable therefore that there are regular periods of shallow and deep hibernation, perhaps of about 12 hours each, and that the periodicity is temperature-independent (see p. 152).

"The ecological significance of a clock independent of temperature in hibernation can be illustrated by the important rule that rodent 24-hour rhythm (which can be represented as a dial of behaviour sequences) can be reversed or 'turned' by 12 hours only by a gradual process taking at least 4 days. Thus, if a free ground squirrel, which is a day-active species, were to awaken at night from hibernation in the spring, it would probably be incapable of causing its behaviour sequence to jump the gap to the day period until several days had elapsed. Apparently this could be avoided by the independence of temperature of the biological clock during hibernation."

As the hours of daylight alter with the changing seasons, mammals tend to change their habits. There may be a minimum period into which an animal can compress the physiological activities that must take place every 24 hours. For example, the nocturnal golden hamster can rest for 16 hours and be active throughout a night of 8 hours so that, even in winter in temperate regions, it is never active during the day. On the other hand, deer mice, which are entirely nocturnal in winter, may show some day-time activity during the summer months when the hours of daylight are long.

Barden (1942) found that the diurnal rhythm of activity in the day-active lizard *Cnemidophorus sexlineatus* persisted under constant conditions. In constant light, however, the peak of activity occurred half an hour earlier each day whilst the initiation of activity was delayed by constant darkness. These observations indicate that shifts in the activity peaks of a day-active animal are just the opposite to that of nocturnal animals in response to continuous light or darkness.

In general, it seems that the activities of nocturnal animals are delayed by constant darkness while those of day-active animals are delayed by constant light. In this way their diurnal rhythm can be shifted as the days lengthen or draw in according to the season. Synchronisation with environmental periodic changes cannot be achieved both at dawn and at dusk, as the time of each of these is altering. In fact, the synchroniser tends to be the dusk in the case of nocturnal forms, dawn in that of diurnal animals.

In this connection the work of Aschoff and Meyer-Lohmann (1952–58) at Heidelberg is specially important. Aschoff takes the view that an animal shows a spectrum of frequencies of oscillations in its activity: in other words it possesses a number of biological 'clocks', not just one. For example, from measurements on 15 mice over a period of 230 days, it was possible to discriminate between two types of activity, one with a frequency of 0.6/hour, the other with a periodicity of 0.4/hour. The average periodicity amounted to 11/24 hours. This was maintained under conditions of complete darkness when the average frequency was 10.7/24 hours (Aschoff and Meyer-Lohmann, 1954b).

Aschoff (1954) has suggested that the occurrence of a number of biological processes in an animal, all following a 24-hour rhythm, necessitates some kind of synchronisation which is achieved in nature chiefly by alternating light and darkness. However, there are always several processes acting at once, and generally in competition with one another so that a change in one will affect the others.

A similar conclusion has been reached by the writer. "Under natural conditions there are probably several clues active at the same time, one of which is generally the ruling factor of an animal's periodicity. However, there can be competition between different clues and changes in the sensitivity and physiological state of an animal may engender considerable changes in the relationship of the various environmental factors involved." (Cloudsley-Thompson, 1952a; 1957a).

Aschoff (1958) points out that periodic environmental 'clues' (*Zeitgeber*) can influence the rhythm of an animal in three ways: (a) by sudden displacement of the *Zeitgeber* without alteration in frequency (phase-leap); (b) by affecting the internal 'clock' of an animal although

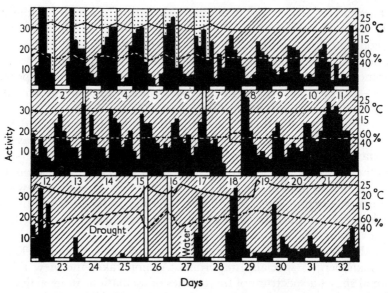

FIG. 27. Periodicity of movement and rest in the cricket, *Gryllus campestris*. At first the activity rhythm was reversed under 'reversed' lighting and this persisted under constant conditions. The rhythm was then reset by a 2-hour light period (day 13) and again by a return to 20°C (day 18). Finally the reappearance of a rhythm is shown in an arhythmic insect whose activity was later suppressed by drought. Water was given at noon (day 27) and activity recommenced at 18.00 hrs., reaching a peak from 21.00 to 24.00 hrs. (After Cloudsley-Thompson, 1958d)

the frequency of the external periodicity remains constant. For example, Aschoff and Meyer-Lohmann (1954a) found that rats and mice, like most other mammals show two distinct peaks of activity every 24 hours. In general, light-active animals show a maximum at the beginning of the light period, nocturnal forms at nightfall. The distance between these maxima is not strongly fixed and in the course of the year the rhythm will alter as sunrise and sunset are followed by these peaks of activity. (c) By a sudden change in frequency.

Individual mice show significant differences in the length of their natural period under constant conditions, but their rhythm can be 'entrained' as Pittendrigh (1958) calls it, by a periodic *Zeitgeber* (Aschoff,

1955c). Again, lizards hatching in constant darkness and temperature show individual differences in the period of their activity rhythm (Hoffman, 1957b), although the time between peaks varies somewhat with temperature, being less at 35°C than at 25°C or 16°C (Hoffman, 1957a). It is evident that temperature independence of the rhythm in this case is by no means perfect.

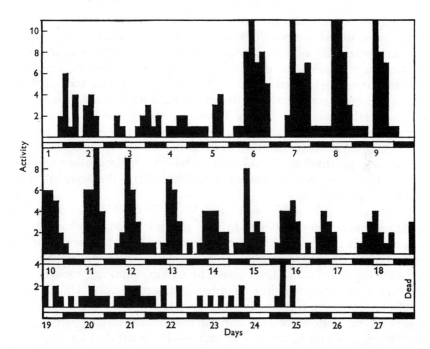

FIG. 28. Persistence of rhythmic activity in the tropical millipede, *Ophistreptus* sp., in constant temperature (21.5°C) humidity (damp medium) and lighting. (After Cloudsley-Thompson, 1951b). As Aschoff (1958) points out, the frequency of the period is about 24.8 hours whilst that of the same animal in constant darkness is 23.0 hours.

The different rhythms in an animal tend to develop a regular pattern, forming an hierarchy in which each rhythm has a shorter frequency than the one above it. Thus, a frequency of a few minutes is dominated by one with a period of 2 to 3 hours which, in turn, is subordinate to the 24-hour period. The majority of 24-hour rhythms observed in nature show two peaks, as we have seen, of which the smaller follows the greater after an interval of less than 24 hours. This smaller peak is more labile than the greater and depends to some extent upon environmental factors less closely related to the *Zeitgeber*.

The natural time of activity of an animal can, therefore, be determined by establishing the time of the major peak of activity; for even crepuscular forms are usually more active at either dusk or dawn (Aschoff, 1957).

It can readily be seen, therefore, that the diurnal rhythm, constantly adjusting itself to an environmental clue, will regulate other periodicities which interact within the animal, so that ultimately all are adjusted.

LOCALISATION OF 'MASTER CHRONOMETERS'

Despite a considerable amount of work on mammals using operative procedures, little has been demonstrated beyond the fact that 24-hour rhythms persist after the removal of major organs and that rhythmic control must therefore be deep-seated. Among invertebrates, however, 'clocks' have been located in at least two instances. I have termed them 'master chronometers' because I believe most, if not all cells, either to be or to contain biological 'clocks' for whose synchronisation a control clock is seldom required. Consequently I do not regard these 'master chronometers' as being the sole 'clocks' in the animals that possess them, but merely as rhythm control centres which regulate other cellular clocks. The behaviour pattern resulting from this is then synchronised by environmental 'clues'.

In an important series of papers, Wells (1937–55) has described spontaneous activity patterns in the physiology and behaviour of various marine Polychaete worms. In several of his experiments, he has housed *Arenicola marina* in glass U-tubes. The lug-worms are able to obtain a supply of water from above by making pumping movements, the water movements being recorded kymographically. Under such conditions the animals generally settle down to give outbursts of irrigation separated by periods of rest, the alternation continuing with great regularity for many hours at a stretch. Wells found that an irrigation outburst consists of three phases, tailward locomotion, headward irrigation and slow headward creeping, followed by tailward irrigation. These three phases follow each other in sequence, but their relative prominence is variable, the second being the most conspicuous when a plentiful supply of oxygenated water is available. The frequency of the period of the irrigation cycle is commonly about 40 minutes.

That the rhythm is spontaneous and produced by conditions internal to the worm is shown by the fact that animals pinned down under sea water continue to show outbursts of rhythmic activity corresponding in timing to the irrigation cycles, the pauses between outbursts being neither shortened nor abolished by lowering the oxygen tension in the water. Moreover, when experimental conditions were arranged so that worms in U-tubes circulated the water without getting an oxygen supply, the timing of the irrigation cycles did not vary although their vigour was greatly increased (Wells 1949a). Observations on the rhythmic activity of strips of body-wall suggest that the pacemaker for the irrigation cycles may lie in the ventral nerve cord (Wells, 1949a).

In addition to and superimposed on the irrigation cycle, lug-worms show a characteristic cyclical pattern of feeding and defaecation when they are allowed to burrow in sand in the laboratory. This is marked by conspicuous diphasic excursions at intervals of about 40 minutes, at the summit of the first phase of which defaecation occurs. In the intervals between the defaecation-irrigation outbursts, the kymograph tracing

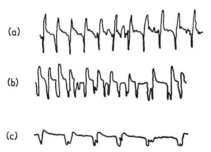

FIG. 29. (a) Record (7 hours long) traced by an actively feeding lug-worm, *Arenicola marina*, with its tail towards the recording float. The worm defaecates at the tip of each of the prominent downward peaks.
(b), (c) Two records (each 4½ hours long) traced by a worm which was not actively feeding. In both cases the worm's head was towards the float. This float was made of paraffin wax moulded on silver wire and connected to a light isotonic lever writing on smoked paper. (After Wells, 1949b)

shows a periodicity of smaller amplitude and frequency. This is probably due to intermittent feeding (Wells, 1949b). For the worms generally show periodic outbursts of proboscis extrusion, gulping and withdrawal which have a frequency of about 7 minutes. These movements are under the influence of an oesophageal pacemaker (Wells, 1937).

When the oesophagus of *Arenicola marina* is excised, divided by a transverse cut into two halves and suspended in sea water, both halves show a primary rhythm of slow contraction waves of small amplitude. In a minority of preparations the oral halves show other types of spontaneous activity. If the proboscis, with a short length of oesophagus attached, is suspended in sea water, it shows outbursts of vigorous rhythmical activity alternating with periods of rest, each cycle taking about 6 or 7 minutes to complete. But if the proboscis is mounted alone, it shows an irregular, more or less continuous rhythm without any trace of the vigorous rhythmic outbursts seen when oesophageal tissue is present (Wells, 1937).

It was, therefore, concluded that the outbursts of feeding activity exhibited by intact worms are probably identical with those of the dissected preparations and therefore due to the pacemaker action of the oesophagus.

Experiments with dissected worms have shown that an inhibitory influence of the oesophageal pacemaker could be detected in the segments responsible for creeping and irrigation.

The alternation described could be due either to a series of reflexes in which each phase is the stimulus for the next, or to a spontaneous pacemaker. But since activity cycles involve bursts of rhythm separated by periods of rest which may be quite long when the oesophageal pacemaker is slowed by excess of magnesium ions (Wells and Ledingham, 1940), it is suggested that there must be a 'clock' mechanism, presumably of the nature of a relaxation oscillator (Wells, 1949b).

The physiological 'master clock' of these Annelida is therefore the oesophagus, or even a slice of this structure *in vitro*. The rhythm of this tissue can be likened to the mammalian heart. But unlike that of the heart, it is transferred through the nervous system to the entire physiology and behaviour of the animal. Thus "the oesophagus drives the proboscis and the rest of the body". (Wells, 1955).

Wells and Albrecht (1951a) have shown that the oesophageal rhythm is transmitted to the muscles of the proboscis, where it causes vigorous contraction, and thence to the body wall, where it causes correlated contractions in the first three segments but periodic inhibition in the brancheate segments. A second component consists of vigorous rhythmic activity in the body wall and tail and can appear after their connection has been severed with the isolated extrovert preparation (consisting of the proboscis with a short length of oesophagus attached). Neither pacemaker directly affects the rhythm of the other, but the integration of the activities which they determine probably depends on variation in the extent to which their influences spread through the neuromuscular system. They appear to compete for territory, and if they happen to discharge outbursts simultaneously the irrigation-defaecation pacemaker dominates over most of the body wall and the feeding cycle pacemaker over the proboscis and mouth region.

The relation between irrigation pattern and the timing of defaecation has been discussed by Wells (1953) who sums up as follows:

"(I) Defaecation and the *i-d* outbursts are essentially independent, cyclically repeated events. (II) When the worm is living under favourable conditions in an established burrow, the familiar pattern in which defaecation is closely coupled to the *i-d* cycle gives a workable means of integrating its activities. (III) The coupling may perhaps be brought about by two factors, a tendency to defaecate just before the onset of headward irrigation and a 'fine adjustment' of the intervals between *i-d* outbursts to match the feeding rate. (IV) The factors controlling irrigation behaviour and the timing of defaecation in other circumstances are still obscure."

Spontaneous activity patterns have also been described in other Polychaetes: in *Arenicola ecaudata* there is a similar organisation of outbursts, but in a more variable and fluctuating pattern. Here the oesophageal rhythm appears to be under the control of the central nervous system rather than of an oesophageal pacemaker. The fact that *Chaetopterus variopedatus* and *Nereis diversicolor* (Wells and Dales, 1951) as well as *Sabella spallanzani*, *S. pavonia* and *Mysicola infundibulum* (Wells, 1951, 1952) also show similar activity patterns suggests that the mechanism of control may be similar in all.

Despite its apparent improbability, Wells suggests that the method of control of these rhythms may have survival value. The flat beaches inhabited by lugworms are often covered with puddles and sheets of water at low tide. "On a sunny day, this water may be several degrees hotter than the under-lying sand, and well above the highest temperatures which the worms can tolerate. A sharp frost, or a heavy downpour of rain, could also make the surface water harmful to the worms. Normally, the worm drives water through its burrow to get a supply of oxygen; if the surface water became dangerously hot or dilute a reflex hyperpnoea in response to oxygen lack might be disastrous; it would be wiser for the worm to suspend its activities. When placed in a glass tube under unfavourable chemical conditions the worm becomes relatively inactive; but, under the influence of its 40-minute rhythm, it makes periodic backward trips towards the top of the tube and generally draws a little water along on these occasions, as if testing the surface water. We may guess that when unfavourable conditions develop in the field, it behaves in the same way; after the rising tide has covered the burrow again and so removed the danger, the fact will be detected at the next testing excursion, and the worm's full activities will then be resumed." (Wells, 1955).

The second known case in which a 'master clock' has been located is afforded by the work of Harker (1954, 1955, 1956) on the factors controlling the diurnal rhythm of activity in *Periplanata americana*. By means of experiments in which two cockroaches were joined together in parabiosis, Harker first showed that a hormone was involved in the control of the activity rhythm.

"The top cockroach, which had had the legs removed and was immobile, had previously been subjected to normal conditions of light and darkness and been found to have a normal rhythm of activity; the bottom, mobile cockroach had been left in constant light for its whole life and had no rhythm of activity. The activity of this parabiotic pair was then measured under constant light and they were found to have a rhythm of activity corresponding closely to that of the 'normal' top cockroach. If left in constant light over a period of 6 or 7 days the rhythm was gradually lost. The reverse positions were also tested, the top cockroach having before parabiosis no rhythm, and the bottom mobile one a normal rhythm. The bottom cockroach continued to show a normal rhythm of activity." (Harker, 1954).

It had already been shown (Cloudsley-Thompson 1953d) that decapitation or painting over the compound eyes and ocelli of a cockroach will cause a loss of rhythm. Harker (1955, 1956) confirmed this and showed that severing the ocellar nerve will also cause a gradual loss of rhythm. Furthermore, she suggested that the neurosecretory hormone whose periodic secretion is responsible for the activity rhythm, might be secreted by the sub-oesophageal ganglion under the influence of stimulation by light operating through the ocelli.

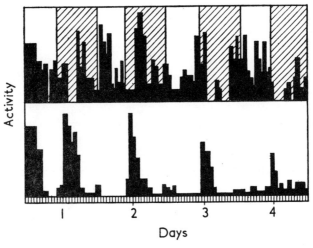

FIG. 30. *Above.* The activity of a headless cockroach, *Periplaneta americana,* in alternating light and darkness. *Below.* The activity in continuous light of a headless cockroach into which had been implanted the sub-oesophageal ganglia from a normal rhythmic cockroach. (After Harker, 1956)

Pairs of sub-oesophageal ganglia were therefore taken from cockroaches with normal activity rhythms and implanted into headless cockroaches. The implanted cockroaches were placed in continuous light, darkness, or in reversed light and darkness; but in each case they showed the rhythm of activity previously exhibited by the donor of the sub-oesophageal ganglion (Harker, 1955, 1956). It was therefore suggested that at least part of the mechanism of the internal clock of the cockroach is an endocrine secretion released by the sub-oesophageal ganglion, and that this is governed by the extrinsic factors of light and darkness through the medium of the ocelli.

In this connection the observation of Harker (1958b) that tumours of the mid-gut develop in normal cockroaches when sub-oesophagael ganglia from insects kept under reversed lighting regimes are implanted in them, may prove to be of great importance in the study of diseases resulting from stress syndromes in man.

Further evidence for the view that a 'master chronometer' may be located in the sub-oesophageal ganglion is afforded by the work of Fingerman, Lago and Lowe (1958) who found that although neither allatectomy (removal of the corpora allata through a triangular opening on top of the brain) nor removal of the entire brain affected the 24-hour periodicity of locomotory activity and oxygen consumption in the American grasshopper, *Romalea microptera:* grasshoppers whose sub-oesophageal ganglion had been removed showed no rhythmicity. However, these results do not prove that the ganglion is the centre of rhythmicity, but merely that the centre must operate through the ganglion which exercises normal control over locomotion.

CHAPTER 10

The Physiological Effects of Temperature on Rhythmic Phenomena

THROUGHOUT this book, constant reference has been made to the temperature independence of rhythmic phenomena. Before the physiological mechanism of this is discussed in detail, reference will be made to other effects of temperature on rhythms, especially the importance of fluctuating temperatures on their maintenance in rhythms.

THE SIGNIFICANCE OF FLUCTUATING TEMPERATURE ON THE PHYSIOLOGY AND ECOLOGY OF INSECTS

Although the more densely populated portions of the earth are affected by daily fluctuations in temperature, there are some well-occupied environments in which the temperature remains nearly constant for long periods. Terrestrial examples of such environments are afforded by the lower levels of the soil, the interiors of trees and fallen logs, and accumulations of stored products. It is therefore to be expected that most animals should be adapted either to fluctuating or to constant temperatures according to their natural habitats. Despite this, nearly all experimental investigations of the effect of heat on the rate of insect development have been carried out at constant temperatures (Uvarov, 1931; Wigglesworth, 1950). The influence of seasonal temperature changes on hibernation and aestivation are of prime importance and the effects of exposure to high and low temperatures on subsequent development are well known (Andrewartha, 1952). In this chapter, however, we are concerned only with the effects of fluctuating temperatures on insects developing without diapause.

As early as 1910, Sanderson had pointed out that when studying development at fluctuating temperatures, the periods spent at each temperature should be evaluated separately. "It is evident," he wrote, "that any accumulation of temperature to secure a thermal or physiological constant cannot be based on a mere addition where variable temperatures are involved, for it is evident that every degree has a different value in relation to the time factor. Thus the mean temperature rises with the advance of the season, both the time for the pupal stage

172

and the total accumulated temperature for the pupal stage of the codling moth decrease with the advancing season."

A few years later, Headlee (1914) studied the development of the grain aphis *Toxoptera graminum* at constant and fluctuating temperatures. Although aphids at a constant temperature of 26.6°C reached maturity in 6 days instead of in 8 at fluctuating temperatures and the daily rate of reproduction increased more than twice, the aphids lived twenty-five times as long at the fluctuating temperature as they did at the constant one. Similar results were obtained with pupae of the codling moth, *Carpocapsa pomonella* which required 8 days less for their development at a constant temperature of 17.22°C than under a diurnal fluctuation varying from 10° to 24.44°C (Headlee, 1929).

Destouches (1921) also found that although the larvae of the wax moth *Galleria melonella* developed at the same rate at alternating as at constant temperatures, yet the life of the adult moths was very much longer at alternating temperatures (30 to 35 days instead of 5), and the total productivity increased from 5 to 25 to 35 eggs per pair. According to Ludwig (1926) the rate of development of the beetle *Popillia japonica* was affected by the fluctuation of the temperature. If the effective temperature was alternated with one above the optimum range, development was retarded, but an alternation with a low temperature had an accelerating effect.

Cook (1927) measured the growth of first instar larvae of the cutworm *Porosagrotis orthogonia* exposed to various high temperatures for short periods each day, and the rate of carbon dioxide production in nearly mature larvae of *Chlorizagrotis auxiliaris* during similar exposures, and reached the conclusion that fluctuations in the temperature had a definitely accelerating effect. Peairs (1927) also obtained a definite but slight acceleration in the development of blowfly larvae and pupae at temperatures changed at intervals of six hours.

According to Shelford (1929), "the crucial variable-temperature experiments must be done with minimal medial temperatures occurring at night and with temperatures rising to maximal medial during the day. These experiments will usually show an acceleration of development as compared with constant temperatures of the same numerical value as the mean hourly reading of the variable temperatures". From his extensive studies on the development of the codling moth under actual weather conditions, Shelford (1927) had previously concluded that the effect of normal daily temperature fluctuations caused a 7 to 8 per cent more rapid development than under constant temperatures, but that short fluctuations might slightly retard development.

Outbreaks of the cotton worm *Prodenia litura* in lower Egypt were studied by Janisch (1930, 1932) who found that short exposures to high temperature (40°C) retarded subsequent development, but that the retarding action of temperature between 33° and 37°C was perceptible only in the later stages of development, while the earlier stages were accelerated as compared with the rate of development under constant optimum conditions. Nevertheless he made the surprising suggestion that all variations from the absolute optimum of temperature, food, moisture, etc., were damaging and resulted in the lengthening of individual instars.

On the other hand, Parker (1929) found that grasshoppers, *Melanoplus atlantis*, developed at a greater rate at fluctuating than at constant temperatures. "This means," he wrote, "that rates of development as determined in constant temperature cabinets cannot be used directly in forecasting when eggs will hatch in Nature when temperatures alternate between high day temperatures and lower night temperatures". Two other species, *Melanoplus mexicanus* and *Camnula pellucida*, were afterwards shown also to develop more quickly at fluctuating temperatures. Eggs held at 22°C for 16 hours and 5°, 10° or 15°C higher for 8 hours daily, showed an average acceleration for *M. mexicanus* of 38.6 per cent and for *C. pellucida* of 30.5 per cent as compared with the rate of development at comparable constant temperatures. Nymphs reared in such alternating conditions were accelerated some 12 per cent over expectation based on results from constant temperatures (Parker, 1930). Payne (1932) found that pupae of the mealworm beetle, *Tenebrio molitor*, exposed to alternating temperatures generally developed somewhat faster than would be predicted from their development rate at constant temperatures, but Dawson (1931) claimed that no acceleration in development occurred in response to fluctuating temperature in the moth, *Telea polyphemus*, of which the cocoons are ordinarily exposed to great variations of temperature (Chapman, 1931).

The rate of pupal development of the fruit-fly, *Drosophila melanogaster*, at constant and alternating temperatures was found by Ludwig and Cable (1933) to have been retarded when one of the temperatures was above the optimum. This retardation might have been due to the reduced rate of development at temperatures above the optimum, so that the total developmental time was longer than at the mean constant temperature: but differences were found in the speed of development at the same alternating temperatures according to whether the higher or the lower were administered first. When both temperatures were between the theoretical threshold and the optimum, neither acceleration nor retardation were produced, but if one of the temperatures lay between the theoretical and the actual threshold of development, the rate was accelerated, probably by development below the theoretical threshold.

Alternating temperatures affected survival as well as the rate of development of the flour beetle, *Tribolium confusum*. The eggs developed more rapidly in constant temperatures than in comparable variable ones, except when the upper temperature lay below the optimum, and the lower was at the developmental zero. Pupae behaved differently, and the most rapid acceleration occurred with an alternating amplitude of 5°C. The range of constant temperatures with a survival greater than 50 per cent, was narrower, however, than the range of mean alternating temperatures producing the same result: and fluctuating temperatures increased survival, especially in the lower part of the favourable thermal range of the insects (Mikulski, 1936a, b).

A study of the relative effects of constant and variable temperatures on insect metabolism, dealing in particular with the mosquito *Aedes aegypti*, confirmed Headlee's (1941) conclusion that the relative effect of temperatures derived from variable and constant sources was dependent, in this species, upon where, in the insect's normal temperature reactions, the constant and variable temperatures lay. He believed that the underlying and governing factors of such temperature differences, as existed in the variable and constant temperatures, was the accumulation of the required amount of heat, regardless of whether the temperature in question came from constant or variable sources.

Describing his investigation of the biology of the red spider mite, *Tetranychus althacae*, Linke (1953) wrote: "The values for the rate of development of *T. althacae* obtained at constant temperatures do not coincide with the results obtained at corresponding average temperatures outdoors. An acceleration of development was observed regularly under changing conditions outdoors. The causes of this can only be assumed but are not definite."

In his important work on the ecology of the bed-bug *Cimex lectularius* in Britain, C. G. Johnson (1940, 1942) showed that there was a decrease in the time from oviposition to hatching when eggs were placed alternatively at 23° and 13.1°C at 90 per cent relative humidity for 24 hours at each temperature until the maximum number had hatched. Similar results were obtained using 27.8° and 17.5°. The transition from one temperature to the other in these experiments was abrupt and not gradual. Johnson argued that such a decrease in the time for development might be due to one of two causes: an acceleration of development due solely to the temperature fluctuations above the mean producing a relatively greater effect than the fluctuations below the mean—this would happen with certain non-linear temperature-velocity curves—or an acceleration of development apart from this and due to the temperature fluctuation itself. He decided that the developmental time for *C. lectularius* eggs was not affected by the alternating temperatures that he used, apart from the effects due to the non-linearity of the temperature-velocity relationship, a conclusion in agreement with the views of Ludwig and Cable (1933).

More recently, the problem of temperature effect on organic development has been treated mathematically by Pradhan (1946), who has given a possible explanation as to why the rise of temperatures up to a certain degree accelerates development but beyond that value begins to have a retarding effect. He has suggested that organic development takes place in accordance with the law of compound interest, the speed of vital activities acting as rate of interest. The amount of development from birth to death and the amount required to complete well-defined stages, such as egg, larva or pupa, are constant quantities for the species, allowing for individual variations, and the amount of vital activity performed in unit time increases with the rise of temperature with a velocity that does not remain constant but is continuously retarded by the same temperature rise. These ideas may prove to be of considerable importance, especially if it can be shown that they are applicable generally.

The present writer has compared the effects of constant and alternating temperatures on insect physiology from a different angle. He found that millipedes *Oxidus gracilis* and *Blaniulus guttulatus* did not thrive in cultures kept at constant temperature, and that under these conditions there was a steady decline in total activity in the large tropical forms *Ophistreptus* sp. and *Oxydesmus platycercus* (Cloudsley-Thompson, 1951b). Drops in temperature were a stimulus to orthokinetic locomotory activity in millipedes, and falling temperature was correlated with nocturnal activity in these animals (Cloudsley-Thompson, 1951a).

Similar results were obtained with the cockroach *Periplaneta americana*. Although fluctuating temperature and humidity alone did not engender a rhythm in this species, constant temperature appeared to have an adverse, depressing effect which was not so apparent when two cockroaches, even of different species (*P. americana* and *P. australasiae*) were kept together (Cloudsley-Thompson, 1953d). "It is not yet possible to say," it was concluded "whether the absence of a rhythm in a normally rhythmic species has a deleterious effect, although this point has a bearing upon problems of pest infestation of stored products, and temperature fluctuations may prove to be of much greater ecological significance than is at present realised" (Cloudsley-Thompson, 1952b; see also below, p. 177).

From the evidence cited above it will be appreciated that it is impossible to use average temperatures for an exact estimation of the influence of weather conditions on the development of insects, for exposure to variable temperatures often affects the rate of development which is usually accelerated, except when one of the alternating temperatures is well above the optimum. It is probable that in many cases this acceleration may be additional to the effect produced by a non-linear temperature-velocity relationship. The amount of acceleration varies with different stages of the life history, with different species and with the combinations of temperature that are used. In addition, the thermal optimum in the action of fluctuating temperatures may differ from the constant temperature optimum, and in those cases in which development is accelerated by constant temperatures, the length of life of the insects is often considerably reduced.

It is probably best to regard fluctuating temperatures as 'normal' and constant temperatures as 'abnormal' for those species that inhabit places in which there are diurnal variations in the air temperature. Conversely the ability of different species to withstand constant temperatures may depend upon the constancy of conditions in their normal habitats, and this may influence their success in competing with other species in environments such as accumulations of stored products which exhibit varying degrees of thermal 'abnormality'. For many biotic factors will naturally be involved, and not every species inhabits the ecological niche which climatically and geographically would appear to be most suited to its requirements.

The paragraphs above have been quoted from Cloudsley-Thompson (1953b). The stimulatory effect they reveal of fluctuating temperatures upon most species of animals, is clearly related to the second function of 'clues' (p. 5), that of maintaining rhythms.

TEMPERATURE INDEPENDENCE IN RHYTHMS

If an endogenous rhythm is to be of any service to an organism, the biological 'clocks' by which it is controlled must be relatively independent of temperature changes. If our clocks, for example, were to double their rates when the temperature rose 10°C and halve them when it fell a similar amount, they would be rather useless. Consequently the existence of temperature independence should not cause surprise when considered from a functional viewpoint. On the other hand it is clear that the timing of biological 'clocks' cannot depend upon any simple metabolic process or else their rate would depend upon the temperature.

In 1948 Brown and Webb established that in the fiddler crab, *Uca pugnax*, the frequency of the rhythm of colour change was independent of temperature over a 20°C range. This study marked the beginning of a period during which the temperature-independent nature of the phenomenon was stressed and the small dependence unemphasised.

As Stephens (1957a) points out: "It is possible to advance a number of explanations to account for this temperature independence. Thus one may invoke a rate-controlling process which is characterised by a Q_{10}

of 1.0. This has the virtue of simplicity, but when one searches the literature in physiology to find some metabolic process with the required characteristics, there is nothing to be found."

In all organisms so far investigated there appears to be a critical temperature at which rhythms cease. This temperature may vary for different types of rhythm within the same organism. Although low temperatures above the critical temperature affect the frequency of the 'clocks' of poikelothermic animals, it is natural to expect that physiological responses may be slowed. For example, an animal may start moving at the correct time, but it will nevertheless move more slowly at lower temperatures. Therefore, although the period of a rhythm is relatively unaffected by temperature, its amplitude will show a normal physiological temperature dependence.

Kayser and Marx (1951) found this to be the case in lizards (*Lacerta agilis* and *L. muralis*). These animals are normally active between 10.00 and 16.00 hours. When their degree of activity was measured at 19°C and 29°C a Q_{10} of 2.9 was found, but the interval between successive activity periods remained 24 hours. The rhythm could be reversed by reversed lighting, but it was not found possible to induce two peaks of activity in the day by illuminating the animals for 4 hours in the morning and 4 hours at night. Neither thyroidectomy nor hypophysectomy affected the rhythm, but the former induced some reduction in the amount of activity that took place.

Brown, Webb, Bennett and Sandeen (1954) showed that the frequency of the endogenous tidal rhythm of melanophore contraction in the fiddler crab, *Uca pugnax*, is little or not influenced by temperature within the range 13° to 30°C. As with day length, the tidal cycles of the physical environment are independent of temperature, so, if the crabs are to utilise endogenous rhythms to synchronise their behaviour patterns with their rhythmic environment, the endogenous mechanisms must also be temperature-insensitive.

Stephens (1957a) has shown that the diurnal melanophore rhythm can be shifted by exposing animals maintained in darkness to low temperatures below a critical threshold lying between 9.5° and 18.0°C. This exposure must continue for a minimum time of at least 6, but not more than 12 hours. The response also depends upon the time of day when the animals are chilled and also on the time when they are warmed after chilling. The initial response is considerably greater than the final persistent shift which the treatment produces, which suggests that the timing of the first cycle following treatment is more labile than subsequent cycles.

Bünning (1958b) has found that the periodicity of the cockroach *Periplaneta americana* is temperature-independent between 18° and 31°C.

If the temperature is increased for a few hours only, disturbances of the rhythm occur, but temperature dependence is in no way demonstrated. Consequently temperature independence cannot be explained in terms of two phases of temperature dependence, each of about 12 hours and following one another in a cycle, that cancel each other out. A period of cold during one phase of the cycle does not affect the rhythm but if the cockroach is subjected to a period of cold during the other part of the cycle, that is, about 12 hours before the time of maximum activity, the 'clock' misfires. The result obtained is similar to that found in plants: the phase of activity that was due to appear when the animal was subjected to the cold, does not do so. Instead, a state of rest is initiated due to a relaxation of the system. The return to normal temperature acts as a stimulus to the oscillator, therefore as a '*Zeitgeber*' (time giver) for the new phases that are being entered upon.

Although, in general, the phases of the 24-hour rhythm are independent of temperature, if the light factor is held constant, a temperature-determined rhythm has been shown to persist in the cockroach *Periplaneta americana* by Cloudsley-Thompson (1953d), in the spider-beetle *Ptinus tectus* by Bentley, Gunn and Ewer (1941) and in the spider *Amaurobius ferox* by Cloudsley-Thompson (1957a). Rhythms of emergence of insects appear also to some degree to be affected by temperature. For example Scott (1936) was able to impose a rhythm on *Ephestia kühniella* (see p. 121). Amongst mammals, temperature-determined rhythms have been produced in the rat by Browman (1943) who found that if the temperature varied, the daily peak of activity of blinded rats was correlated with the cool period, and the onset of proestrous occurred at the end of the cool 12-hour period. The persistence of this rhythm was not recorded. Menaker (1959) has recently shown that the endogenous clocks demonstrated by fluctuating rectal temperature, in the bats *Myotis bicifugus* and *Eptesicus fuscus* continue to function with a period of 24 hours while the animals are in hibernation in constant darkness and at various ambient temperatures of 3° to 10°C.

From a detailed physiological study of the effect of temperature changes on the activity of poikelothermic animals, Kerkut and Taylor (1958) have shown that the spontaneous activity of isolated ganglia of cockroaches, crayfish and slugs varies with temperature and shows anomalous temperature transients. When the temperature is increased, the activity shows a transient decrease, while decreasing the temperature brings about an increase in activity. Furthermore, intact animals become temporarily more active when the temperature is lowered below the optimum and less active when the temperature is raised, a point previously observed in millipedes (Cloudsley-Thompson, 1951a, b), cockroaches (Cloudsley-Thompson, 1957a) and slugs (Dainton, 1954).

Again, Sand (1938) found that the ampullae of Lorenzini of Elasmobranch fishes respond to cooling by an acceleration and to warming by an inhibition of the rhythm of impulse discharge. Such responses occur throughout the physiological temperature range, from 3° to 20°C approximately, though they are most sensitive in the region 10° to 15°C. Sand suggested an hypothesis to account for this effect involving the assumption of underlying reactions with different time factors of kinetic equilibration.

It is obvious, therefore, that there must be some kind of temperature-compensating device in the nervous system of poikelotherms. It is quite possible that a similar mechanism occurs in other types of cells, for Bruce and Pittendrigh (1956) have shown that the endogenous diurnal rhythm in the phototactic response of *Euglena gracilis* is temperature-independent in the range 16.7 to 33.0°C. They conclude that "no satisfactory physiological explanation of the remarkable fact of temperature-independent endogenous rhythms has been advanced. Three types of mechanisms have been suggested. They are as follows: (1) The diurnal periodicity is maintained by some uncontrolled variable with a diurnal periodicity. (2) The periodicity of the clock derives from some relatively temperature-independent physical (as contrasted to chemical) process. (3) Temperature independence is achieved by virtue of a temperature-compensating medium within the organism, although component parts of the clock may be temperature-dependent. The first mechanism is unsatisfactory for these cases such as *Euglena*, where the periodicity in 'constant conditions' is not exactly 24-hours. The following consideration favours an interpretation in terms of a temperature-compensating mechanism. Repeated and non-repeated temperature changes have been demonstrated to affect endogenous rhythms in several ways. The entrainability to periodic temperature cycles and the influence of single temperature shocks in initiating rhythms, introducing transients, or shifting the phase of a rhythm are examples which have been demonstrated in several organisms. An argument against the second mechanism hinges on the fact that the diurnal (24-hour) rhythm in *Euglena* persists even when the cells are growing in organic media so rapidly that they divide more frequently than once every 24 hours. There is implied in the second mechanism for achieving temperature independence the idea that the periodicity of the 'clock' is intimately tied into the physical localisation of the components of the 'clock'. The ability of the 'clock' to continue running while it is duplicating itself is an argument against this mechanism."

In this connection the opinion of Bünning (1958b) is also of interest. He writes: "Experiments on the influence of temperature on endogenous rhythms are of interest in the study of the 'clock' mechanism. In the range of 15° to 30°C, or even 10° to 30°C, the speed of the 'clock' is not at all or only very little influenced by temperature in the higher plants, unicellular algae, arthropods or vertebrates. The absence of a marked influence of temperature is especially surprising, since immediately after a reduction in temperature there is a distinct increase of the first period by some 5to10 hours. It looks as if plants and animals become accustomed to the new temperature within a single day. There is still another striking fact. While the 'clock' is independent of temperature between about 10° and 30°C, a drop in temperature to 0° to 10°C seems to stop the 'clock'. That means that after chilling the plants or animals for several hours, the next maximum of the rhythm to be observed after re-establishing the higher temperature will be delayed by several hours. A further analysis, however, shows that this is due to something other than stopping the 'clock'. After a period of chilling to values in the vicinity of 5°C for more than about 10 hours the same period at normal temperature must always elapse before a new maximum of the cycle occurs. This implies that the abnormally low temperature does not fix the oscillator in the phase which

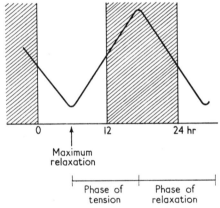

Fig. 31. The endodiurnal oscillator of plants and animals regulated by light-dark cycles. Quantitative details based on results with beans. Dark period hatched. (After Bünning, 1958a, c.)

was prevailing at the onset of chilling: instead, the effect of low temperature is to make the oscillator relax into its zero position. This suggests that the cycles may be regarded as the periods of a relaxation oscillator. This is confirmed by offering the low temperature in different phases of the cycle. There is, in both plants and animals, one phase of several hours which cannot be delayed very much by chilling; but low-temperature treatment of the other phase makes the oscillator drop to its zero value, thus causing a delay. The former is the relaxation-, the latter the tension-phase. Replacing oxygen by nitrogen causes a similar strong delay, during the phase of tension.

"The speed of tension and relaxation always seems to be independent of temperature, but if we replace, say, 25°C by 15°C, the oscillator drops to a lower energy-level than before, since the supply of energy is delayed. This delay only allows the oscillator, when again entering the phase of tension, to reach a lower level of energy than during tension at higher temperatures. Thus at lower temperatures the system oscillates between lower levels of energy than at higher temperatures, and the first cycle after a fall in temperature is necessarily longer. After bringing the plant to a still lower temperature (for example, 8°C), the energy supply will be so much delayed that the oscillator drops to zero energy-level during relaxation, and very little tension is possible. Consequently the periods are much reduced (say, about 10 hours instead of 24 hours). Still lower temperatures allow no tension at all; the oscillator relaxes to zero energy-level and will keep this as long as the very low temperature prevails.

"Experimental results from plants (diurnal leaf movements of beans) and animals (running activity of the cockroach, *Periplaneta americana*) are in harmony with these theoretical conclusions.

"Thus it appears that the endogenous periodicity is a relaxation oscillation. The tension requires a supply of energy by respiration, but this does not necessarily mean that the oscillator itself is a chemical system.

"Organisms use their 'clocks' for very different purposes. Plants use them in order to establish diurnal fluctuations in the photoperiodic light sensitivity. They do this, at any rate in the better-known cases, through an effect of the endogenous periodicity on the so-called photomorphogenetic pigment system. A phase of high sensitivity to red light alternates with a phase of high sensitivity to the far-red. Much more complicated is the utilization of the 'clock' in the case of animals, among which it may serve quite different purposes. Even lower animals like arthropods, which use the 'clock' in connection with their Sun navigation, may also employ it in order to visit feeding places at suitable times of the day. The 'clock' even allows them to have a memory for different suitable daily feeding times, and to know at which of several different places they are to search during these different times of the day. Still more complex are the processes which can be coupled with the internal 'clock' in higher animals, and human beings.

"We are not yet sure whether the 'clock' in plants, and that in the lower and higher animals, depends on the same type of clock-work, although this assumption would be the simplest working hypothesis. The similarities in the qualities of the 'clocks' of the different organisms are striking."

Some other scanty evidence suggests physiological mechanisms which increase their activity when the temperature is lowered.

For example, cooling the central nerve cord by lowering the temperature of the surrounding medium causes marked augmentation of spinal reflex responses before depression occurs. Temperature gradients within the cord cannot be responsible for these augmented responses, because when the spinal cord is cooled by cooling both the surrounding medium and the aortic blood supplying it, reflex responses are likewise augmented between certain critical temperature ranges (35° to 27°) below which depression predominates in all recordings and desynchronisation of evoked response occurs.

Similar studies have been made on the effects of cooling on the electro-corticograms and evoked potentials recorded from the sensory-motor cortex and the cerebellum. Cooling of the blood reaching the brain and cooling the brain surface alone or in conjunction with blood cooling also produce an augmented response and electrocorticogram records show an increase in amplitude though the wave frequency remained the same (Suda, Koizumi and Brooks, 1956).

There is no direct evidence of enzymes whose activity increases at lower temperatures, but Precht (1958) has shown that some oxidative enzymes of fish show a decrease in activity after acclimatisation to a raised temperature. Presumably these enzymes also show an increase in activity when the temperature is lowered.

The causes of temperature adaptation in poikelothermic animals is little known; according to Precht, Christophersen and Hensel (1958) it may be due to the central nervous system as well as to hormones. In *Carassius vulgaris*, cold adaptation is probably brought about through some form of cell regulation whereas heat adaptation is achieved through hierarchial factors (central nervous system and other organ functions). The heat resistence of tissue respiration and succinodehydrogenase activity rises with a fall in temperature. This may be a side effect, as with the cold resistance of the same enzyme systems from liver and muscle. Contrary to expectation, the cold resistance of the oxygen consumption of muscle tissue increases with rising adaptive temperature.

The presence of a heat-stable enzyme coupled with a heat-labile inhibitor has been described by Schwartz, Kaplan and Frech (1956). In the course of assays on the pyridine nucleotide content of various micro-organisms, these workers isolated two enzymes that were normally present in an inhibited state. Only after these were placed in a boiling water bath for several minutes could any significant activity be shown. The explanation of this apparent heat-activation lies in the fortuitous coicidence of a heat-stable enzyme and a heat-labile inhibitor. "The existence of certain enzymes in a normally inhibited state could conceivably be a mechanism of cellular control of enzyme action. It would be possible to control enzymatic patterns, then, not only through the synthesis or lack of synthesis of a specific inhibitory protein or RNA. Indeed, it has been possible to obtain cultures of *Proteus vulgaris* that are essentially free of the inhibitor of pyrophosphatase by growing the organisms on a medium containing yeast extract rather than on the usual minimal medium."

Bünning (1956c) provides a slightly different theory: "It is by no means impossible to imagine a chemical mechanism that also has no temperature dependence. If part of the mechanism were concerned with supplying a particular substance while a second process destroyed it and both processes were equally temperature-dependent, then the substance would accumulate at the same rate irrespective of temperature."

Pittendrigh and Bruce (1957) have described an oscillation model of the basic biological rhythm in any animal. They refer to this as an endogenous self-sustaining oscillation (ESSO) but believe that the control or clock presiding over this oscillation is a complex system with constituent oscillatory processes and that the control system is not a single temperature-insensitive process. "The mutual entrainment (synchronisation) of constituent oscillators would result in temperature independence over a limited range provided that key members of the system had reciprocal temperature coefficients."

They also point out that temperature has been used to replace light for reversing rhythms by 12 hours. It is difficult, however, to conceive a 'clock' or process which at the same time responds to and is also insensitive to temperature.

Pittendrigh's argument supports his hypothesis of the 'clock' as a system of compensating processes, some of which respond to temperature and can restore synchronisation of a rhythm whilst others are insensitive to temperature changes.

In a review of the phenomenon of compensation for temperature in poikelothermic animals, Bullock (1954) has shown that many species exhibit in their metabolism or activity some degree of independence of their temperature. The evidence points to the conclusion that multiple levels of adaptive regulation exist: for example, compensatory changes are found at biochemical, cellular, organ and behavioural levels, although there are many exceptions too. In general adaptation is achieved by a compensation for temperature rather than a fundamental insensitivity of metabolism or of the rate function measured. Bullock concludes that even in the same organism there are several simultaneous mechanisms with different time courses. Thus the activity of several enzymes may alter with temperature while that of others shows little or no change. The limiting factor in the use of temperature-compensating mechanisms for overcoming temperature barriers to distribution is presumed to be such failure to balance the regulation of different processes.

The metabolic clock system in poikelothermic animals, which is independent of temperature within ecological limits, must be regarded as part of this wider, but equally little understood phenomenon. At present nothing is known of the physiological mechanisms involved but, hazarding a guess, I would suggest that it is achieved as a result of the buffering action of numerous metabolic periodicities at each level of organisation, synchronised into an organic whole.† The initial delay followed by overshoot in the peak of pupal emergence observed by Pittendrigh (1954) could be accounted for by enzyme systems buffering each other. Alternatively if the control process is one involving a change in entropy rather than heat change, there would be but a slight temperature coefficient and the clock mechanism would tend to be independent of temperature. In the denaturation of most proteins, for example, there is a large change in entropy accompanied by correspondingly large heat changes of opposite sign, but if there were some protein in which such heat change was small, it could, perhaps, provide a mechanism for temperature independence. In any case the analogy between this problem and that involved in the field of morphogenesis outlined in the introduction (p. 1) is probably valid.

† See also Hastings (1959).

CHAPTER 11

Consideration of Special Themes

ANIMAL BEHAVIOUR DURING ECLIPSES

ONE of the first records of the effects of a solar eclipse on animal behaviour is that of Newport (1837) who described observations made during a total eclipse of the sun on 15th May, 1836. At 14.15 hours when the eclipse began and the sunlight was sensibly diminished, bees started flocking to the hives. At 15.15 hours when little light remained and the temperature dropped from 20° to 15°C, the hive was quiet as in the evening and a solitary *Geotrupes stercorarius* was noticed on the wing. Full activity was resumed at 16.00 hours when the eclipse was nearly over.

Some years ago, Mori (1939) described the behaviour of various animals at Ômu village in Hokkaido, Japan during a total eclipse which occurred there on 19th June, 1936 from 14.08 to 16.26 hours. Mori found that the activity of the fly, *Protofucellia syuitimorii*, was remarkably reduced, its movements apparently being correlated with light intensity. The crepuscular swarming activity of the midge, *Spanistoma* sp., the nocturnal croaking of a tree frog, *Hyla arborea japonica*, the roosting of a crow, *Corvus corone*, and the crepuscular crowing of the domestic fowl were all more or less induced out of time by the eclipse. On the other hand, the nocturnal hopping of the sand-hopper, *Orchestia* sp. as well as the roosting behaviour of the starling, *Spodiopsar cineraceus* and the red-cheeked mynah *Sturnia violacea* were apparently not induced. Nor was the diurnal migration of the eye pigments of the crayfish, *Cambaroides japonicus*, in any way affected.

More recently, Weber (1952) has described the effects of a total solar eclipse on 25th February, 1952 in southern Iraq. He gives a minute to minute account of the behaviour of every animal observed, including the local inhabitants who believe that a whale is attempting to swallow the sun during an eclipse and therefore beat drums and cooking utensils with much shouting and wailing. Bioclimatic readings were taken throughout. Weber compares his observations with those of Wheeler *et al.* (1935) who made observations on the behaviour of animals during the total solar eclipse of 31st August, 1932 in the north-eastern United States of America. Again many mammals were observed, some apparently

186

responding, others not, whilst the numerous bird records led to the conclusion that most species showed reactions of an unusual nature. Cockroaches emerged into the open both in Iraq and U.S.A., and crickets responded with much chirping. Records of Diptera and Lepidoptera were comparable and significant observations were made on the behaviour of honeybees.

It can be concluded, therefore, that the unique field observations made during total eclipses of the sun, do not in any way contradict results obtained by means of laboratory experiment. Some animals show exogenous rhythms, others are more markedly endogenous.

THEORIES TO ACCOUNT FOR ENDOGENOUS RHYTHMICITY

A number of theories have been proposed as to the way in which persistent rhythms are maintained. It has been suggested that there may be rhythmical metabolic changes of various kinds or control resulting from the accumulation of toxic depressents or the elaboration and exhaustion of reserve products or hormones (see discussion by Harker, 1958a). The results of feeding experiments showing that endogenous rhythms are not related to feeding time and the fact that some periodicities become immediately synchronised in new environmental conditions render the first two of these methods of control unlikely. The case for hormones (Mori, 1948; Park, 1940, etc.) is less clear but there are several examples in Protozoa and in tissue cultures where it would seem unlikely that hormonic control could be responsible.

Hoagland (1935) adopts a physico-chemical attitude to behaviour. He believes that biochemical reactions are not usually reversible and that a thermodynamic treatment of their equilibria is therefore impossible. He develops kinetically an equation for the steady state of a chain of two successive irreversible macromolecular reactions and suggests that the master reaction, or pacemaker, is the slowest and the one therefore upon which the velocity of the entire chain depends. He has investigated this concept especially from the viewpoint of the effect of temperature upon it.

Several workers have suggested ways in which rhythms might be self-perpetuating. For example, Bethe (1946) points out in a discussion of the various forms of biological irritability and rhythm, and the trigger action and catalytic reaction of models, that if a relatively slow accumulation of energy takes place in a system, it will trigger-discharge at its maximum value although an excitatory process may stimulate discharge before this has been reached. If no external interference occurs, discharge may become rhythmical and in this way a 24-hour rhythm could be endogenous yet at the same time influenced by environmental changes.

Some years ago van der Pol (1926) carried out some mathematical research concerning a non-linear differential equation containing one parameter only. If this parameter was small, the solution yielded the well known sinusoidal or harmonic oscillations which seem to form a mathematical interpretation of truly rhythmic phenomena, but together with their building-up processes produce a steady amplitude. On the other hand, with a large value of this parameter new forms of periodic phenomena were obtained which possessed properties that led van der Pol to call them 'relaxation oscillations'. In a later paper (1940) he discussed their biological significance, pointing out that they are the basis of most periodic phenomena found in nature where the period is not rigidly constant but is given by some form of relaxation or decay time. Relaxation oscillations are characterised by the following:

(a) Their periodicity is determined by some form of relaxation time. (b) They constitute a periodic automatic repetition of a typical aperiodic phenomenon, the system periodically reaching an unstable condition. (c) Their form is widely different from the well-known sinusoidal or harmonic oscillations, relaxation oscillations showing discontinuous jumps. (d) They show the typical phenomenon of synchronisation even on a sub-harmonic of an applied external periodic force. (e) The phenomenon of resonance, so typical of harmonic oscillation, is wholly absent in relaxation oscillations. (f) Their time period is not by far as constant as that of sinusiodal oscillations because external circumstances such as temperature variation more easily influence a relaxation time than a sinusoidal periodicity. (g) They were found from a non-linear differential equation implying the presence of a threshold value resulting in the applicability of the "all-or-nothing" law.

In concluding the above-mentioned paper, van der Pol (1940) pointed out that different sciences are governed by common mathematical laws and relations, so that a clearer and deeper insight into some phenomenon may give us a vivid picture of what is happening in other apparently totally unrelated phenomena in fields belonging to other sciences.

A notable example of an organ showing periodicity is afforded by the heart and van der Pol (1940) has selected this as an example of the way in which electrical models showing relaxation oscillations can be applied to biological systems. In the model the beat of the heart is imitated by three relaxation systems representing respectively the sinus, the auricle and the ventricle. The first acts unidirectionally on the second which, with a retardation, acts also unidirectionally on the ventricle. Electrocardiograms can be obtained from this model similar to those of the normal heart beat as well as several anomalous rhythms comparable with an early ventricular extrasystole, an auricular systole with the ventricle responding, an auricular systole with the ventricle still in the refractory period, a sinus extrasystole, a sino-auricular block and so on.

The flashes of a neon lamp were also cited by van der Pol as an example of relaxation oscillations and they show what, in biology, is called a 'refractory period', because if a single small impulse is brought to the lamp it will be without effect when it is applied immediately after the lamp has flashed. On the other hand, if the impulse is supplied later in the period the voltage may reach the flashing potential so that the condenser discharges the full charge. This provides an electrical demonstration of the 'all-or-nothing' principle and provides an analogy with the passage of nerve impulses across a synapse. The synapse or junction of one nerve fibre to another, like the nerve-muscle junction, acts as a valve so that it allows an impulse to pass in one direction only.

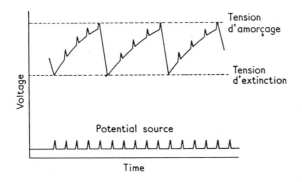

FIG. 32. Potential of a neon lamp showing the phenomenon of frequency demultiplication. (After van der Pol, 1940).

A relaxation process is characterised by the gradual build-up of some energy or material, followed by its sudden dissipation. When the wind blows against telegraph wires and causes a whistling noise, the time period of that sound is determined by a diffusion or relaxation time and has nothing to do with the natural period of the string when oscillating in a sinusoidal way. Other physical examples of relaxation oscillations are afforded by a pneumatic hammer, the squeak of a knife on a plate and the waving of a flag in the wind. An example from the field of biology is afforded by the accumulation of liquid in a contractile vacuole and its sudden release which is paralleled by the filling of the bladder and its periodic emptying.

Kris (1958) investigated correo-fundal potential variations during light and dark adaptation of the human eye and found that a step-change in illumination produces an initial transient effect lasting between 60 and 80 seconds followed by a fluctuation resembling a damped oscillation of 30 minutes period lasting one hour. This suggests a homoeostatic mechanism.

Mori (1947) suggests that all vital phenomena, including rhythms, are based on chemical reactions and obey chemical laws. The number of these reactions is finite and it is assumed that those within the animal's body are correlated and harmonise with one another. Consequently, if the balance is temporarily upset and a transition to the state of equilibrium evoked, this will affect future reactions. If these changes take place rhythmically, day by day, their external manifestation may be rhythmic activity. Thus a rhythm which is at first purely exogenous will, in time, become endogenous. Some rhythms are more persistent than others, and Mori (1948) suggests that the harmony between environmental and behaviour rhythm is mediated by various physiological rhythms within the organism. Thus periodicity in behaviour acquired during the developmental stages of *Drosophila melanogaster* will persist through later instars (Mori, 1949a, b). Doubt is shed on this conclusion, however, by the experiments of Pittendrigh (1954), Scott (1936), etc. described above (p. 121).

For references to Mori's numerous papers on diurnal rhythms published in recent years, see Harker (1958a).

Pittendrigh (1958) and Pittendrigh and Bruce (1957) suggest that a better model than a 'clock' for the endogenous controlling system would be a self-sustaining oscillator, with a natural period which can be initiated by any single perturbance of light or temperature. As a further step in the analogy, Pittendrigh suggests that after one perturbation of the environment, the oscillator may show transients before a steady state is reached. As a result of this work he abandoned his earlier concept (1954) of a temperature-sensitive 'terminal clock' controlling the period just before the emergence of *Drosophila melanogaster*.

As Harker (1958a) points out: "Convincing as these experiments are, the rhythm of only one function was being examined; and it may be that transients are being produced by the interaction of rhythms . . . Whatever the cause of the effect, Pittendrigh's results may help to explain those anomalies which have been remarked when animals are subjected to environmental cycles of lengths other than 24 hours. If transients are developed in these conditions then temporary upset of the endogenous 24-hour rhythm may result in cycles which are neither representative of the 24-hour rhythm nor of the environmental rhythm."

Bünning (1958a, b, c, 1959) also subscribes to the relaxation oscillator hypothesis, as a result of experiments in which he offered low temperature or poisons at different phases of the cycle. He found in both plants and animals (cockroaches) one phase of several hours which could not be delayed very much by chilling: but low temperature treatment of the other phase caused a delay which he ascribed to the oscillator dropping to its zero value. The former is believed to be the relaxation, the latter the tension phase. If chilling is less extreme, the system may still oscillate, but the tension is interrupted by relaxation earlier than normally. This explains the extremely short cycles sometimes obtained with these temperatures. That the first cycles after transition to lower temperature or after the application of a poison are often longer than the normal ones finds an explanation by this hypothesis too. These treatments make the oscillator drop to a lower level of energy, i.e. the first relaxation continues for a longer time than the normal ones; but the ensuing tensions are very small, thus causing shorter cycles. This looks like a delay, followed by processes of compensation (Bünning, 1959).

It is difficult to see how a purely physical model can explain processes which must, since they occur in living organisms, be basically bio-chemical in nature. The suggestion of Aschoff (1954 etc.) that a number of biological processes are synchronised by means of a *"Zeitgeber"* has already been discussed and is more in accordance with the writer's views, as is that of Harker (1958a). Harker postulates that there is a basic 24-hour rhythm present in the cells of all animals, that this rhythm is inherited and continues unchanged even when concealed by the immediate influence of the environment. "The cells of any animal may not all be in phase with one another, and any cell or group of cells may constitute a 'physiological clock' regulating certain activities, although always running to a 24-hour cycle, so that any animal may have a number of 'clocks' all operating at once, either in phase or at variance with each other."

This concept is similar to that reached in the preceding chapter, and would appear to be not only very much simpler than the complex ideas of Pittendrigh outlined above, but more susceptible to experimental investigation.

Gooddy (1958) outlines the hypothesis of a mammalian 'master clock' derived from a study of the human nervous system. He suggests that navigation and chronometry demonstrated in the control of ships and aeroplanes and in the construction of clocks are but "the exteriorised examples of personal navigation and chronometry. We should, then, be able to detect and describe physiological chronometric mechanisms (clocks, clock systems) in the same way that spatial orienta-tional mechanisms have already been described." All that is necessary for a clock is 'the detectable phenomena of accurate repetition'! Thus many bodily structures which show rhythmic activity, such as cardio-vascular and respiratory systems, the alimentary cardiorenal, glandular and autonomic systems fulfil the requirements of repetition necessary for clock form. The nervous system, because of its fundamentally rhythmic type of activity associated with 'all-or-none' phenomena, its mediation of sensory and motor activity of other clock systems, may be regarded as a 'master clock'. Gooddy cites the electroencephalograph as evidence of the highly abstracted cerebral cortical clock-system and claims that it is 'a neuro-physiological demonstration at cortical level' of the whole theory underlying his paper, since it has a simplified rhythm abstracted from the multitudes of nerve-cells, processes, channels and impulses of the nervous system. [A similar suggestion has been made by the writer (1953c)]. Gooddy continues: "It is generally agreed that these processes or faculties loosely classified under the titles of 'memory', 'foresight', 'judgment', 'intelligence', 'behaviour', 'concentration', 'reasoning' are disordered in cases where we find evidence of damage to parts or the whole of the cerebral cortex. Such processes, for all their apparent diversity, have one common underlying feature—namely the loss of 'timing'. Thus when memory fails, we find a defect of recall and arrangement of time past. A failure of concentration is an inability to maintain a 'fine-scale' sensorimotor activity ranged immediately about the present. Foresight, judgement and reasoning imply a failure of forward memory or 'prediction'. When these powers are lacking, it is easy to show that the patient can no longer estimate odds of probability concerning future events on the information available from the past. The patient with a frontal-lobe tumour or cerebral atrophy, who is incontinent of faeces, has forgotten what it will be like, *in the future*, to have been incontinent."

THE CELLULAR 'CLOCK'

It has been suggested that probably all cells possess an inherent 24-hour rhythm. Consequently it is necessary to examine next what data is available as to the nature of the cellular 'clock'.

Many of the fundamental physiological processes of living cells are conspicuously rhythmic. On a molecular level the citric acid and other biochemical cycles are essentially rhythmical phenomena as are cycles of mitosis and cell division. These two processes are dissociated, and it has been suggested (Swann, 1957) that different media provide the essentials of growth on the one hand and division on the other, in different amounts.

Evidence in favour of this hypothesis is afforded by temperature-induced synchrony in cultures of the Ciliate, *Tetrahymena pyriformis*. Scherbaum and Zeuthen (1954) showed that if the temperature were shifted repeatedly from the optimum of 29°C to the sublethal value of 34°C (at which the organisms do not divide and grow little if at all) and back, on their final return to 29°C, the cells divide several times, with 85 per cent synchrony. It is suggested by the authors that the sub-lethal temperature not only blocks the division mechanism, but in some way sets it back, perhaps as far as the end of the previous division. On its return to 29°C, it grows and prepares to divide again, but before it can do so, it receives another shock at 34°C, and so on. After a time all the cells have grown sufficiently to divide, and have, in fact, doubled or trebled their volume so that when they are finally returned to 29°C, they divide more or less synchronously.

Zeuthen and Scherbaum (1954) have also found that slight synchrony can be achieved by single cold shocks. At 7°C division is slowed down but growth is less affected so that on return to normal temperatures a degree of synchrony becomes apparent. Similar experiments have been carried out on other micro-organisms (for references, see Swann, 1957) and found to give varying degrees of synchrony.

Bünning (1957) described experiments in which it has been possible to interfere with the diurnal rhythm of the cells of the scarlet runner bean, *Phaseolus multiflorus*, without killing them. When colchicine is applied via the transpiration stream there occurs a distinct retardation of the rhythmicity which can be extended to 35 hours. Other chemicals have a disturbing effect on the rhythm too. Bünning continues: "The results are somewhat surprising since mitotic processes are not in all cases involved in periodicity. The leaf movements for example are due to processes in cells which no longer show any cell division.

"It seems that the mitotic cycle itself is a consequence of cyclic structural changes within the cell. These cycles are still going on while mitosis, due to the ageing of the cell, no longer occurs. The structural cycles reveal themselves in diurnal changes of the nuclear volume. The beginning of mitosis is well known to be connected with an increase in nuclear volume. Now we may state that these volume changes are still continuing while mitosis has stopped due to ageing. But other consequences of the structural changes, for example the periodicity of enzyme activity, are still possible."

Unfortunately this ingenious theory cannot be accepted. Bruce and Pittendrigh (1956) have shown that the 24-hour phototactic rhythm of *Euglena gracilis* persists even when the cells are growing in organic media so rapidly that they divide more frequently than once every 24 hours (see p. 180).

Furthermore, it has been shown that when the nucleus of one strain of *Amoeba* is implanted in the cytoplasm of another, the rate of cell division of the hybrid organism varies according to the temperature: at higher temperatures (27°C) it is similar to that of the parent strain from which the nucleus was derived, but at lower temperatures (11°C) it is similar to that of the cytoplasmic strain (Miss S. E. Hawkins, personal communication).

In this connection it may be important to note that Danielli (1958) has shown that whereas the evidence is overwhelming for cytoplasmic control of binary fission in *Amoeba proteus*, a predominance of nuclear control appears when antigens are studied singly and in the rate of multiplication under standard conditions. In order to explain the large measure of cytoplasmic inheritance, he has advanced the hypothesis that whereas the nucleus controls the nature of the molecules which can be synthesised within a cell, the cytoplasm controls the way in which these are organised into functional units.

In the following section, another interesting speculation is discussed.

Evidence from the 'Gonyaulax clock'

Gonyaulax polyedra is an armoured marine Dinoflagellate that is both photosynthetic and luminescent. Hastings and Sweeney (1957) have found that it possesses a rhythm of induced luminescent flashing: the organism normally emits light as a discrete flash only when it is stimulated. In experiments this was achieved by bubbling air through a suspension of cells in a test tube for a period of 1 minute. With continued stimulation the luminescent response was found to decline sharply due to fatigue, so that after 1 minute, only a very small amount of light was produced. The light emitted was measured with a photomultiplier apparatus which permitted integration of light by accumulating the current output from the phototube on a capacitor. The index of luminescence was therefore a fixed proportion of the total amount of light emitted by a cell suspension during a 1-minute period of stimulation. After each determination, the particular cell suspension used was discarded.

When cultures were grown in conditions of alternating 12-hour periods of light and darkness, the amount of luminescence produced during the dark period was found to be 40 to 60 times greater than that during the light period. These fluctuations continued as a persistent endogenous diurnal rhythm if the cultures were transferred to conditions of constant dim light (100 to 200 ft.-candles) at constant temperature. In darkness, the rhythm continued for several days also, but with decreasing amplitude because the organism requires light for its nutrition.

Cells of *Gonyaulax* were shown to acquire unnatural rhythms when exposed to alternating light and darkness with periods of other than 24-hour; but in constant conditions the 24-hour periodicity reasserted itself. Again, as in the case of the *Drosophila* emergence rhythms described in the last chapter and in the locomotory rhythm of the field-cricket (p. 164), the phase could be shifted by a non-repeated, relatively brief exposure to changed environmental conditions such as light or temperature.

Four overt manifestations of rhythmicity have been observed in *Gonyaulax*. The rhythm of induced luminescent flashing, already mentioned, as well as a rhythm of flashing in undisturbed cultures, which is probably related to it and may result from cells bumping into one another or into the side of the culture tube. Thirdly, there is a rhythm of steady, but very faint light emission or 'glow'; and finally a rhythm of cell division.

The period of each of these rhythms under constant conditions is always close to, but not necessarily exactly 24 hours and the phase may be set to siderial time. In each of three overt rhythms studied (Hastings and Sweeney, 1957), the period was found to be essentially temperature-independent although it was slightly *longer* at higher temperatures. This suggests that the 'clock' may have a temperature compensation mechanism which is not precisely balanced.

The fact that several rhythmic functions in *Gonyaulax* have similar properties supports the idea of a single master clock. These similarities include a loss of rhythmicity in constant bright light and its retention in constant dim light, the aquisition of an exogenous ('entrained') rhythm in cycles of alternating light and darkness which differ from 24 hours, and a phase shift of the endogenous rhythm upon changes in illumination. In addition the period of each rhythm is essentially independent, and what temperature sensitivity does exist has a Q_{10} of less than unity.

At first, Hastings and Sweeney (1957) considered that there might be several independently oscillating systems in *Gonyaulax*, and that the luminescent system in particular was such an oscillator. This was because the effect of temperature upon period was found to be similar to its effect upon the amplitude of luminescence, which implied that a specific inhibitor system was present, and that its action was exerted directly upon the luminescent system rather than via a 'master clock'.

Cellular interaction does not take place, however, as shown by experiments in which two cultures maintained in alternating light-dark conditions for several weeks with their phases different by 5 hours were mixed in equal proportions. If two typical curves showing the luminescence rhythms are summated, the resultant curve differs only slightly in shape from the original curves and dies precisely midway between their maxima. In the actual experiment this also occurred. Moreover, the shape of the curve from the mixed cultures was very similar to that obtained when the measured luminescence of the separate cultures was summated.

More recent experiments (Hastings, 1959; Hastings and Sweeney, 1958, 1959), however, appear to exclude the luminescent system as an independently oscillating system, for if cells are stimulated to exhaustion at a time when they are sensitive to resetting by light, their luminescence falls to a low value. "The effect of stimulation is thus overtly similar to the perturbation by light, both presumably resulting in an exhaustion of a component(s) of the luminescent system. If the luminescent system were itself a clock, then perturbation by stimulation should be an effective way by which phase shifting could be accomplished. When the luminescence of aliquots was assayed at times subsequent to stimulation it was found that the rhythmicity persisted, but that no phase shift whatsoever occurred. This tells us not only that the luminescent system is not a clock; it also tells us that its precise chemical status has no effect upon the clock. In other words, there is no feedback from the luminescent system to the clock. These experiments may be of significance in directing our approach towards finding the essential components of the clock, since

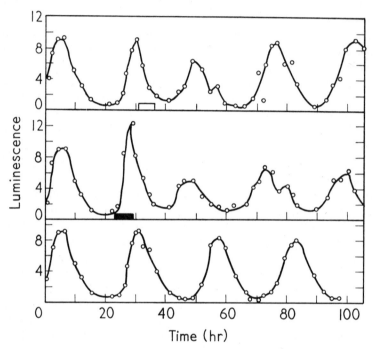

FIG. 33. Phase shift in the rhythm of the marine Dinoflagellate, *Gonyaulax polyedra*, following changes in light intensity. Cells previously kept under light-dark conditions were placed at constant temperature (23.5°C) and constant light intensity (100 ft.-candles) at the end of a 12-hour dark period. Two days later (zero time on graph) measurements of luminescence were begun and the endogenous rhythm was apparent.

Upper curve. Cultures transferred to bright light (1,400 ft.-candles) for a period of 6 hours and then returned to the previous conditions.

Middle curve. Cultures transferred to darkness for 6 hours and returned to dim light at 200 ft.-candles.

Lower curve. Cultures left in dim light all the while—average period of control: 25.7 hours.

The phase shifts illustrated above were found to be stable since, in experiments where measurements were continued for an additional 48 hours, the phase difference between controls and the treated cells remained unchanged. (After Hastings and Sweeney, 1958).

feedback is a critical property to be expected in any biological clock mechanism.

"If we look for a single biological element or class of elements which may function to regulate a variety of physiological processes, our attention is drawn to the nucleus since it does have a 'master' role in the control of cellular processes. Is there any known aspect of nuclear metabolism which might be involved in the clock mechanism? From a variety of experiments it seems clear that cell division and the mitotic cycle may be excluded as a possibility. In the absence of cell division the clock continues to run. When cell division does occur, the population may be heterogeneous with respect to the mitotic cycle, with no evident change in clock activity. It is therefore not possible to identify the clock with processes involved in the mitotic cycle, although it is clear that the mitotic cycle may be clock controlled.

"From what we know of clock systems on the one hand, and from our knowledge of nuclear metabolism on the other, it seems that a detailed study of the ribose nucleic acid (RNA) metabolism in clock systems would be of value. Its known metabolic role suggests it as a likely candidate for a 'master' oscillator, and a model for the way in which it might oscillate is not difficult to envision. From the studies of Mazia (1956) we know that RNA is formed in the nucleus and moves unidirectionally into the cytoplasm. Specific enzymes, formed in response to RNA, could decrease the level of substrates specific for new RNA synthesis, thereby decreasing the rate of RNA production. Via an appropriate turnover of the components involved a rhythmic RNA production could occur, giving rise to a rhythmic aspect to all RNA coupled systems, which we might measure as overt physiological rhythms. Such a system has the possibility of controlling many diverse cellular reactions, and at the same time the feedback in the system might be rather specific.

"This model is essentially a prey-predator type, in the general class considered by Lotka (1920). In the simple case which he considers the period is inversely proportional to the square root of the product of the velocity constants. All that would be necessary to expect temperature independence is that the period be, instead, a function of the ratio of the velocity constants. Additional assumptions concerning the nature of the mechanism might result in this. Since very little is known concerning the chemical events involved in a clock system under constant conditions, a great variety of specific models is possible.

"The need for biochemical information is evident; what does RNA metabolism look like in such a system, for example? We certainly are not suggesting that RNA is the only component which could be supposed to function as the 'master' oscillator. We merely point to it as a likely example, in order to illustrate the fact that additional information concerning the nature of the key compounds involved in the clock system will be of indispensible value in understanding the mechanism."

The work of Halberg and his co-workers in Minnesota (1953–59) on the cellular events of metabolism throughout the 24-hour cycle lends support to this type of hypothesis. Their assumption was that if cellular functions normally exhibit 24-hour changes in rate, periodic analysis ought to reveal important differences in phase of rhythms for those functions that are dissociated in time. The results obtained for a few variables were studied by a combination of periodicity analysis, the use of radiotracer and of differential centrifugion. At the same time, the proportion of cells in mitosis was determined on slices from the mouse livers used for metabolic work. "A two- to threefold decrease in the relative specific activity of DNA (counts/min/μg of DNA P as percentage of counts/min/ μg of acid soluble P) was noted from 08.00 to 24.00 and was followed by a sharp peak at 04.00. The interval between the peak in the RSA of DNA and that of mitosis was $\sim$ 8 hour. This may be considered to be an estimate of the lag period between DNA synthesis and mitosis in intact immature mouse liver." It is in accord with the 6 to 12-hour lag period noted for regenerating liver. "In contrast to DNA, however, RSA of both microsomal and nuclear RNA increased rapidly from 16.00 to 20.00 and then gradually dropped to the lower morning values. These results indicate, first, that the metabolism of nucleic acids as well as mitosis, are 24-hour periodic metabolic functions. Second, that certain aspects of cytoplasmic and nuclear DNA metabolism are roughly in phase with each other, and third, that they are dissociated in phase from peak DNA metabolism by a lag of $\sim$ 8 hour. Finally, another lag period of $\sim$ 8 hour normally exists between DNA synthesis and mitosis in immature growing liver." (Halberg, Halberg, Barnum and Bittner, 1959).

Appendix

THE main problems posed by the rhythms of animals and especially the ubiquitous 24-hour rhythm, are:

(a) Is the periodicity learned by 'imprinting' as suggested by Thorpe (1956) and others, or inherited, or dependent upon the reception of cosmic stimuli? For the reasons already given, I think the probable answer, at any rate in most cases, to be that they are inherited although the presence of cyclic exogenous factors may always be necessary.

(b) How does a rhythm represent a biological process that is independent of temperature? A number of theories have been suggested of which perhaps the more promising depend upon postulating some buffering effect of enzyme balance.

(c) What advantages of survival value are there in the possession of an endogenous chronometer by an organism normally inhabiting a fluctuating environment? The answer to this is complex. The advantage would appear to lie in the maintenance of regularity in the temporary absence of environmental 'clues'; in the ability of the organism to pre-adapt itself to a forthcoming change; in the possession of a time-sense necessary for solar orientation and of advantage to bees which visit flower crops at the time of nectar flow, etc.; in the appreciation of changing photoperiod and the consequent synchronisations of breeding cycles, and the initiation of diapause and other seasonal phenomena. It must be remembered, too, that rhythms of longer frequency appear usually to result from the interaction of other rhythms of shorter phase duration.

Thus 'clues' are not regular in the field, and there is competition between them. For example, sunrise may be completely hidden for a number of days and, at the same time, the temperature may be consistently high. When such disturbed conditions occur, the animal can maintain its normal rhythm by means of its internal 'clock' and will not get out of phase with other members of its species. Again, it will obviously benefit an animal to be pre-adapted for some forthcoming event such as the dawn, or the incoming tide, thus ensuring that it is not caught at a disadvantage.

A number of examples have been cited of vertebrates and invertebrates that navigate by maintaining a fixed angle to the sun, or to polarised light in the sky and allow for the change in angle necessitated by the sun's movements by means of an endogenous chronometer.

A time sense is necessary, too, for organisms to perceive seasonal changes in day length and thereby synchronise their reproduction rhythms, seasonal diapause and so on.

Although it can be postulated in the Metazoa that some organ may act as a 'clock' to control the rhythm of the entire animal, the fact that Protozoa also possess inherent periodicity indicates that a 'clock' must also occur within a single cell and the question arises as to whether such organisms are a 'clock' or contain a 'clock'. Perhaps this question should not be asked, however. At least, not by a biologist: it savours too much of that other perennial regarding the relationship between purpose and directiveness in ethology.

Pittendrigh (1958) has classified biological 'clocks' as (a) "Continuously consulted clocks": the mechanisms used in sun navigation would come under this category. (b) "Interval timers": examples are afforded by the rhythms of pupal eclosion which occur once in a lifetime but at a particular time of day. (c) "Pure rhythms" such as persistent rhythms of activity, heart rate, colour change and so on. These include both 'physiological' and 'cosmic rhythms' as defined by Stephens (1957b). This may be a useful analysis and would appear to have many advantages over previous attempts at classification, but it must always be remembered that different types of rhythm tend to grade into one another. Indeed, it is suggested above (p. 9) that the only difference between exogenous and endogenous rhythms may be that the former become synchronised more rapidly with environmental 'clues'.

In his inaugural lecture entitled "The sources of animal behaviour", Wells (1955) draws a parallel between the behaviour of marine Polychaetes, controlled by inherent oesophageal 'clocks', with that of birds. He suggests that the lug-worm is a creature of 'moods' and has several alternative behaviour rhythms which can be employed according to conditions. In a similar way, the singing behaviour of birds is rhythmically organised. First is the pattern of the individual song-phrase which is highly specific and has the function of warning off other birds of the same species and sex. To some extent these song-phrases are learned, to some extent they are innate (Thorpe, 1956).

The second level of organisation in the distribution of song-phrases is time. The song-phrases are sung at regular, and presumably innate, intervals.

Kendeigh (1952) and Whitehouse and Armstrong (1953) have shown that a wren divides her time between sitting on her eggs and other activities. Her diurnal rhythm can be split up into a number of 'sessions' and 'recesses'. The lower the temperature, the more time she spends on her eggs, as might be expected, but the sum of the 'session' and the following 'recess' is not affected. As Wells (1955) says: "This looks like a clear case of an inherent rhythm with environmental temperature playing a secondary, modifying role. Every twenty minutes or so, some kind of 'physiological alarm clock' goes off inside the wren, and she gets off her eggs; the colder it is, the sooner she comes back. Later in the season, when she is feeding her young, another rhythm appears; the frequency with which she visits the nest shows a well-marked peak every 4 or 5 hours.

"The facts encourage us to believe that a large part of a bird's behaviour springs from within—not only in reflex response to physiological urgencies, but also in obedience to timing mechanisms which are essentially arbitrary . . . I venture the opinion that we should diagrammatise the dividing forces behind animal behaviour, not so much in terms of the familiar tank in which water collects at ever-increasing pressure until it escapes through a spring-guarded outlet, as of a complicated system which can never rest, but has to oscillate in one or other of a number of predetermined alternative rhythms."

As we saw in the first chapter, the rhythmic nature of the physiological activity of nervous tissue is ultimately responsible even for human behaviour. Although we concluded that the various cycles at different levels of biological organisation have nothing in common, it is true that they are related insofar as they are the inevitable manifestation of natural phenomena.

Nerve impulses arriving at the central nervous system in a disorderly way produce sensations of pain and discomfort. Conversely, rhythmic stimuli are associated with pleasure and relaxation. It is worth remembering that aesthetic delights arise from causes that are essentially rhythmic: light and colour, music and poetry. For the essence of beauty lies in rhythm and harmony.

Bibliography

No attempt has been made to compile a complete bibliography of publications on rhythmic activities in animals. Sources for further references, however, have frequently been cited in the text. Bibliographical works are indicated below by an asterisk (*). The references given here are those to which specific mention has been made. Whilst the majority have been consulted in the original, a few have been quoted from *Biological Abstracts* and the reviews of Calhoun (1944–46), Caspers (1951), Park (1940, 1949a) and Harker (1958a) in particular. Papers published after 1959 have not been included.

Agren, G., Wilander, O. and Jorpes, E. (1931) Cyclic changes in the glycogen content of the liver and muscle of rats and mice. *Biochem. J.* **25**, 777–85.

Alexander, A. J. (1957) Notes on Onychophorous behaviour. *Ann. Natal Mus.* **14**, 35–43.

*Allee, W. C., Emerson, A. E., Park, O. and Park, T. (1949) "Principles of Animal Ecology". Saunders, Philadelphia and London.

*Andrewartha, H. G. (1952) Diapause in relation to the ecology of insects. *Biol. Rev.* **27**, 50–107.

Arbit, J. (1957) Diurnal cycles and learning in earthworms. *Science*, **126**, 654.

*Armstrong, E. A. (1947) "Bird Display and Behaviour. An introduction to the study of bird psychology". Witherby, London.

Arnould-Taylor, W. E. and Malewski, A. M. (1955) The factor of topographical clues in bird homing experiments. *Ecology*, **36**, 641–6.

Aschoff, J. (1952a) Aktivitätsperiodik von Mäusen im Dauerdunkel. *Pflüg. Arch. ges. Physiol.* **255**, 189–96.

—— (1952b) Frequenzänderung der Aktivitätsperiodik bei Mäusen im Dauerlicht und Dauerdunkel. *Ibid.* **255**, 197–203.

—— (1953) Aktivitätsperiodik bei Gimpeln unter natürlichen und künstlichen Belichtungsverhältnissen. *Z. vergl. Physiol.* **35**, 159–66.

*—— (1954) Zeitgeber der tierischen Tagesperiodik. *Naturwissenschaften*, **3**, 49–56.

—— (1955a) Tagesperiodik von Mäusestämmen unter konstanten Umgebungsbedingungen. *Pflüg. Arch. ges. Physiol.* **262**, 51–9.

*—— (1955b) Jahresperiodik der Fortpflanzung bei Warmblütern. *Stud. Gen.* **12**, 742–76.

—— (1955c) Exogene und endogene Komponente der 24-Stunden Periodik bei Tieren und Mensch. *Naturwissenschaften*, **21**, 569–75.

—— (1957) Aktivitätsmuster der Tagesperiodik. *Ibid.* **13**, 361–7.

*—— (1958) Tierische Periodik unter dem Einfluss von Zeitgebern. *Z. Tierpsychol.* **15**, 1–30.

—— and Meyer-Lohmann, J. (1954a) Die 24-Stunden-Periodik von Nagern im natürlichen und künstlichen Belichtungswechsel. *Z. Tierpsychol.* **11**, 476–84.

—— and Meyer-Lohmann, J. (1954b) Die Schubfolge der lokomotorischen Aktivität bei Nagern. *Pflüg. Arch. ges. Physiol.* **260**, 81–6.

—— and Meyer-Lohmann, J. (1954c) Angeborene 24-Stunden-Periodik beim Kücken. *Ibid.* **260**, 170–6.

—— and Meyer-Lohmann, J. (1955a) Die Aktivität gekäfigter Grünfinken im 24-Stunden-Tag bei unterschiedlich langer Lichtzeit mit und ohne Dämmerung. *Z. Tierpsychol.* **12**, 254–65.

—— and Meyer-Lohmann, J. (1955b) Die Aktivitätsperiodik von Nagern im Künstlichen 24-Stunden-Tag mit 6–20 Stunden Lichzeit. *Z. vergl. Physiol.* **37**, 107–17.

Backlund, H. O. and Ekerood, S. (1950) An aktograph for small terrestrial animals. *Oikos*, **2**, 213–6.

Bacq, Z. M. (1931) The effects of abdominal sympathectomy, adrenal inactivation and removal of the stellate ganglia on the spontaneous activity of the albino rat. *Endocrinology*, **15**, 34–40.

—— (1932) The effect of sympathectomy on sexual functions, lactation and the maternal behaviour of the albino rat, with a description of the technique of sympathectomy in the rat. *Amer. J. Physiol.* **99**, 444–53.

Bailey, S. W. and McCabe, J. B. (1957) A controller for a light source. *Bull. ent. Res.* **48**, 463–5.

*Baker, J. R. (1938) The evolution of breeding seasons. In "Evolution. Essays on aspects of Evolutionary Biology presented to Professor F. S. Goodrich on his seventieth birthday", 161–77. (G. R. de Beer, ed.) Oxford University Press, London.

—— (1939) The relation between latitude and breeding seasons in birds. *Proc. zool. Soc. Lond.* **A108**, 557–82.

—— (1947) The seasons in a tropical rain-forest (New Hebrides). Part 7 (Final part). Summary and general conclusions. *J. Linn. Soc. (Zool.)* **41**, 248–58.

—— and Baker, I. (1936a) The seasons in a tropical rain-forest (New Hebrides). Part 2. Botany. *J. Linn. Soc. (Zool.)* **39**, 507–19.

—— and Baker, Z. (1936b) The seasons in a tropical rain-forest (New Hebrides). Part 3. Fruit-bats (Pteropidae). *Ibid.* **39**, 123–41.

—— and Bird, T. F. (1936) The seasons in a tropical rain-forest (New Hebrides). Part 4. Insectivorous bats (Vespertilionidae and Rhinolophidae). *Ibid.* **40**, 143–61.

—— , Marshall, A. J. and Harrison, T. H. (1940) The seasons in a tropical rain-forest (New Hebrides). Part 5. Birds (*Pachycephala*). *Ibid.* **41**, 50–70.

—— and Ranson, R. M. (1938) The breeding seasons of southern hemisphere birds in the northern hemisphere. *Proc. zool. Soc. Lond.* **A153**, 101–41.

Baldwin, F. M. (1917) Diurnal activity of the earthworm. *J. Anim. Behav.* **7**, 187–90.

Ball, N. G. and Dyke, I. J. (1954) An endogenous 24-hour rhythm in the growth rate of the *Avena* coleoptile. *J. exp. Bot.* **5**, 421–33.

Barden, A. (1942) Activity of the lizard, *Cnemidophorus sexlineatus*. *Ecology*, **23**, 336–44.

Bateman, M. A. (1955) The effect of light and temperature on the rhythms of pupal ecdysis in the Queensland fruit-fly *Dacus (Strumata) tryoni* (Frogg.) *Austr. J. Zool.* **3**, 22–33.

Beach, F. A. (1941) Effects of brain lesions upon running activity in the male rat. *J. comp. Psychol.* **31**, 145–79.

Belding, D. L. (1941) "Textbook of Clinical Parasitology". Appleton-Century, New York.

Beling, I. (1929) Über das Zeitgedächtnis der Biene. *Z. vergl. Physiol.* **9**, 259–338.

Bennett, M. F. (1954) The rhythmic activity of the quahog, *Venus mercenaria*, and its modification by light. *Biol. Bull. Woods Hole*, **107**, 174–91.

Bennett, M. F., Shriner, J. and Brown, R. A. (1957) Persistent tidal cycles of spontaneous motor activity in the fiddler crab, *Uca pugnax*, *Biol. Bull. Woods Hole*, **112**, 267-75.

Bentley, E. W., Gunn, D. L. and Ewer, D. W. (1941) The biology and behaviour of *Ptinus tectus* Boie (Coleoptera, Ptinidae), a pest of stored products. I.—The daily rhythm of locomotory activity, especially in relation to light and temperature. *J. exp. Biol* **18**, 182-95.

Bethe, A. (1946) Irritabilität, Rhythmik und Periodik. *Naturwissenschaften*, **33**, 86.

Bissonnette, T. H. (1930) Studies on the sexual cycles in birds. I.—Sexual maturity, its modification and possible control in the European starling (*Sturnus vulgaris*). *Amer. J. Anat.* **45**, 289–305.

—— (1932) Modification of mammalian sexual cycles; reactions of ferrets (*Putorius vulgaris*) of both sexes to electric light added after dark in November and December. *Proc. roy. Soc.* **B110**, 322–36.

—— (1933) Light and sexual cycles in starlings and ferrets. *Quart. Rev. Biol.* **8**, 201–8.

Blake, G. M. (1958) Diapause and the regulation of development in *Anthrenus verbasci* (L.) (Col., Dermestidae). *Bull. ent. Res.* **49**, 751–75.

Bodenheimer, F. S. (1934) Studies on the ecology of palastinian Coleoptera. II.—Seasonal and diurnal appearance and activity. *Bull. Soc. ent. Égypt*, **1934**, 1–2, 211–41.

—— and Klein, H. J. (1930) Über die Temperaturabhängigkeiten von Insekten. II.—Die Abhängigkeit der Aktivität bei der Ernteameise *Messor semirufus* E. Änderung von Temperatur und anderen Faktoren. *Z. vergl. Physiol.* **11**, 345–85.

Bohn, G. (1903) Sur les movements oscillatoires des *Convoluta roscoffensis*. *C.R. Acad. Sci., Paris*, **137**, 576–8.

—— (1904) Periodicité vitale des animaux soumis aux oscillations du neveau des hautes mers. *C.R. Acad. Sci., Paris*, **139**, 610–11.

—— (1906) La persistance du rhythme des marées chez l'*Actinia equina*. *C.R. Soc. Biol., Paris*, **61**, 661–3.

Brehm, E. and Hempel, G. (1952) Untersuchung tagesperiodischer Aktivitäts-schwankungen bei Käfern. *Naturwissenschaften*, **11**, 265–6.

Bremer, H. (1926) Über die tageszeitliche Konstanz im Schlüpftermine der Imagine einiger Insekten und ihre experimentelle Beeinflussbarkeit. *Z. wiss. Insekt Biol.* **21**, 209–16.

Brereton, J. L. (1957) The distribution of woodland isopods. *Oikos*, **8**, 85–106.

Brett, W. J. (1955) Persistent diurnal rhythmicity in *Drosophila* emergence. *Ann. ent. Soc. Amer.* **48**, 119–31.

Brian, M. V. (1947) On the ecology of beetles of the genus *Agriotes* with special reference to *A. obscurus*. *J. Anim. Ecol.* **16**, 210–24.

Browman, L. G. (1943) The effect of controlled temperatures upon the spontaneous activity rhythms of the albino rat. *J. exp. Zool.* **94**, 477–89.

—— (1952) Artificial sixteen-hour day activity rhythms in the white rat. *Amer. J. Physiol.* **168**, 694–7.

Brown, F. A. Jr. (1954) Persistent activity rhythms in the oyster. *Amer. J. Physiol.* **178**, 510–14.

—— (1957a) The rhythmic nature of life. In "Recent Advances in Invertebrate Physiology", 287–304. University of Oregon Publications.

—— (1957b) Biological chronometry. *Amer. Nat.* **91**, 129–31.

—— (1958a) An exogenous reference-clock for persistent, temperature-independent, labile biological rhythms. *Biol. Bull. Woods Hole*, **115**, 81–100.

—— (1958b) Studies of the timing mechanisms of daily tidal and lunar periodicities in organisms. In "Perspectives in Marine Biology", 269–82. (A. Buzzati Traverso, ed.) Scripps Institution of Oceanography, California.

—— (1959) Living clocks. *Science*, **130**, 1535–44.

——, Bennett, M. F. and Ralph, C. L. (1954) An apparent influence of alteration in cosmic-ray induced showers on a living system. *Anat. Rec.* **120**, 796.

——, Bennett, M. F., Webb, H. M. and Ralph, C. L. (1956) Persistent daily, monthly, and 27-day cycles of activity in the oyster and quahog. *J. exp. Zool.* **131**, 235–62.

—— , Fingerman, M., Sandeen, M. I. and Webb, H. M. (1953) Persistent diurnal and tidal rhythms of colour change in the fiddler crab, *Uca pugnax. J. exp. Zool.* **123**, 29–60.

—— , Freeland, R. O. and Ralph, C. L. (1955) Persistent rhythms of O₂-consumption in potatoes, carrots and the seaweed, *Fucus. Plant Physiol.* **30**, 280–92.

—— , Shriner, J. and Ralph, C. L. (1956) Solar and lunar rhythmicity in the rat in 'constant conditions' and the mechanisms of physiological time measurement. *Amer. J. Physiol.* **184**, 491–6.

—— and Stephens, G. C. (1951) Studies of the daily rhythmicity of the fiddler crab, *Uca*. Modifications by photoperiod. *Biol. Bull. Woods Hole*, **101**, 71–83.

—— and Webb, H. M. (1948) Temperature relations of an endogenous daily rhythmicity in the fiddler crab, *Uca. Physiol. Zool.* **21**, 371–81.

—— (1949) Studies of the daily rhythmicity of the fiddler crab, *Uca*. Modification by light. *Ibid.* **22**, 136–48.

—— , Webb, H. M. and Bennett, M. F. (1955) Proof for the endogenous component in persistent solar and lunar rhythmicity in organisms. *Proc. nat. Acad. Sci., Wash.* **41**, 93–100.

—— , Webb, H. M., Bennett, M. F. and Sandeen, M. I. (1954) Temperature-independence of the frequency of the endogenous tidal rhythm of *Uca. Physiol. Zool.* **27**, 345–9.

—— , Webb, H. M., Bennett, M. F. and Sandeen, M. I. (1955) Evidence for an exogenous contribution to persistent diurnal and lunar rhythmicity under so-called constant conditions. *Biol. Bull. Woods Hole*, **109**, 238–54.

—— , Webb, H. M. and Brett, W. J. (1959) Exogenous timing of solar and lunar periodisms in metabolism of the mud snail, *Ilyanassa* (=*Nassarius*) *obsoleta*, in laboratory and constant conditions. *Gunma J. med. Sci.* **8**, 233–42.

Browne, L. B. (1956) The effect of light on the fecundity of the Queensland fruit-fly, *Strumeta tryoni* (Frogg.). *Austr. J. Zool.* **4**, 125–45.

Bruce, V. G. and Pittendrigh, C. S. (1956) Temperature independence in a unicellular "clock". *Proc. nat. Acad. Sci., Wash.* **42**, 676–82.

Bruce-Chwatt, L. J. (1950) Recent studies on insect vectors of yellow fever and malaria in British West Africa. *J. trop. Med. (Hyg.)* **53**, 71–9.

Bruns, H. (1954) Beobachtungen zum Verhalten (insbesondere Tagesrhythmus) der roten Waldameise (*Formica rufa*) während des Nahrungserwerbes. *Z. Tierpsychol.* **11**, 151–4.

Buck, J. B. (1937) Studies on the firefly. I.—The effects of light and other agents on the flashing in *Photinus pyralis* with special reference to periodicity and diurnal rhythm. *Physiol. Zool.* **10**, 45–58.

*—— (1938) Synchronous rhythmic flashing of fireflies. *Quart. Rev. Biol.* **13**, 301–4.

Bünning, E. (1935) Zur Kenntnis der endogen Tagesrhythmik bei Insekten und bei Pflanzen. *Ber. dtsch. bot. Ges.* **53**, 594–623.

—— (1956a) Endogenous rhythms in plants. *Annu. Rev. Plant Physiol.* **7**, 71–90.

—— (1956b) Versuche zur Beeinflussung der endogenen Tagesrhythmik durch chemische Faktoren. *Z. Bot.* **44**, 515–29.

—— (1956c) Die physiologische Uhr. *Naturwissenschaften*, **9**, 351–7.

—— (1957) Endogenous diurnal cycles of activity in plants. In "Rhythmic and Synthetic Processes in Growth", 111–26. (D. Rudnick, ed.) 15th Growth Symposium, Princeton University Press.

—— (1958a) Cellular Clocks. *Nature, Lond.* **181**, 1169–71.

—— (1958b) Über den Temperatureinfluss auf die endogene Tagesrhythmik besonders bei *Periplaneta americana. Biol. Zbl.* **77**, 141–52.

—— (1958c) "Die physiologische Uhr". Springer, Berlin.

—— (1959) Physiological mechanism and biological importance of the endogenous diurnal periodicity in plants and animals. In "Photoperiodism and Related Phenomena in Plants and Animals", 507–35. American Assocation for the Advancement of Science, Washington, D.C.

*Bullock, T. H. (1954) Compensation for temperature in the metabolism and activity of poikelotherms. *Biol. Rev.* **30**, 311–42.

*Bullough, W. S. (1951) "Vertebrate Sexual Cycles". Methuen, London.

Burrows, W. (1945) Periodic spawning of 'Palolo' worms in Pacific waters. *Nature, Lond.* **155**, 47–8.

Busnel, R.-G. (1958) Quelques applications de techniques électro-acoustiques à la métrologie de certains aspects du comportement. *Ann. Soc. Zool. Belg.*, **89**, 49–92.

Buxton, P. A. (1923) "Animal Life in Deserts. A study of the fauna in relation to the environment." Arnold, London.

—— (1924a) Heat, moisture and animal life in deserts. *Proc. roy. Soc.* **B96**, 123–31.

—— (1924b) The temperature of the surface of deserts. *J. Ecol.* **12**, 127–34.

*Calhoun, J. B. (1944) Twenty-four hour periodicities in the animal kingdom. Part I. The invertebrates. *J. Tenn. Acad. Sci.* **19** (2) 179–200; (3) 252–62.

—— (1945) *Idem.* Part II. The vertebrates. *Ibid.* **20** (2) 228–32; (3) 291–308; (4) 373–78.

—— (1946) *Ibid.* **21** (2) 208–16; (3) 281–2.

Carpenter, J. R. (1934) Diurnal fluctuations in communities adjoining the forest edge near Urbana, Illinois. *Proc. Okla. Acad. Sci.* **14**, 29–31.

Carter, G. S. (1951a) "A general Zoology of the Invertebrates", 3rd Edition. Sidgwick and Jackson, London.

—— (1951b) "Animal Evolution. A study of recent views of its causes". Sidgwick and Jackson, London.

*Caspers, H. (1951) Rhythmische Erscheinungen in der Fortpflanzung von *Clunio marinus* (Dipt: Chiron.) und das Problem der lunaren Periodizität bei Organismen. *Arch. Hydrobiol.* Suppl. **18**, 415–594.

*Chapman, R. N. (1931) "Animal Ecology with especial Reference to Insects". McGraw-Hill, New York and London.

Chauvin, R. (1943) Deux appareils pour l'étude de l'activité des petits animaux. *Bull. Soc. zool. Fr.*, **68**, 53–6.

—— (1944) L'effet de groupe et la régulation de l'activité sociale chez les fourmis du genre *Leptothorax* etudiés au moyen du microactographe optique. I. La fourmillière en hibernation. *Bull. biol.* **78**, 197–205.

Clark, A. H. (1914) Nocturnal animals. *J. Wash. Acad. Sci.* **4**, 139–42.

Clark, F. N. (1925) The life history of *Leuresthes tenuis* an Atherine fish with tide-controlled spawning habits. *Fish Bull.*, *Sacramento*, No. 10, 1–51.

Cloudsley-Thompson, J. L. (1950) The water-relations and cuticle of *Paradesmus gracilis* (Diplopoda: Strongylosomidae). *Quart. J. micr. Sci.* **91**, 453–64.

—— (1951a) On the responses to environmental stimuli and the sensory physiology of millipedes (Diplopoda). *Proc. zool. Soc. Lond.* **121**, 253–77.

—— (1951b) Studies in diurnal rhythms. I.—Rhythmic behaviour in millipedes. *J. exp. Biol.* **28**, 165–72.

—— (1952a) Studies in diurnal rhythms. II.—Changes in the physiological responses of the woodlouse *Oniscus asellus* to environmental stimuli. *Ibid.* **29**, 295–303.

—— (1952b) Diurnal rhythms. *Trans. IX. int. Congr. Ent., Amsterdam* 1951, **1**, 305–10.

—— (1953a) Diurnal rhythm of locomotory activity in isolated migratory locusts. *Ent. mon. Mag.* **89**, 233–5.

—— (1953b) The significance of fluctuating temperatures on the physiology of insects *Entomologist*, **87**, 153–61.

—— (1953c) Diurnal rhythms in animals. *Sci. News*, **28**, 77–98.

—— (1953d) Studies in diurnal rhythms. III.—Photoperiodism in the cockroach *Periplaneta americana* (L). *Annu. Mag. nat. Hist.* (12) **6**, 705–12.

—— (1953e) Studies in diurnal rhythms. IV.—Photoperiodism and geotaxis in *Tenebrio molitor* L. (Coleoptera: Tenebrionidae). *Proc. R. ent. Soc. Lond.* **A28**, 117–32.

—— (1954a) The ecological significance of diurnal rhythms in terrestrial arthropods. *Sci. Progr.* **42**, 46–52.

—— (1954b) Problems of dispersal in some terrestrial arthropods. *Advanc. Sci.* **11**, 73–5.

—— (1955a) Arthropods and terrestrial life. *Sci. News*, **36**, 95–108.

—— (1955b) The design of entomological aktograph apparatus. *Entomologist*, **88**, 153–61.

—— (1956a) The effect of rock cover on the diurnal range of microclimatic conditions. *Entomologist*, **89**, 213–5.

—— (1956b) The ecological significance of diurnal rhythms in terrestrial arthropods. *Proc. XIV. int. Cong. Zool. Copenhagen, 1953*, 415–7.

—— (1956c) Studies in diurnal rhythms. VI.—Bioclimatic observations in Tunisia and their significance in relation to the physiology of the fauna, especially woodlice, centipedes, scorpions and beetles. *Annu. Mag. nat. Hist.* (12) **9**, 305–29.

—— (1956d) Studies in diurnal rhythms. VII.—Humidity responses and nocturnal activity in woodlice (Isopoda). *J. exp. Biol.* **33**, 576–82.

*—— (1957a) Studies in diurnal rhythms. V.—Nocturnal ecology and water relations of the British cribellate spiders of the genus *Ciniflo* Bl. *J. Linn. Soc. (Zool.)* **43**, 134–52.

—— (1957b) Some comments on the natural control of animal populations with especial reference to insects. *Entomologist*, **90**, 195–203.

*—— (1958a) "Spiders, Scorpions, Centipedes and Mites, The ecology and natural history of woodlice, 'myriapods' and arachnids", Pergamon, London and New York.

—— (1958b) Water relations and diurnal rhythms in woodlice. *Ann. appl. Biol.* **46**, 117–9.

—— (1958c) The effect of wind on the nocturnal emergence of woodlice and other terrestrial arthropods. I–III. *Ent. mon. Mag.* **94**, 106–8, 184–5, 283–4.

—— (1958d) Studies in diurnal rhythms. VIII.—The endogenous chronometer in *Gryllus campestris* L. (Orthoptera: Gryllidae). *J. Insect Physiol.* **2**, 175–80.

—— (1959a) The evolution of twenty-four-hour periodicities in terrestrial Arthropoda. *Proc. XV int. Congr. Zool. London, 1958*, 812–15.

*—— (1959b) Microclimate, diurnal rhythms and the conquest of the land by arthropods. *Internat. J. Biochem. Biomet.* **3** (3) B, 1–8.

—— (1959c) Animal clocks. *Nature, Lond.* **184**, 763–5.

—— (1959d) Studies in diurnal rhythms. IX.—The water-relations of some nocturnal tropical arthropods. *Ent. Exp. & Appl.* **2**, 249–56.

—— and Sankey, J. H. P. (1957) Some aspects of the fauna of the district around the Étang de Berre, Bouches-du-Rhône, France. *Annu. Mag. nat. Hist.* (12) **10**, 417–24.

Cole, L. C. (1957) Biological clock in the Unicorn. *Science*, **125**, 874–6.

Cook, W. C. (1927) Some effects of alternating temperatures on the growth and metabolism of cutworm larvae. *J. econ. Ent.* **20**, 769–82.

Corbet, P. S. (1952) An adult population study of *Pyrrhosoma nymphula* (Sulzer): (Odonata: Coenagrionidae). *J. Anim. Ecol.* **21**, 206–22.

—— (1957a) The life-history of the Emperor dragonfly, *Anax imperator* Leach (Odonata: Aeshnidae). *Ibid.* **26**, 1–69.

—— (1957b) The life-histories of two summer species of dragonfly (Odonata: Coenagriidae). *Proc. zool. Soc., Lond.* **128**, 403–18.

—— and Tjønneland, A. (1956) The flight activity of twelve species of East African Trichoptera. *Univ. Bergen Arb. naturv. R.* [1955] No. 9, 1–49.

*Cott, H. B. (1940) "Adaptive Coloration in Animals" Methuen, London.

*Crawford, S. C. (1934) The habits and characteristics of nocturnal animals. *Quart. Rev. Biol.* **9**, 201–14.

Crawshay, L. R. (1935) Possible bearing of a luminous Syllid on the question of the landfall of Columbus. *Nature, Lond.* **136**, 559–60.

Cresswell, E. (1959) A cattle rangemeter. *Anim. Behav.* **7**, 244.

Crowcroft, P. (1954) The daily cycle of activity in British shrews. *Proc. zool. Soc. Lond.* **123**, 715–29.

*Cushing, D. H. (1951) The vertical migration of planktonic Crustacea. *Biol. Rev.* **26**, 158–92.

D'Aguillar, J. (1952) L'activité cinésthesique des imagos de certains Agriotes (Col. Elateridae). *Trans. IX int. Congr. Ent. Amsterdam,* 1951, **1**, 465–71.

Dainton, B. H. (1954) The activity of slugs. I. The induction of activity by changing temperature. *J. exp. Biol.* **31**, 165–87.

Danielli, J. F. (1958) Studies of inheritance in amoebae by the technique of nuclear transfer. *Proc. roy. Soc.* **B148**, 321–31.

Dawson, R. W. (1931) The problem of voltinism and dormancy in the Polyphemus moth (*Telea polyphemus* Cramer). *J. exp. Zool.* **59**, 87–132.

Dehnel, P. A. (1958) Effect of photoperiod on the oxygen consumption of two species of intertidal crabs. *Nature, Lond.* **181**, 1415–17.

Destouches, L. (1921) Prolongation de la vie chez les *Galleria melonella*. *C.R. Acad. Sci., Paris,* **172**, 998–9.

Dice, L. R. (1914) The factors determining the vertical movement of *Daphnia*. *J. Anim. Behav.* **4**, 229–65.

Drzewina, A. (1907) Les variations périodiques du signe du phototropisme chez les Pagures misanthropes. *C.R. Acad. Sci., Paris,* **145**, 1208–9.

Dunning, R. A. (1956) A diurnal rhythm in the emergence of *Pegomyia betae* Curtis from the puparium. *Bull. ent. Res.* **47**, 645–53.

Dyson-Hudson, V. R. D. (1956) The daily activity rhythm of *Drosophila subobscura* and *D. obscura*. *Ecology,* **37**, 562–7.

Eastop, V. F. (1951) Diurnal variation in the aerial density of Aphididae. *Proc. R. ent. Soc. Lond.* **A26**, 129–34, 1 fig.

Edney, E. B. (1937) A study of spontaneous locomotor activity in *Locusta migratoria migratorioides* (R. and F.) by the actograph method. *Bull. ent. Res.* **28**, 243–78.

—— (1951) The evaporation of water from woodlice and the millipede *Glomeris*. *J. exp. Biol.* **28**, 91–115.

—— (1954) Woodlice and the land habitat. *Biol. Rev.* **29**, 185–219.

*—— (1957) "The Water Relations of Terrestrial Arthropods". Cambridge University Press, London.

*Elton, C. (1942) "Voles, Mice and Lemmings—Problems in Population Dynamics". Oxford University Press, London.

Engstrom, H., Holmgren, H. and Walhfart, G. (1938) Untersuchungen über 24-stundenrhythmische Veränderung in der Blutkörperchenmenge der Leber, der Nebennieren und der Schildrüse. *Anat. Anz.* **86**, 129–49.

Everett, J. W. and Sawyer, C. H. (1950) A 24-hour periodicity in the 'L-H-release apparatus' of female rats, disclosed by barbiturate sedation. *Endocrinology,* **47**, 198–218.

Everly, R. T. (1929) Preliminary experiments on the reaction of *Melanoplus differentialis* Uhler. *Ohio J. Sci.* **29**, 309–15.

Eyden, D. (1923) Specific gravity as a factor in the vertical distribution of plankton. *Proc. Camb. phil. Soc. biol.* **1**, 49–55.

Eyster, M. B. (1954) Quantitative measurement of the influence of photoperiod, temperature, and season on the activity of captive songbirds. *Ecol. Monogr.* **24**, 1–28.

Fauré-Fremiet, E. (1948) Le rhythme de marée du *Strombidium oculatum*. *Bull. biol.* **82**, 3–23.

Fingerman, M. (1955) Persistent daily and tidal rhythms of color change in *Callinectes sapidus. Biol. Bull. Woods Hole*, **109**, 255–64.

—— (1956) Phase difference in the tidal rhythms of color change of two species of fiddler crab. *Ibid.* **110**, 274–90.

—— (1957) Lunar rhythmicity in marine organisms. *Amer. Nat.* **91**, 167–78.

—— and Lago, A. D. (1957) Endogenous twenty-four hour rhythms of locomotor activity and oxygen consumption in the crawfish *Orconectes clypeatus. Amer. Midl. Nat.* **58**, 383–93.

——, Lago, A. D. and Lowe, M. E. (1958) Rhythms of locomotor activity and O_2-consumption of the grasshopper *Romalea microptera. Ibid.* **59**, 67–81.

——, Lowe, M. E. and Mobberly, W. C. Jr. (1958) Environmental factors involved in setting the phases of tidal rhythm in the fiddler crab *Uca pugilator* and *U. minax. Limnol. Oceanogr.* **3**, 271–82.

Floersheim, C. (1906) On some enemies of the diurnal Lepidoptera. *Ent. Rec.* **18**, 36–9.

Folk, G. E., Jr. (1957) Twenty-four hour rhythms of mammals in a cold environment. *Amer. Midl. Nat.* **91**, 153–66.

—— (1959) Modification by light of 24-hour activity of white rats. *Proc. Iowa. Acad. Sci.* **66**, 399–406.

——, Meltzer, M. R. and Grindeland, R. E. (1958) A mammalian activity rhythm independent of temperature. *Nature, Lond.* **181**, 1598.

—— and Schellinger, R. R. (1954) The diurnal rhythm of body temperature in the hamster. *Anat. Rec.* **120**, 787.

Forel, A. (1906) Mémoire du temps et association des souvenirs chez les abielles. *Bull. Inst. gén. psychol.* **1906**, 257–9.

Fox, H. M. (1922) Lunar periodicity in living organisms. *Sci. Progr.* **17**, 273–82.

—— (1923) Lunar periodicity in reproduction. *Proc. roy. Soc.* **B95**, 523–50.

—— (1925) The effect of light on the vertical movement of aquatic organisms. *Proc. Camb. phil. Soc. Biol.* **1**, 219–24.

—— (1932) Lunar periodicity in reproduction. *Nature, Lond.* **130**, 23.

—— (1956) The moon and life. *Proc. roy. Instn. GB.* **37**, (163) 1–12.

Fraps, R. M. (1954) Neural basis of diurnal periodicity in release of ovuli-inducing hormone in fowl. *Proc. nat. Acad. Sci., Wash.* **40**, 348–56.

Gamble, F. W. and Keeble, F. (1903) The bionomics of *Convoluta roscoffensis* with special reference to its green cells. *Proc. roy. Soc., Lond.* **B72**, 93–8.

—— (1904) The bionomics of *Convoluta roscoffensis* with special reference to its green cells. *Quart. J. Micr. Sci.* **47**, 363–431.

Gaul, A. T. (1952) The awakening and diurnal flight activities of Vesperine wasps. *Proc. R. ent. Soc., Lond.* **A27**, 33–8.

Gause, G. F. (1934) "The Struggle for Existence". Williams and Wilkins, Baltimore.

Ghidini, G. M. (1947) L'impiego degli "attogrammi" nel saggio biologico degli insetticidi. *Boll. Ist. Ent. Univ. Bologna*, **16**, 279–90.

—— (1948) Saggio biologico di insetticidi per contatto con il metodo degli attogrammi. *Ibid.* **17**, 122–9.

Gibson, N. H. E. (1945) On the mating swarms of certain Chironomidae (Diptera). *Trans. R. ent. Soc., Lond.* **95**, 263–94.

Gillett, J. D. (1957) Age analysis of the biting-cycle of the mosquito *Taeniorhynchus* (*Mansonioides*) *africanus* Theobald, based on the presence of parasitic mites. *Ann. trop. Med. Parasit.* **51**, 151–8.

——, Haddow, A. J. and Corbet, P. S. (1959) Observations on the oviposition cycle of *Aedes* (*Stegomyia*) *aegypti* Linnaeus 11. *Ann. trop. Med. Parasit.* **53**, 35–41.

Godfrey, G. K. (1954) Tracing field voles (*Microtus agrestis*) with a Geiger-Müller counter. *Ecology*, **35**, 5–10.

Gompel, M. (1937) Recherches sur la consommation d'oxygène de quelques animaux aquatiques littoraux. *C.R. Acad. Sci., Paris*, **205**, 816–8.

Gooddy, W. (1958) Time and the nervous system. The brain as a clock. *Lancet* i. 1139–44.

—— (1959) *Idem. Ibid.* ii. 1155–6.

Grabensberger, W. (1933) Untersuchungen über das Zeitgedächtnis der Ameisen und Termiten. *Z. vergl. Physiol.* **20**, 1–54.

—— (1934a) Experimentelle Untersuchungen über das Zeitgedächtnis von Bienen und Wespen nach Verfütterung von Euchinin und Jodthyreoglobulin. *Ibid.* **20**, 338–42.

—— (1934b) Der Einfluss von Salicylsäure, gelbem Phosphor und weissem Arsenik auf das Zeitgedächtnis der Ameisen. *Z. vergl. Physiol.* **20**, 501–10.

Gray, J. (1950) The role of peripheral sense organs during locomotion in the vertebrates. In "Physiological Mechanisms in Animal Behaviour", 112–26. *Symp. Soc. exp. Biol.* IV (J. F. Danielli, and R. Brown, eds.) Cambridge.

Griffin, D. R. (1952) Bird navigation. *Biol. Rev.* **27**, 359–93.

Gunn, D. L. (1940) The daily rhythm of activity of the cockroach, *Blatta orientalis* L. I. Aktograph experiments, especially in relation to light. *J. exp. Biol.* **17**, 267–77.

——, Jenkin, P. M. and Gunn, A. L. (1937) Menstrual periodicity; statistical observations on a large sample of normal cases. *J. Obstet. Gynaecol.* **44**, 839–79.

—— and Kennedy, J. S. (1936) Apparatus for investigating the reactions of land arthropods to humidity. *J. exp. Biol.* **13**, 450–59.

—— and Walsh, B. M. (1941) Klino-kinesis in *Paramecium*. *Nature, Lond.* **148**, 565–6.

Guyselman, J. B. (1957) Solar and lunar rhythms of locomotor activity in the crayfish *Cambarus viriles*. *Physiol. Zool.* **30**, 70–87.

Haddow, A. J. (1945a) The mosquitoes of Bwamba County, Uganda. II. Biting activity with special reference to the influence of microclimate. *Bull. ent. Res.* **36**, 33–73.

—— (1945b) The mosquitoes of Bwamba County, Uganda. III. The vertical distribution of mosquitoes in a banana plantation and the biting cycle of *Aedes* (*Stegomyia*) *simpsoni*, Theobald. *Ibid.* **36**, 297–304.

—— (1947) The mosquitoes of Bwamba County, Uganda. V. The vertical distribution and biting-cycle of mosquitoes in rain-forest, with further observations on microclimate. *Ibid.* **37**, 301–30.

—— (1954) Studies of the biting-habits of African mosquitoes. An appraisal of methods employed, with special reference to the twenty-four hour catch. *Ibid.* **45**, 199–242.

—— (1956) Rhythmic biting activity of certain East African mosquitoes. *Nature, Lond.* **177**, 531–2.

Haddow, A. J. and Mahaffy, A. F. (1949) The mosquitoes of Bwamba County, Uganda. VII. Intensive catching on tree platforms, with further observations on *Aedes* (*Stegomyia*) *africanus*, Theobald. *Bull. ent. Res.* **40**, 169–78.

Halberg, F. (1953) Some physiological and clinical aspects of 24-hour periodicity. *J. Lancet*, **73**, 20–32.

—— (1959) Physiologic 24-hour periodicity; general and procedural considerations with reference to the adrenal cycle. *Z. Vitam.- Horm.- u. Fermentforsch.* **10**, 225.

——, Barnum, C. P., Silber, R. H. and Bittner, J. J. (1958) 24-hour rhythms at several levels of integration in mice on different lighting regimens. *Proc. Soc. exp. Biol. Med.* **97**, 897–900.

——, Halberg, E., Barnum, C. P. and Bittner, J. J. (1959) Physiologic 24-hour periodicity in human beings and mice the lighting regimen and daily routine. In "Photoperiodism and Related Phenomena in Plants and Animals", 803–77. (A. P. Withrow, ed.) American Association for the Advancement of Science, Washington, D.C.

——, French, L. A. and Gully, R. J. (1958) 24-hour rhythms in rectal temperature and blood eosinophils after hemidecortication in human subjects. *J. appl. Physiol.* **12**, 381–4.

—— and Visscher, M. B. (1956) Daily variations in physiologic parameters in various mammals. *Fed. Proc.* Part II. **15**, 761.

——, Visscher, M. B. and Bittner, J. J. (1953) Eosinophil rhythm in mice: range of occurrence; effects of illumination, feeding and adrenalectomy. *Amer. J. Physiol.* **174**, 109–22.

——, Visscher, M. B. and Bittner, J. J. (1954) Relation of visual factors to eosinophil rhythm in mice. *Amer. J. Physiol.* **179**, 229–35.

Haldane, J. B. S. (1941) "New Paths in Genetics". Allen and Unwin, London.

—— (1954) "The Biochemistry of Genetics". Allen and Unwin, London.

*Hammond, J. H. (1954) An aktograph for small insects. *J. Sci. Inst.* **31**, 43–4.

Harder, W. and Hempel G. (1954) Studien zur Tagesperiodik der Aktivität von Fischen. I. Versuche an Plattfischen. *Kurze Mitt. Inst. Fisch. Hamb.* No. 5, 22–31.

Hardy, A. (1956) "The Open Sea—its Natural History. The world of plankton". Collins, London.

Harker, J. E. (1953) The diurnal rhythm of activity of mayfly nymphs. *J. exp. Biol.* **30**, 525–33.

—— (1954) Diurnal rhythms in *Periplaneta americana* L. *Nature, Lond.* **173**, 689.

—— (1955) Control of diurnal rhythms of activity in *Periplaneta americana* L. *Ibid.* **175**, 733.

—— (1956) Factors controlling the diurnal rhythm of activity of *Periplaneta americana* L. *J. exp. Biol.* **33**, 224–34.

—— (1958a) Diurnal rhythms in the animal kingdom. *Biol. Rev.* **33**, 1–52.

—— (1958b) Experimental production of midgut tumours in *Periplaneta americana* L. *J. exp. Biol.* **35**, 251–9.

Harris, J. E. and Mason, P. (1956) Vertical migration in eyeless *Daphnia*. *Proc. roy. Soc.* **B145**, 280–90.

—— and Wolfe, U.K. (1955) A laboratory study of vertical migration. *Proc. roy. Soc.* **B144**, 329–54.

Harrison, J. L. (1952a) Moonlight and the pregnancy of Malayan forest rats. *Nature, Lond.* **170**, 73.

—— (1952b) Breeding rhythms of Selangor rodents. *Bull. Raffles Mus.* **24**, 109–31.

—— (1954a) Moonlight and the pregnancy of Malayan forest rats. *Nature, Lond.* **173**, 1002.

—— (1954b) The moonlight effect on rat breeding. *Bull. Raffles Mus.* **25**, 166–70.

—— (1955) Data on the reproduction of some Malayan mammals. *Proc. zool. Soc. Lond.* **125**, 445–60.

Hartland-Rowe, R. (1955) Lunar rhythm in the emergence of an Ephemeropteran. *Nature, Lond.* **176**, 657.

—— (1958) The biology of a tropical mayfly, *Povilla adusta* Navas (Ephemeroptera, Polymitarcidar), with special reference to the lunar rhythm of emergence. *Rev. Zool. Bot. afr.* **5B**, 185–202.

Haskell, P. T. (1954) An automatic recording maze for insect behaviour studies. *J. Anim. Behav.* **2**, 153–8.

Hastings, J. W. (1959) Unicellular clocks. *Annu. Rev. Microbiol.* **13**, 297–312.

—— and Sweeney, B. M. (1957) On the mechanisms of temperature independence in a biological clock. *Proc. nat. Acad. Sci. Wash.* **43**, 804–11.

—— and Sweeney, B. M. (1958) A persistent diurnal rhythm of luminescence in *Gonyaulax polyedra*. *Biol. Bull. Woods Hole,* **115**, 440–58.

—— and Sweeney, B. M. (1959) The *Gonyaulax* clock. In "Photoperiodism and Related Phenomena in Plants and Animals", 567–84. (A. P. Withrow, ed.) American Association for the Advancement of Science, Washington, D.C.

Hauenschild, C. (1955) Photoperiodizität als Ursache des von der Mondphase abhängegen Metamorphose-Rhythmes bei dem Polychaeten *Platynereis dumerlii*. *Z. Naturf.* **10b** (II) 658–62.

Hawking, F. (1953) The periodicity of microfilariae. III. Transfusion of microfilariae into a clean host. *Trans. R. Soc. trop. Med. Hyg.* **47**, 82–3.

—— (1955) *Idem.* VII. Periodicity of microfilariae of *Loa loa*. *Ibid.* **49**, 132–42.

—— (1956) *Idem. Ibid.* **50**, 397–417.

—— and Thurston, J. P. (1951a) The periodicity of microfilariae. I. The distribution of microfilariae in the body. *Ibid.* **45**, 307–29.

—— and Thurston, J. P. (1951b) *Idem.* II. The explanation of its production. *Ibid.* **45**, 329–40.

Headlee, T. J. (1914) Some data on the effect of temperature and moisture on the rate of insect metabolism. *J. econ. Ent.* **7**, 413–7.

—— (1929) Climate and insect investigations. *Rep. N.J. agric. Exp. Sta.* **1928**, 133–8.

—— (1941) Further studies of the relative effects on insect metabolism of temperatures derived from constant and variable sources. *J. econ. Ent.* **34**, 171–4.

Hediger, H. (1950) "Wild Animals in Captivity". Butterworths, London.

Hemmingsen, A. M. and Krarup, N. B. (1937) Rhythmic diurnal variation in the oestrus phenomena of the rat and their susceptibility to light and dark. *Biol. Medd. Kbh.* **13** (17) 1–64.

Higginbotham, A. C. (1939) Studies on amphibian activity. 1—Preliminary report on the rhythmic activity of *Bufo americanus americanus* Holbrook and *Bufo fowleri* Hinckley. *Ecology,* **20**, 58–70.

Hinman, E. H. (1936) Attempted reversal of filarial periodicity in *Dirofilaria immitis*. *Proc. Soc. exp. Biol. N.Y.* **33**, 524.

Hinton, H. E. (1954) The initiation, maintenance and rupture of diapause: a new theory *Entomologist,* **86**, 279–91.

—— (1957) Some aspects of diapause. *Sci. Progr.* **45**, 307–20.

Hitchcock, L. F. (1955) Studies on the parasitic stages of the cattle tick, *Boophilus microplus* (Conestrini) Acarina: Ixodidae) *Austr. J. Zool.* **3**, 145–55.

Hoagland, H. (1935) "Pacemakers in Relation to Aspects of Behaviour". Macmillan, New York.

—— (1936) Some pacemaker aspects of rhythmic activity in the nervous system. *Cold Spr. Harb. Symp. quant. Biol.* **4**, 267–76.

Hoar, W. S. (1956) Photoperiodism and thermal resistance of goldfish. *Nature, Lond.* **178**, 364–5.

Hoffmann, K. (1954) Versuche zu der im Richtungsfinden der Vögel enthaltenen Zeitschätzung. *Z. Tierphysiol.* **11**, 453–75.

—— (1957a) Über den Einfluss der Temperatur auf die Tagesperiodik bei einem Poikelthermen. *Naturwissenschaften,* **12**, 358.

—— (1957b) Angeborene Tagesperiodik bei Eidechsen. *Ibid.* **12**, 359–60.

—— (1958) Repetition of an experiment on bird orientation. *Nature, Lond.* **181**, 1435–7.

Holmgren, H. (1936). Studien über 24-Stunden rhythmische Variationen des Darm-, Lungen-, und Leberfetts. *Acta. med. scand. Suppl.* **74**, 1–202.

—— (1938) Leber Rhythmus und Fettresorption. *Dtsch. med. Wschr.* **64**, 744–6.

—— and Swensson, Å (1953) Der Einfluss des Lichtes auf den 24-Stunden-Rhythmus der Aktivität, des Leberglykogens und der Körpertemperatur. *Acta. med. scand. Suppl.* **278**, 71–6.

Howe, R. W. (1956) A method for obtaining a controlled daily temperature cycle. *Ann. appl. Biol.* **44**, 188–94.

Ilse, D. and Mulherkar, L. (1954) Mating reactions in the common Indian housefly, *Musca domestica nebulo* (Fabricius). *Curr. Sci.* **23**, 227–8.

Janda, V. and Mrciak, M. (1957) Gesamtstoffwechsel der Insekten. VI. Die Bewegungs-aktivität der Schabe *Periplaneta americana* L. während des Tages und ihre Beziehung zum Sauerstoffverbrauch. *Mém. Soc. zool. tchécosl.* **21**, 244–55.

Janisch, E. (1930) Experimentelle Untersuchungen über die Wirkung der Umwelt-faktoren auf Insekten. I—Die Massenvermehrung der Baumwolleneule *Prodenia littoralis* in Ägypten. *Z. Morph. Ökol. Tiere.* **17**, 339–416.

—— (1932) The influence of temperature on the life-history of insects. *Trans. R. ent. Soc. Lond.* **80**, 137–68.

Jennings, H. S. (1906) "Behaviour of the Lower Organisms". Columbia University Press, New York.

Johnson, C. G. (1940) Development, hatching and mortality on the eggs of *Cimex lectularius* L. (Hemiptera) in relation to climate, with observations on the effects of pre-conditioning to temperature. *Parasitology,* **32**, 127–73.

*—— (1942) The ecology of the bed-bug, *Cimex lectularius* L. in Britain. Report on research, 1935–40. *J. Hygiene,* **41**, 345–461.

—— (1950) A suction trap for small airborne insects which automatically segregates the catch into successive hourly samples. *Ann. appl. Biol.* **37**, 80–91.

—— (1951) The study of wind-borne insect populations in relation to terrestrial ecology, flight periodicity and the estimation of aerial populations. *Sci. Progr.* **39**, 41–62.

—— (1952) The role of population level, flight periodicity and climate in the dispersal of aphids. *Trans. IX int. Cong. Ent. Amsterdam, 1951,* **1**, 429–31.

*—— (1954) Aphid migration in relation to weather. *Biol. Rev.* **29**, 87–118.

—— and Taylor, L. R. (1955) The development of large suction traps for airborne insects. *Ann. appl. Biol.* **43**, 51–61.

Johnson, M. S. (1939) Effect of continuous light on periodic spontaneous activity of white-footed mice (*Peromyscus*). *J. exp. Zool.* **82**, 315–28.

*Jores, A. (1937) Die 24-Stunden Periodik in der Biologie. *Tab. Biol.* **14**, 77–109.

Kachkarov, O. N. and Korovine, E. P. (1942) "La Vie dans les Déserts". (Th. Monod, ed. fr.), Payot, Paris.

Kalabukhov, N. I. (1939) Some ecological peculiarities of closely related species of rodents. Peculiarities of the reaction of wood-mice and yellow-necked field mice (*Apodemus sylvaticus* L. and *A. flavicollis* Melch.) . . . to the temperature gradient. [In Russian] *Zool. Zh.* **18**, 915–23.

Kalmus, H. (1934) Ueber die Natur des Zeitgedächtnisses der Bienen. *Z. vergl. Physiol.* **20**, 405–19.

—— (1935) Periodizität und Autochronie (Ideochronie) als zeitregelnde Eigen-schaften der Organismen. *Biol. gen.* **11**, 93–114.

—— (1938a) Tagesperiodisch verlaufende Vorgänge an der Stabheuschrecke (*Dixippus morosus*) und ihre experimentelle Beeinflussung. *Z. vergl. Physiol.* **25**, 494–508.

*—— (1938b) Über das Problem der sogenannten exogenen und endogenen sowie der erblichen Rhythmik und über organische Periodizität Überhaupt. *Riv. Biol.* **24**, 191–225.

—— (1940) Diurnal rhythms in the axolotl larva and in *Drosophila. Nature, Lond.* **145**, 72–3.

—— (1953) Repetition, autonomy and synchronization in the living world. *Acta. med. scand. Supp.* No. **278**, 19–25.

—— (1956) Sun navigation of *Apis mellifica* L. in the southern hemisphere. *J. exp. Biol.* **33**, 554–65.

Kayser, Ch. and Marx, Ch. (1951) Le rhythme nycthéméral de l'activité et la mémoire du temps chez le lézard (*Lacerta agilis* et *Lacerta muralis*). *XX Congr. int. phil. Sci. Paris, 1949,* **6**, Biol. 96–103.

*Kellerman, K. F. (1926) A review of the discovery of photoperiodism: the influence of the length of daily light periods upon the growth of plants. *Quart. Rev. Biol.* **1**, 87–94.

Kendeigh, S. C. (1952) Parental care and its evolution in birds. *Ill. biol. Monogr.* **22**, 1–358.

Kennedy, C. H. (1928) Evolutionary level in relation to geographic, seasonal and diurnal distribution of insects. *Ecology,* **9**, 367–79.

Kennedy, J. S. (1939) The behaviour of the desert locust (*Schistocerca gregaria* (Forsk.) (Orthopt.)) in an outbreak centre. *Trans. R. ent. Soc. Lond.* **89**, 385–542.

Kerkut, G. A. and Taylor, B. J. R. (1958) The effect of temperature changes on the activity of poikelotherms. *Behaviour,* **13**, 259–79.

Kettle, D. S. (1957) Preliminary observations on weather conditions and the activity of biting flies. *Proc. R. ent. Soc. Lond.* **A32**, 13–20.

*Kikuchi, K. (1930) Diurnal migrations of plankton Crustacea. *Quart. Rev. Biol.* **5**, 189–206.

Kitching, J. A. (1954) The physiology of contractile vacuoles. IX. Effects of sudden changes in temperature on the contractile vacuole of a suctorian; with a discussion of the mechanism of contraction. *J. exp. Biol.* **31**, 68–75.

Klauber, L. M. (1939) Studies of reptile life in the arid southwest. Part I. Night collecting on the desert with ecological statistics. *Zool. Soc. San Diego Bull.* **114**, 7–64.

Kleitman, K. and Kleitman, N. (1953) Effect of non-twenty-four-hour routines of living on oral temperature and heart rate. *J. appl. Physiol.* **6**, 283–91.

*Kleitman, N. (1939) "Sleep and Wakefulness as Alternating Phases in the Cycle of Existence". University of Chicago Press, Chicago.

—— (1940) The modifiability of the diurnal pigmentary rhythm in isopods. *Biol. Bull. Woods Hole,* **78**, 403–6.

*—— (1949) Biological rhythms and cycles. *Physiol. Rev.* **29**, 1–30.

Korringa, P. (1941) Experiments and observations on swarming, pelagic life and settling in the European flat oyster, *Ostrea edulis* L. *Arch. néerl. Zool.* **5**, 1–249.

*—— (1947) Relations between the moon and periodicity in the breeding of marine animals. *Ecol. Monogr.* **17**, 347–8.

Koskimies, J. (1955) Ultimate causes of cyclical fluctuations in numbers in animal populations. *Pap. Game-Res., Helsingf.* No. 15, 1–29.

*Kramer, G. (1952) Experiments on bird orientation. *Ibid.* **94**, 265–85.

Kris, C. (1958) Corneo-fundal potential variations during light and dark adaptation. *Nature, Lond.* **182**, 1027–8.

Krumbiegel, I. (1932) Untersuchungen über physiologische Rassenbildung. *Zool. Jb.* **63**, 183–280.

*Lack, D. (1954) "The Natural Regulation of Animal Numbers". Oxford University Press, London.

Lane, F. W. (1948) "Animal Wonderland". Country Life, London.

Larsen, E. Bro., (1943) The importance of master factors for the activity of noctuids. Studies on the activity of insects I. *Ent. Medd.* **23**, 352–74.

—— (1949) Activity and migration of *Plusia gamma* L. Studies on the activity of insects III. *Biol. Medd., Kbh.* **21**, (4)1-32.

—— (1948) Observations on the activity of some Culicids. Studies on the activity of insects IV. *Ent. Medd.* **25**, 263–77.

Lees, A. D. (1953) Environmental factors controlling the evocation and termination of diapause in the fruit tree red spider mite *Metatetronychus ulmi* Koch (Acarina: Tetranychidae). *Ann. appl. Biol.* **40**, 449–86.

*—— (1955) "The Physiology of Diapause in Arthropods". Cambridge University Press.

—— and Milne, A. (1951) The seasonal and diurnal activities of individual sheep ticks (*Ixodes ricinus* L.). *Parasitology*, **41**, 189–208.

Leinweber, F. J. (1956) Über die Temperaturabhängigkeit der Periodenlänge bei der endogenen Tagesrhythmik von *Phaseolus*. *Z. Bot.* **44**, 337–64.

Levinson, L., Welsh, J. H. and Abramowitz, A. A. (1941) Effect of hypophysectomy on diurnal rhythm of spontaneous activity in the rat. *Endocrinology*, **29**, 41–6.

Lewis, C. B. and Bletchly, J. D. (1943) The emergence rhythm of the dung-fly, *Scopeuma* (= *Scatophaga*) *stercoraria* (L.) *J. Anim. Ecol.* **12**, 11–18.

Lewis, H. E. and Masterton, J. P. (1957) Sleep and wakefulness in the Arctic. *Lancet.* i. 1262–6.

Lewis, P. R. and Lobban, M. C. (1957a) The effects of prolonged periods of life on abnormal time routines upon excretory rhythms in human subjects. *Quart. J. exp. Physiol.* **42**, 356–71.

—— (1957b) Dissociation of diurnal rhythms in human subjects living on abnormal time routines. *Ibid.* **42**, 371–86.

Linke, W. (1953) Investigation of the biology and epidemiology of the common spider mite, *Tetranychus althaeae* v Hanst. with particular consideration to the hop as a host. *Höfchenbr. Wiss.* **6**, 181–232.

Long, D. B. (1958a) Field observations on adults of the wheat bulb fly, (*Leptohylemyia coarctata* (Fall.)). *Bull. ent. Res.* **49**, 77–94.

—— (1958b) Observations on oviposition in the wheat bulb fly, *Leptohylemyia coarctata* (Fall.). *Ibid.* **49**, 355–66.

Lotka, A. J. (1920) Analytical note on certain rhythms in organic systems. *Proc. nat. Acad. Sci., Wash.* **6**, 410–15.

Ludwig, D. (1926) Effects of temperature on the rate of development of the "Jap" beetle (*Popillia japonica*). *Anat. Rec.* **39**, 121.

—— and Cable, R. M. (1933) The effect of alternating temperatures on the pupal development of *Drosophila melanogaster* Meigen. *Physiol. Zool.* **6**, 493–508.

Lumsden, W. H. R. (1952) The crepuscular biting activity of insects in the forest canopy in Bwamba, Uganda. A study in relation to the sylvan epidemiology of yellow fever. *Bull. ent. Res.* **42**, 678–721.

—— (1958) A trap for insects biting small vertebrates. *Nature, Lond.* **181**, 819–26.

Lutz, F. E. (1932) Experiments with Orthoptera concerning diurnal rhythms. *Amer. Mus. Novit.* **550**, 1–24.

McClure, A. G. (1938) Insect aerial populations. *Ann. ent. Soc. Amer.* **31**, 504–14.

McFadzean, J. A. and Hawking, F. (1956) The periodicity of microfilariae. V. Stimuli affecting the periodic migration of the microfilariae of *Wuchereria bancrofti* and of *Loa loa* in man. *Trans. R. Soc. trop. Med. Hyg.* **50**, 543–62.

McGinnis, M. O. (1911) Reaction of *Branchipus serratus* to light, heat and gravity. *J. exp. Zool.* **10**, 227–40.

Makings, P. (1956) An aktograph which records the time, rate and duration of walking-movements and oviposition, of moths. *Proc. Linn. Soc. Lond.* **167**, 7.

Manson-Bahr, P. H. (1948) "Manson's Tropical Diseases. A manual of the diseases of warm climates". 12th edition, Cassell, London.

Marshall, A. J. (1938) Bird and animal activity in the Arctic. *J. Anim. Ecol.* **7**, 248–50.

*—— (1954) "Bower-birds, their Displays and Breeding Cycles. A preliminary statement". Oxford University Press, London.

*Marshall, F. H. A. (1910) "The Physiology of Reproduction". Longmans, London,

—— (1936) Sexual periodicity and the causes which determine it. *Phil. Trans.* **B226** 423–56.

*—— (1942) Exteroceptive factors in sexual periodicity. *Biol. Rev.* **17**, 68–90.

Matthews, G. V. T. (1955) "Bird Navigation". Cambridge University Press, London.

Mattingly, P. F. (1949) Studies on West Africa forest mosquitos. Part 1. The seasonal distribution, biting cycle and vertical distribution of four of the principal species. *Bull. ent. Res.* **40**, 149–68.

—— (1952) Recent work on cyclical behaviour in the Nematocera. *Trans. IX int. Congr. Ent. Amsterdam*, 1951. **1**, 375–9.

Mayer, A. G. (1914) The relation between the degree of concentration of the electrolytes of sea water and the rate of nerve conduction in *Cassiopea*. *Carnegie Inst. Publ.* No. 183, 1–30.

Mazia, D. (1956) Nuclear products and nuclear reproduction. In "Enzymes: Units of Biological Structure and Function." (O. H. Gaebler, ed.) Academic Press, New York.

Mellanby, K. (1939) The physiology and activity of the bed-bug (*Cimex lectularius* L.) in a natural infestation. *Parasitology*, **31**, 200–11.

—— (1940) The daily rhythm of activity in the cockroach *Blatta orientalis* L. II. Observations and experiments on a natural infestation. *J. exp. Biol.* **17**, 278–85.

Menaker, M. (1959) Endogenous rhythms of body temperature in hibernating bats. *Nature, Lond.* **184**, 1251–2.

Meunier, K. (1928) Experimentelles über den Schwärmtrieb und das periodische Auftreten verschiedener Aktivitätsformen beim Maikäfer (*Melolontha melolontha* L.). *Z. angew. Ent.* **14**, 91–139.

Meyer-Lohmann, J. (1955) Über den Einfluss täglicher Futtergaben auf die 24-Stunden-Periodik der lokomotorischen Aktivität weisser Mäuse. *Pflüg. Arch. ges. Physiol.* **260**, 292–305.

Michal, K. (1931) Oszillationen im Sauerstoffverbrauch der Mehlwurmlarven (*Tenebrio molitor*). *Zool. Anz.* **95**, 65–75.

Mikulski, J. S. (1936a) The effect of constant and alternating temperatures on the survival of some developmental stages of *Tribolium confusum* Duval. *Bull. int. Acad. Cracovie (Acad. pol. Sci.)* **B1936**, 361–72.

—— (1936b) On the changes of developmental velocity of some developmental stages of *Tribolium confusum* when influened by constant and alternating temperatures. *Ibid.* **1936**, 373–85.

Miller, R. S. (1955) Activity rhythms in the wood mouse, *Apodemus sylvaticus* and the bank vole *Clethrionomys glareolus Proc. zool. Soc. Lond.* **125**, 505–19.

Mills, J. N. (1951) Diurnal rhythm in urine flow. *J. Physiol.* **113**, 528–36.

Mitchell, D. F. and Epling, C. (1951) The diurnal periodicity of *Drosophila pseudoobscura* in Southern California. *Ecology*, **32**, 696–708.

Mori, S. (1939) Effects of the total solar eclipse on the rhythmic diurnal activities of some animals. *Ann. Zool. Japan*, **18** (2) 115–32.

—— (1947) A concept of mechanisms of the endogenous daily rhythmic activity. *Mem. Coll. Sci. Kyoto*, **B19**, (1) 1–4.

—— (1948) Harmony between behaviour rhythm and environmental rhythm. *Ibid.* **19** (2) 71–74.

—— (1949a) Inheritance of daily rhythmic types in emerging behaviour in some *Drosophila*-mutants. [In Japanese] *Jap. J. Genet.* **24**, 150–6.

—— (1949b) Daily rhythmic phenomena in the life history of *Drosophila*.[In Japanese] *Seibut. Gyos.* **4**, 121–8.

—— (1954) Population effect on the daily periodic emergence of *Drosophila. Mem. Coll. Sci. Kyoto*, **B21**, 49–54.

—— and Ondô, Y. (1957) Daily rhythmic activity of the sea-pen, *Cavernularia obesa* Valenciennes. XV.—Controlling of the activity by light (3). *Publ. Seto. mar. biol. Lab.* **6**, 79–98.

Müller, H. J. (1956) Über die Wirkung von Umweltfaktoren auf die Variabilität saisondimorpher Insekten, insbesondere der Gattung *Euscelis. Verh. dtsch. zool. Ges.* **1956**, 450–62.

Muirhead-Thomson, R. C. (1951) "Mosquito Behaviour in relation to Malaria Transmission and Control in the Tropics". Arnold, London.

Naylor, E. (1958) Tidal and diurnal rhythms of locomotory activity in *Carcinus moenas* (L). *J. exp. Biol.* **35**, 602–10.

Neal, E. (1948) "The Badger". Collins, London.

Newell, G. (1948) A contribution to our knowledge of the life history of *Arenicola marina* L. *J. Mar. biol. Ass. U.K.* **27**, 554–80.

Newport, G. (1837) On the temperature of insects and its connection with the function of respiration and circulation in this class of invertebrate animals. *Phil. Trans.* **1837**, 259–338.

*Nicholson, A. J. (1933) The balance of animal populations. *J. Anim. Ecol.* **2**, 132–78.

Nielsen, E. T. (1938) Zur Oekologie der Laubheuschrecken. *Ent. Medd.* **20**, 121–64.

—— (1957) Use of the electronic flash to record the activity of small animals. *Nature, Lond.* **179**, 1308.

—— and Greve, H. (1950) Studies on the swarming habits of mosquitoes and other Nematocera. *Bull. ent. Res.* **41**, 227–58.

Norgaard, E. (1951) Notes on the biology of *Filistata insidiatrix* (Forsk.). *Ent. Medd.* **26**, 170–84.

Noüy, Lecomte du (1936) "Biological Time". Methuen, London.

Osborn, C. M. (1940) Spontaneous diurnal activity in a genetically hypopituitary animal, the dwarf rat. *Anat. Rec.* **78**, 137.

*Palmén, E. (1955) Diel periodicity of pupal emergence in natural populations of some Chironomids (Diptera). *Ann. Soc. zool.-bot. fenn. Vanamo* **17** (3) 1–30.

—— (1956) Periodic emergence in some chironomids—an adaptation to nocturnalism. In "Bertil Hanström, Zoological papers in honour of his sixty-fifth birthday". (K. G. Wingstrand, ed.) Lund.

Pantin, C. F. A. (1935) The nerve net of the Actinozoa. I.—Facilitation. *J. exp. Biol.* **12**, 119–38.

Papi, F. (1955a) Experiments on the sense of time in *Talitrus saltator* (Crustacea-Amphipoda). *Experientia*, **11**, 210–13.

—— (1955b) Ricerche sull'orientamento astronomico di *Arctosa perita* (Latr.) (Araneae Lycosidae). *Publ. Staz. zool. Napoli.* **27**, 76–103.

—— (1955c) Astronomische orientierung bei der Wolfspinne *Arctosa perita* (Latr.). *Z. vergl. Physiol.* **37**, 230–3.

—— and Pardi, L. (1953) Ricerche sull'orientamento di *Talitrus saltator* (Montagu) (Crustacea-Amphipoda). *Ibid.* **35**, 490–518.

—— and Serretti, L. (1955) Sull'esistenza di un senso del tempo in *Arctosa perita* (Latr.) (Araneae-Lycosidae). *P.V. Soc. tosc. Sci. nat.* **B62**, 98–104.

Pardi, L. and Papi, F. (1953) Ricerche sull'orientamento di *Talitrus saltator* (Montagu) (Crustacea-Amphipoda) I. L'orientation durante il giorno in una popolozione del litorale Tierrenico. *Z. vergl. Physiol.* **35**, 459–89.

Park, O. (1935) Studies in nocturnal ecology, III. Recording apparatus and further analysis of activity rhythm. *Ecology*, 16 pp. 152–63.

—— (1937) Studies in nocturnal ecology. Further analysis of activity in the beetle, *Passalus cornutus*, and description of audio-frequency recording apparatus. *J. Anim. Ecol.* **6**, 239–53.

—— (1938) Studies in nocturnal ecology VII. Preliminary observations in Panama rain forest animals. *Ecology*, **19**, 208–23.

*—— (1940) Nocturnalism—the development of a problem. *Ecol. Monogr.* **10**, 485–536.

—— (1941a) Quantitative determination of rhythmicity in organisms. *Ohio J. Sci.* **41**, 39–45.

—— (1941b) Concerning community symmetry. *Ecology*, **22**, 164–7.

*—— (1949a) Community organization: periodicity. 528–62 in Allee, W. C. *et al.* (q.v.)

—— (1949b) Application of the converse Bergmann principle to the Carabid beetle, *Dicaclus purpuratus*. *Physiol. Zool.* **22**, 359–72.

——, Barden, A. and Williams, E. (1940) Studies in nocturnal ecology, IX. Further analysis of activity in Panama rain forest animals. *Ecology*, **21**, 122–34.

—— and Keller, J. G. (1932) Studies in nocturnal ecology, II. Preliminary analysis of activity rhythm in nocturnal forest insects. *Ibid.* **13**, 335.

——, Lockett, J. A. and Myers, D. J. (1931) Studies in nocturnal ecology with special reference to climax forest. *Ibid.* **12**, 709–27.

——, Roberts, T. W. and Harris, S. J. (1941) Preliminary analysis of activity of the cave crayfish, *Cambarus pellucidus*. *Amer. Nat.* **75**, 154–71.

—— and Sejba, O. (1935) Studies in nocturnal ecology, IV. *Megalodacne heros*. *Ecology*, **16**, 164–72.

—— and Strohecker, H. F. (1936) Studies in nocturnal ecology, V. An experiment in conducting field classes at night. *Ohio J. Sci.* **36**, 46–54.

—— and Woods, L. P. (1940) A modified Hemmingsen-Krarup mammalian activity recorder. *Proc. Soc. exp. Biol. Med.* **43**, 366–70.

Parker, G. H. (1948) "Animal Colour Changes and their Neurohumours". Cambridge University Press, London.

Parker, J. R. (1929) Some effects of temperature and moisture upon the activities of grasshoppers and their relation to grasshopper abundance and control. *Trans. 4th int. Congr. Ent. Ithaca, 1928,* **2**, 322–32.

—— (1930) Some effects of temperature and moisture upon *Melanoplus mexicanus* Saussure and *Camnula pellucida* Scudder. *Bull. Univ. Mont. agric. Exp. Sta.* No. 223: 132 pp.

*Parkes, A. S. (1952) (Ed.) "Marshall's Physiology of Reproduction", (2 vols.). Longmans, London.

Pavan, M. (1950) Ricerche sperimentali sul comportamento degli Artropodi. I. Apparecchio per lo studio delle tassie *Boll. Soc. ent. ital.* **80**, 27–32.

—— (1952a) Ricerche sperimentali sul comportamento degli Artropodi. III. Apparecchio per lo studio del comportamento cinetico. *Boll. Zool. agr. Bachic.* **17** (3) 1–20.

—— (1952b) Attografo multiplo per lo studio del comportamento cinetico di Artropodi. *Trans. IX int. Congr. Ent. Amsterdam, 1953.* **1**, 315–20.

Payne, N. M. (1932) Duration of the pupal state of *Tenebrio molitor* Linnaeus at constant and at alternating temperatures (Coleop. Tenebrionidae). *Ent. News,* **43**, 6–7.

Peairs, L. M. (1927) Some phases of the relation of temperature to the development of insects. *Bull. W. Va. agric. Exp. Sta.* **208**: 62 pp.

Perttunen, V. (1952) Seasonal changes in the humidity reaction of the common earwig, *Forficula auricularia. Nature, Lond.* **170**, 209.

—— (1953) Reactions of diplopods to the relative humidity of the air. Investigations on *Orthomorpha gracilis, Iulus terrestris* and *Schizophyllum sabulosum. Ann. Soc. zool.-bot. fenn. Vanamo,* **16**, 1–69.

—— (1955) The reversal of the humidity reaction at the onset of the egg-laying period in the diplopod *Schizophyllum sabulosum. Arch. Soc. zool.-bot. fenn. Vanamo,* **9**, 231–4.

—— and Lagerspetz, K. (1957) Dissociation of the pulsation rhythm in the anterior and posterior parts of the heart at low and high temperatures in the larva of *Corethra plumicornis* (Dipt., Culicidae) *Ann. Ent. Fenn.* **23**, 179–81.

Piéron, H. (1958) "De l'Actinie a l'Homme L'anticipation et mémoire bases de l'evolution psychique". Presses universitaires de France, Paris.

Pittendrigh, C. S. (1954) On temperature independence in the clock system controlling emergence in *Drosophila. Proc. nat. Acad. Sci. Wash.* **40**, 1018–29.

—— (1958) Perspectives in the study of biological clocks. In "Perspectives in Marine Biology", 239–68. (A. A. Buzzati-Traverso, ed.) Scripps Institution of Oceanography, California.

—— and Bruce, V. G. (1957) An oscillator model for biological clocks. In "Rhythmic and Synthetic Processes in Growth", 75–109. (D. Rudnick, ed.) 15th Growth Symposium, Princeton University Press.

——, Bruce, V. and Kaus, P. (1958) On the significance of transients in daily rhythms. *Proc. nat. Acad. Sci. Wash.* **44**, 965–73.

Pitts, G. C. (1943) A diurnal rhythm in the blood sugar of the white rat. *Amer. J. Physiol.* **139**, 109–16.

Pohl, R. (1948) Tagesrhythmik im phototaktischen Verhalten der *Euglena gracilis. Z. Naturf.* **3b**, 367–74.

Pradhan, S. (1945) Rate of insect development under variable temperatures of the field. *Proc. nat. Inst. Sci. India,* **11**, 73–80.

—— (1946) Insect population studies. IV.—Dynamics of temperature effect on insect development. *Proc. nat. Inst. Sci. India,* **12**, 385–404.

Precht, H. (1958) Concepts of temperature adaptation of unchanging reaction systems of cold-blooded animals. In "Physiological Adaptation", 50–78. (C. L. Prosser, ed.) American Physiological Society, Washington.

——, Christophersen, J. and Hensel, H. (1958) "Temperatur und Leben". Springer, Berlin.

Ralph, C. L. (1957) Persistent rhythms of activity and O$_2$-consumption in the earthworm. *Physiol. Zoöl.* **30**, 41–55.

Ramanathan, O. (1932) Light and sexual periodicity in Indian buffaloes. *Nature, Lond.* **130**, 169–70.

Ranson, S. W. (1939) Somnolence caused by hypothalamic lesions in the monkey. *Arch. Neurol. Phychiat., Lond.* **41**, 1–23.

Rao, K. P. (1954) Tidal rhythmicity of rate of water propulsion in *Mytilus,* and its modifiability by transplantation. *Biol. Bull. Woods Hole,* **106**, 353–9.

Ratner, S. C. and Ringer, R. K. (1959) An activity cage and recorder for domestic fowl. *Anim. Behav.* **7**, 245–7.

Rau, P. (1938) Additional observations on the sleep of insects. *Ann. ent. Soc. Amer.* **31**, 540–57.

—— and Rau, N. (1916) The sleep of insects: an ecological study. *Ibid.* **9**, 227–74.

—— (1929) The sex attraction and rhythmic periodicity in giant saturniid moths. *Trans. Acad. Sci. St. Louis*, **26**, 81–221.

Reichle, F. (1943) Untersuchungen über Frequenzrhythmen bei Ameisen. *Z. vergl. Physiol.* **30**, 227–51.

Reinberg, A. and Ghata, J. (1957) "Rhythmes et Cycles Biologiques". Presses universitaires de France, Paris.

Remmert, H. (1955) Untersuchungen über das tageszeitlich gebundene Schlüpfen von *Pseudosmittia arenaria* (Dipt., Chironomidae) *Z. vergl. Physiol.* **37**, 338–54.

Renner, M. (1955) Ein Transozeanversuch zum Zeitsinn der Honigbiene. *Naturwissenschaften*, **42**, 540–1.

Ribbands, C. R. (1953) "The Behaviour and Social Life of Honey-bees". Bee Research Association, London.

Richter, C. P. (1933) The role played by the thyroid gland in the production of gross bodily activity. *Endocrinology*, **17**, 73–87.

—— and Wislocki, G. (1930) Anatomical and behaviour changes produced by the rat by complete and partial extirpation of the pituitary gland. *Amer. J. Physiol.* **95**, 481–92.

Riley, C. F. C. (1925) Some aspects of the general ecology and behaviour of the water-strider, *Gerris rufoscutellatus*, Latreille III. *Ent. Rec.* **37**, 107–14.

Robertson, A. G. (1939) The nocturnal activity of crane-flies. *J. Anim. Ecol.* **8**, 300–22.

Rockwood, L. P. (1925) On night flying and attraction to light in Acrididae and the relation of meteorological conditions thereto. *Pan-Pacif. Ent.* **2**, 36–8.

Rose, M. (1925) Contribution à l'étude de la biologie du plankton: le problème des migrations verticales journalières. *Arch. Zool. exp. gen.* **64**, 387–542.

Rothmann, H. (1923) Zusammenfassender Bericht über den Rothmarnschen grosshunlosen Hund nach klinischer und anatomischer Untersuchung. *Z. ges. Neurol. Psychiat.* **87**, 247–313.

Rowan, W. (1926) On photoperiodism, reproductive periodicity, and the annual migrations of birds and certain fishes. *Proc. Boston Soc. nat. Hist.* **38**, 147–89.

—— (1929) Experiments in bird migration. I.—Manipulation of the reproductive cycle: seasonal histological changes in the gonads. *Ibid.* **39**, 151–208.

*Russell, F. S. (1927) The vertical distribution of plankton in the sea. *Biol. Rev.* **2**, 213–63.

Sand, A. (1938) The function of the ampullae of Lorenzini, with some observations on the effect of temperature on sensory rhythms. *Proc. roy. Soc.* **125**, 524–53.

Sandeen, M. I., Stephens, G. C. and Brown, F. A., Jr. (1954) Persistent daily and tidal rhythms of oxygen consumption in two species of marine snails. *Physiol. Zool.* **27**, 350–6.

Sanderson, E. D. (1910) The relations of temperature to the growth of insects. *J. econ. Ent.* **3**, 113–39.

Sargent, F. (1955) An application of statistics. *Science*, **121**, 402.

Sauer, E. G. F. (1958) Celestial navigation in birds. *Sci. Amer.* **199** (2) 42–7.

Sauer, F. and Sauer, E. (1955) Zur Frage der nachtlichten Zugorientierung von Grasmücken. *Rev. suisse Zool.* **62**, 250–9.

Scherbaum, O. and Zeuthen, E. (1954) Induction of synchronous cell division in mass cultures of *Tetrahymena pyriformis*. *Exp. Cell Res.* **6**, 221–7.

Schmidt-Nielsen, B. and Schmidt-Nielsen, K. (1950) Evaporative water loss in desert rodents in their natural habitat. *Ecology*, **31**, 75–85.

Schuett, J. F. (1934) Studies in mass physiology: the activity of goldfish under different conditions of aggregation. *Ibid.* **15**, 258–62.

Schwartz, M. N., Kaplan, N. O. and Frech, M. E. (1956) Significance of "heat-activated" enzymes. *Science*, **123**, 50–3.

Scott, W. N. (1936) An experimental analysis of the factors governing the hour of emergence of adult insects from their pupae. *Trans. R. ent. Soc. Lond.* **85**, 303–30.

Shelford, V. E. (1927) An experimental investigation of the relations of the codling moth to weather and climate. *Bull. Ill. nat. Hist. Survey*, **16**, 307–440.

—— (1929) "Laboratory and Field Ecology". Williams and Wilkins, Baltimore, and Bailliere, London.

Shipton, H. W., Emde, J. W. and Folk, G. E. Jr. (1959) A multiple point recorder of small animal locomotory activity. *Proc. Iowa Acad. Sci.* **66**, 407–12.

Siivonen, L. and Koskimies, J. (1955) Population fluctuations and the lunar cycle. *Pap. Game-Res. Helsingf.* **14**, 1–10.

*Solomon, M. E. (1949) The natural control of animal populations. *J. Anim. Ecol.* **18**, 1–35.

Southern, H. N. (1942) Periodicity of refection in the wild rabbit. *Nature, Lond.* **149**, 553.

*—— (1954) (Ed.) "Control of Rats and Mice. 3-House Mice". Oxford University Press.

——, Watson, J. S. and Chitty, D. (1946) Watching nocturnal animals by infra-red radiation. *J. Anim. Ecol.* **15**, 198–202.

Spencer, W. P. (1939) Diurnal activity in fresh-water fishes. *Ohio. J. Sci.* **39**, 119–32.

Spoor, W. A. (1941) A method for measuring the activity of fishes. *Ecology,* **22**, 329–331.

—— (1946) A quantitative study of the relationship between the activity of oxygen consumption of the goldfish, and its application to the measurement of respiratory metabolism in fishes. *Biol. Bull. Woods Hole,* **91**, 312–25.

Stauber, L. A. (1939) Factors influencing the asexual periodicity of avian malarias. *J. Parasit.* **25**, 95–116.

Stephens, G. C. (1955) Induction of moulting in the crayfish, *Cambarus* by modification of daily photoperiod. *Biol. Bull. Woods Hole,* **108**, 235–41.

—— (1957a) Influence of temperature fluctuations on the diurnal melanophore rhythm of the fiddler crab, *Uca. Physiol. Zool.* **30**, 55–69.

—— (1957b) Twenty-four hour cycles in marine organisms. *Amer. Nat.* **91**, 135–51.

——, Sandeen, M. I. and Webb, H. M. (1953) A persistent tidal rhythm of activity in the mud snail, *Nassa obsoleta. Anat. Rec.* **117**, 635.

Stewart, C. C. (1898) Variations in daily activity with description of recording methods. *Amer. J. Physiol.* **1**, 40–56.

Suda, I., Koizumi, K. and Brooks, C. McC. (1956) Effects of cooling on central nervous system responses. *Fed. Proc.* **15**, 182.

Swann, M. M. (1957) The control of cell division: A review. I.—General mechanisms. *Cancer Res.* **17**, 727–58.

—— (1958) *Idem.* II.—Special mechanisms. *Ibid.* **18**, 1118–60.

Sweeney, B. M. and Hastings, J. W. (1958) Rhythmic cell division in populations of *Gonyaulax polyedra. J. Protozool.* **5**, 217–24.

Szymanski, J. S. (1914) Eine Methode zur Untersuchung der Ruhe—und Aktivitätsperioden bei Tieren. *Pflüg. Arch. ges. Physiol.* **158**, 343–85.

—— (1918a) Abhandlungen zum Aufbau der Lehre von den Handlungen der Tiere. *Ibid.* **170**, 1–244.

—— (1918b) Die Verteilung von Ruhe- und Aktivitätsperioden bei einigen Tierarten. *Ibid.* **172**, 430–48.

Taylor, L. R. (1951) An improved suction trap for insects. *Ann. appl. Biol.* **38**, 582–91.

—— and Kalmus, H. (1954) Dawn and dusk flight of *Drosophila subobscura* Collin. *Nature, Lond.* **174**, 221.

Tembrock, G. (1958) Zur Aktivitätsperiodik bei *Vulpes* und *Alopex. Zool. Jb. Phys.* **68**, 297–324.

*Thorpe, W. H. (1956) "Learning and Instinct in Animals". Methuen, London.

*Tinbergen, N. (1951) "The Study of Instinct". Oxford University Press, London.

Tretzel, E. (1955) Intragenerische Isolation und interspazifische Konkurrenz bei Spinnen. *Z. Morph. Ökol. Tiere*, **44**, 43–162.

Tsang, Y. (1938) Hunger motivation in gastrectomized rats. *J. comp. Psychol.* **26**, 1–17.

*Uvarov, P. B. (1931) Insects and climate. *Trans. R. ent. Soc. Lond.* **79**, 1–247.

Vachon, M. (1952) "Études sur les Scorpions". Institut Pasteur d'Algérie, Algiers.

—— (1953) The biology of scorpions. *Endeavour*, **12**, 80–9.

van der Pol, B. (1926) On relaxation oscillations. *Phil. Mag.* (7) **2**, 978–92.

—— (1940) Biological rhythms considered as relaxation oscillations. *Acta. med. scand. Suppl.* **108**, 76–88.

Volterra, V. (1926) Variazione e fluttuazioni del numero d'individui in specie animali conviventi. *Mem. Accad. Lincei* (6) **2**, 31–113.

—— (1931) Variations and fluctuations of the number of individuals in animal species, living together. In "Animal Ecology", 409–48. (R. N. Chapman) McGraw-Hill, New York.

von Frisch, K. (1950) Die Sonne als Kompass im Leben der Bienen. *Experientia*, **6**, 210–21.

—— (1952) Die Richtungsorientierung der Bienen. *Verh. dtsch. Zool. Freiburg*, **1952**, 58–72.

——(1954) "The Dancing Bees. An account of the life and senses of the honey-bee". Methuen, London.

von Stein-Beling, I. (1935) Über das Zeitgedächtniss bei Tieren. *Biol. Rev.* **10**, 18–41.

Wahl, O. (1932) Neue Untersuchungen über das Zeitgedächtnis der Bienen. *Z. vergl. Physiol.* **16**, 529–89.

*Walls, G. L. (1942) "The Vertebrate Eye and its Adaptive Radiation". University of Michigan Press, Chicago.

Waloff, N. (1941) The mechanisms of humidity reactions of terrestrial isopods. *J. exp. Biol.* **18**, 115–35.

Webb, H. M. (1950) Diurnal variations of response to light in the fiddler crab, *Uca. Physiol. Zool.* **23**, 315–37.

Weber, N. A. (1952) The 1952 animal behaviour eclipse expedition of the College of Arts and Science. *Baghdad Coll. Arts Sci. Publ.* No. 2, 1–23.

Wells, G. P. (1937) Studies on the physiology of *Arenicola marina* L. I. The pace-maker role of the oesophagus and the action of adrenaline and acetylcholine. *J. exp. Biol.* **14**, 117–57.

—— (1949a) Respiratory movements of *Arenicola marina* L.: intermittent irrigation of the tube, and intermittent aerial respiration. *J. Mar. biol. Ass. U.K.* **28**, 447–64.

—— (1949b) The behaviour of *Arenicola marina* L. in sand, and the role of spontaneous activity cycles. *Ibid.* **28**, 465–78.

—— (1950) Spontaneous activity cycles in polychaete worms. In "Physiological Mechanisms in Animal Behaviour", 127–42. (J. F. Danielli and R. Brown, eds.) *Symp. Soc. exp. Biol.* IV. Cambridge.

—— (1951) On the behaviour of *Sabella. Proc. roy. Soc.* **B138**, 278–99.

—— (1952) The respiratory significance of the crown in the polychaete worms *Sabella* and *Myxicola. Ibid.* **B140**, 70–82.

—— (1953) Defaecation in relation to the spontaneous activity cycles of *Arenicola marina* L. *J. Mar. biol. Ass. U.K.* **32**, 51–63.

Wells, G. P. (1955) "The Sources of Animal Behaviour". H. K. Lewis, London.

—— and Albrecht, E. B. (1951a) The integration of activity cycles in the behaviour of *Arenicola marina*, L. *J. exp. Biol.* **28**, 41–50.

—— and Albrecht, E. B. (1951b) The role of oesophageal rhythms in the behaviour of *Arenicola ecaudata* Johnston. *Ibid.* **28**, 51–6.

—— and Dales, R. P. (1951) Spontaneous activity patterns in animal behaviour: the irrigation of the burrow in the polychaetes *Chaetopterus variopedatus* Renier and *Nereis diversicolor* O. F. Müller. *J. Mar. biol. Ass. U.K.* **29**, 661–80.

—— and Ledingham, I. C. (1940) Studies in the physiology of *Arenicola marina* L. II.—Accommodation to magnesium concentration in the isolated extrovert. *J. exp. Biol.* **17**, 353–62.

Welsh, J. H. (1930) Diurnal rhythm of the distal pigment cells in the eyes of certain crustaceans. *Proc. nat. Acad. Sci.* **16**, 386–95.

—— (1935) Further evidence of a diurnal rhythm in the movement of pigment cells in the eyes of crustaceans. *Biol. Bull.* **68**, 247–53.

—— (1936) Diurnal movements of the eye pigments of *Anchistioides*. *Ibid.* **70**, 217–27.

*—— (1938) Diurnal rhythms. *Quart. Rev. Biol.* **13**, 123–39.

—— (1941) The sinus gland and twenty-four hour cycles of retinal pigment migration in crayfish. *J. exp. Zool.* **86**, 35–49.

—— and Osborn, C. M. (1937) Diurnal changes in the retina of the catfish *Ameiurus nebulosus*. *J. comp. Neurol.* **66**, 349–59.

——, Chace, F. A. Jr. and Nunnemacher, R. F. (1937) The diurnal migration of deep-water animals. *Biol. Bull.* **73**, 185–96.

Wheeler, J. F. G. and Brown, F. A. (1936) The periodic swarming of *Anchistioides antiguensis* (Schmitt) (Crustacea, Decapoda) at Bermuda. *J. Linn. Soc. Lond.* (*Zool.*) **39**, 413–38.

Wheeler, W. M. (1913) "Ants: their Structure, Development and Behaviour". Columbia University Press, New York.

—— MacCoy, C. V., Grescom, L., Allen, G. M. and Collidge (1935) Observations on the behaviour of animals during the solar eclipse of August 31, 1932. *Proc. Amer. Acad. Sci.* **70**, 33–70.

Whitehouse, H. L. K. and Armstrong, E. A. (1953) Rhythms in the breeding behaviour of the European wren. *Behaviour*, **5**, 261–88.

*Wigglesworth, V. B. (1950) "The Principles of Insect Physiology". 4th Ed. Methuen, London.

Williams, C. B. (1935) The times of activity of certain nocturnal insects, chiefly Lepidoptera, as indicated by a light trap. *Trans. R. ent. Soc.* **85**, 523–55.

—— (1936) The influence of moonlight on the activity of certain nocturnal insects, particularly of the family Noctuidae, as indicated by a light trap. *Phil. Trans.* **B226**, 357–89.

—— (1954) Some bioclimatic observations in the Egyptian desert. In "Biology of Deserts", 18–27. (J. L. Cloudsley-Thompson, ed.) Institute of Biology, London.

——, Singh, B. P. and el Ziady, S. (1956) An investigation into the possible effects of moonlight on the activity of insects in the field. *Proc. R. ent. Soc. Lond.* (A) **31**, 135–44.

Williams, G. (1958) Mechanical time-sorting of pitfall captures. *J. Anim. Ecol.* **27**, 27–35.

Wolf, E. (1930) Die Aktivität der japanischen Tanzmaus und ihre rhythmische Verteilung. *Z. vergl. Physiol.* **11**, 321–44.

Wynne-Edwards, V. C. (1930) On the waking-time of the nightjar (*Caprimulgus e. europaeus*). *Brit. J. exp. Biol.* **7**, 241–7.

Young, J. Z. "Doubt and Certainty in Science". Oxford University Press.

Zeuthen, E. and Scherbaum, O. (1954) Synchronous divisions in mass cultures of the ciliate Protozoon *Tetrahymena pyriformis*, as induced by temperature changes. In "Cell Physiology", 141–56. (J. A. Kitching, ed.) Butterworths, London.

Author Index

A

Abramowitz, A. A., 149
Agren, G., 148
Albrecht, E. B., 168
Alexander, A. J., 39
Allee, W. C., 7, 38
Andrewartha, H. G., 98, 172
Arbit, J., 45
Armstrong, E. A., 76, 96, 102, 200
Arnould-Taylor, W. E., 139
Aschoff, J., 5, 7, 22, 104, 140, 144, 145, 146, 155, 156, 163, 164, 165, 166, 191

B

Backlund, H. O., 14
Bacq, Z. M., 148
Bailey, S. W., 21
Baker, I., 101, 105
Baker, J. R., 101, 103, 105, 106, 107
Baker, Z., 105
Baldwin, F. M., 45
Ball, N. G., 135
Barden, A., 63, 74, 163
Barnum, C. P., 141, 150, 198
Bateman, M. A., 125, 126
Beach, F. A., 150
Belding, D. L., 44
Beling, I., 115, 127, 128, 130
Bennett, M. F., 84, 85, 91, 109, 110, 113, 115, 116, 178
Bentley, E. W., 179
Bethe, A., 187
Bird, T. F., 106
Bissonette, T. H., 102, 103
Bittner, J. J., 141, 150, 198
Blake, G. M.. 100
Bletchly, J. D., 65
Bodenheimer, F. S., 60, 64
Bohn, G., 45, 82
Brehm, E., 66
Bremer, H., 65
Brereton, J. L., 54

Brett, W. J., 117, 121, 125
Brian, M. V., 19, 20, 66
Brooks, C. McC., 183
Browman, L. G., 7, 146, 179
Brown, F. A., Jr., 5, 81, 82, 83, 84, 85, 91, 109, 110, 111, 112, 113, 114, 115, 116, 117, 118, 126, 141, 159, 160, 161, 162, 177, 178
Brown, R. A., 24
Browne, L. B., 95
Bruce, V. G., 5, 7, 42, 119, 125, 131, 158, 180, 184, 190, 193
Bruce-Chwatt, L. J., 70
Bruns, H., 66
Buck, J. B., 67
Bünning, E., 126, 135, 136, 137, 159, 162, 178, 180, 181, 184, 190, 191, 193
Bullock, T. H., 184
Bullough, W. S., 90, 93, 102, 106
Burrows, W., 87
Busnel, R.-G., 14
Buxton, P. A., 41, 58, 60

C

Cable, R. M., 174, 176
Calhoun, J. B., 3, 8, 24, 42, 45, 46, 74, 76, 85, 140, 158
Carpenter, J. R., 8
Carter, G. S., 27, 34
Caspers, H., 85, 87, 91, 92, 120
Chace, F. A., Jr., 48
Chapman, R. N., 23, 174
Chauvin, R., 18, 19
Chitty, D., 11
Christophersen, J., 183
Cicero, 86
Clark, A. H., 40
Clark, F. N., 90
Cloudsley-Thompson, J. L., 4, 5, 7, 17, 18, 19, 34, 40, 41, 51, 52, 53, 54, 55, 56, 57, 58, 59, 60, 61, 62, 63, 64, 67, 70, 121, 126, 131, 132, 155, 158, 159, 164, 165, 170, 177, 179

225

Cole, L. C., 114, 115
Cook, W. C., 173
Corbet, P. S., 65, 67, 70, 91, 99, 100
Cott, H. B., 74
Crawford, S. C., 39
Crawshay, L. R., 88
Cresswell, E., 15
Crowcroft, P., 7, 78
Cushing, D. H., 47, 49
Cuvier, Baron, 47

D

D'Aguillar, J., 17, 18, 19, 66
Dainton, B. H., 46, 179
Dales, R. P., 169
Danielli, J. F., 193
Dawson, R. W., 174
Dehnel, P. A., 95
Destouches, L., 173
Dice, L. R., 47, 48
Drzewina, A., 82
Dunning, R. A., 65
Dyke, I. J., 135
Dyson-Hudson, V. R. D., 70

E

Eastop, V. F., 71
Edney, E. B., 51, 53, 55, 61
Ekerood, S., 14
Elton, C., 34
el Ziady, S., 72, 91
Emde, J. W., 15
Emerson, A. E., 7, 38
Engstrom, H., 148
Epling, C., 70
Everett, J. W., 150, 151
Everly, R. T., 19, 20, 61
Ewer, D. W., 179
Eyden, D., 48
Eyster, M. B., 96

F

Fauré-Fremiet, E., 25
Fingerman, M., 83, 84, 85, 90, 111, 112, 160, 171
Floersheim, C., 39
Folk, G. E., 6, 7, 15, 140, 142, 144, 146, 151, 152, 153, 162
Forel, A., 126, 127
Fox, H. M., 48, 86, 87, 91
Fraps, R. M., 139

Frech, M. E., 183
Freeland, R. O., 113, 117
French, L. A., 141

G

Gamble, F. W., 81, 86
Gaul, A. T., 66
Gause, G. F., 32, 33
Ghata, J., 24
Ghidini, G. M., 15, 16, 19
Gibson, N. H. E., 69
Gillett, J. D., 69, 70
Godfrey, G. K., 11, 79
Gompel, M., 82
Gooddy, W., 9, 191, 192
Grabensberger, W., 128, 129, 130, 131, 132
Gray, Sir James, 29, 30
Greve, H., 69
Griffin, D. R., 137
Grindeland, R. E., 162
Gully, R. J., 141
Gunn, A. L., 22, 92
Gunn, D. L., 5, 16, 19, 22, 31, 63, 92, 179
Guyselman, J. B., 15, 84, 113

H

Haddow, A. J., 12, 69, 70
Halberg, E., 198
Halberg, F., 5, 8, 141, 146, 150, 154, 198
Haldane, J. B. S., 25
Hammond, J. H., 19
Harder, W., 21
Hardy, A., 51
Harker, J. E., 5, 7, 45, 63, 67, 76, 132, 140, 147, 157, 158, 169, 170, 171, 187, 190, 191
Harris, J. E., 7, 49, 50
Harris, S. J., 119
Harrison, J. L., 93
Harrison, T. H., 106
Hartland-Rowe, R., 72, 91
Haskell, P. T., 14
Hastings, J. W., 185, 194, 195, 196
Hauenschild, C., 88
Hawking, F., 43, 44
Hawkins, S. E., 193
Headlee, T. J., 173, 175
Hediger, H., 77
Hemmingsen, A. M., 13, 142

Hempel, G., 21, 66
Hensel, H., 183
Higginbotham, A. C., 74
Hinman, E. H., 43
Hinton, H. E., 99, 100, 101
Hitchcock, L. F., 72
Hoagland, H., 187
Hoar, W. S., 96
Hoffman, K., 134, 137, 138, 161, 165
Holmgren, H., 142, 147, 148
Howe, R. W., 21

I

Ilse, D., 65

J

Janda, V., 63
Janisch, E., 173
Jenkin, P. M., 22, 92
Jennings, H. S., 31
Johnson, C. G., 12, 13, 71, 175
Johnson, M. S., 6, 116, 140, 143, 145, 157
Jores, A., 24
Jorpes, E., 148

K

Kachkarov, O. N., 58
Kalabukhov, N. I., 79
Kalmus, H., 24, 25, 42, 71, 74, 120, 123,
    128, 129, 132, 133
Kaplan, N. O., 183
Kaus, P., 125
Kayser, Ch., 75, 178
Keeble, F., 81, 86
Keller, J. G., 63
Kellerman, K. F., 101
Kendeigh, S. C., 200
Kennedy, C. H., 39, 40, 61
Kennedy, J. S., 16, 19, 65
Kerkut, G. A., 179
Kettle, D. S., 70
Kikuchi, K., 47
Kitching, J. A., 25, 26
Klauber, L. M., 75
Klein, H. J., 64
Kleitman, K., 155
Kleitman, N., 2, 3, 7, 132, 140, 141, 147,
    150, 153, 155
Koizumi, K., 183
Korovine, E. P., 58
Korringa, P., 87, 88, 89, 90

Koskimies, J., 34, 35, 36, 93
Kramer, G., 120, 137
Krarup, N. B., 13, 142
Kris, C., 189
Krumbiegel, I., 63

L

Lack, D., 34
Lagerspetz, K., 161
Lago, A. D., 160, 171
Lane, F. W., 119
Larsen, E. Bro., 18, 64, 68
Ledingham, I. C., 168
Lees, A. D., 72, 91, 98, 99
Leinweber, F. J., 135
Levinson, L., 149
Lewis, C. B., 65
Lewis, H. E., 80, 154
Lewis, P. R., 153, 154, 155
Linke, W., 175
Lobban, M. C., 153, 154, 155
Lockett, J. A., 63
Long, D. B., 68
Lotka, A. J., 197
Lowe, M. E., 85, 171
Ludwig, D., 173, 174, 176
Lumsden, W. H. R., 12, 69
Lutz, F. E., 20, 67

M

McCabe, J. B., 21
McClure, A. G., 68
McFadzean, J. A., 44
McGinnis, M. O., 47
Mahaffy, A. F., 69
Makings, P., 16
Malewski, A. M., 139
Manson-Bahr, P. H., 44
Marshall, A. J., 76, 103, 104, 106
Marshall, F. H. A., 92, 101, 102, 103,
    107
Marx, Ch., 75, 178
Mason, P., 50
Masterton, J. P., 80, 155
Matthews, G. V. T., 120, 137, 138
Mattingly, P. F., 69
Mayer, A. G., 29
Mazia, D., 197
Mellanby, K., 5, 62, 63
Meltzer, M. R., 162
Menaker, M., 152, 179

Meunier, K., 67
Meyer-Lohmann, J., 140, 146, 155, 156, 163, 164
Michal, K., 64
Mikulski, J. S., 175
Miller, R. S., 79, 97
Mills, J. N., 147
Milne, A., 72
Mitchell, D. F., 70
Mobberly, W. C., Jr., 85
Mori, S., 126, 158, 186, 187, 190
Mrciak, M., 63
Müller, H. J., 95
Muirhead-Thomson, R. C., 70
Mulherkar, L., 65
Myers, D. J., 63

N

Naylor, E., 84
Neal, E., 7
Newell, G., 88
Newport, G., 128, 186
Nicholson, A. J., 23
Nielsen, E. T., 11, 66
Norgaard, E., 72
Noüy, Lecomte du, 8
Nunnemacher, R. F., 48

O

Ondô, Y., 158
Osborn, C. M., 74

P

Palmén, E., 65, 120
Pantin, C. F. A., 29
Papi, F., 85, 133, 134, 135
Pardi, L., 85
Park, O., 3, 6, 7, 13, 14, 17, 38, 40, 63, 74, 75, 79, 119, 187
Park, T., 7, 38
Parker, G. H., 74
Parker, J. R., 174
Parkes, A. S., 102
Pavan, M., 15
Payne, N. M., 174
Peairs, L. M., 173
Perttunen, V., 94, 161
Piéron, H., 82
Pittendrigh, C. S., 5, 7, 42, 113, 115, 119, 120, 121, 122, 123, 124, 125, 131, 135, 157, 158, 159, 164, 180, 184, 185, 190, 191, 193, 200

Pitts, G. C., 147
Pliny, 86
Pohl, R., 42
Pradham, S., 176
Precht, H., 183

R

Ralph, C. L., 45, 113, 117, 141
Ramanathan, O., 92
Ranson, S. W., 101, 103, 150
Rao, K. P., 82, 83
Ratner, S. C., 14
Rau, N., 61
Rau, P., 61
Reichle, F., 130
Reinberg, A., 24
Remmert, H., 126
Renner, M., 115, 116
Ribbands, C. R., 127, 130
Richter, C. P., 149
Riley, C. F. C., 41
Ringer, R. K., 14
Roberts, T. W., 119
Robertson, A. G., 68
Rockwood, L. P., 41
Roosevelt, 7
Rose, M., 47, 48
Rothmann, H., 150
Rowan, W., 102, 103
Russell, F. S., 47, 49, 50

S

Sand, A., 180
Sandeen, M. I., 82, 83, 91, 109, 110, 111, 112, 113, 178
Sanderson, E. D., 172
Sankey, J. H. P., 70
Sargent, F., 2
Sauer, E., 138
Sauer, E. G. F., 138
Sauer, F., 138
Sawyer, C. H., 150, 151
Schellinger, R. R., 151
Scherbaum, O., 192, 193
Schmidt-Nielsen, B., 76
Schmidt-Nielsen, K., 76
Schuett, J. F., 73
Schwartz, M. N., 183
Scott, W. N., 121, 179, 190
Sejba, O., 63
Serretti, L., 135

Shelford, V. E., 173
Shipton, H. W., 15
Shriner, J., 84, 141
Siivonen, L., 35, 36, 93
Silber, R. H., 141
Singh, B. P., 72, 91
Solomon, M. E., 23
Southern, H. N., 11, 78, 79
Spencer, W. P., 20, 73
Spoor, W. A., 20
Stauber, L. A., 42, 43
Stephens, G. C., 6, 7, 8, 82, 83, 94, 95,
    159, 160, 177, 178, 200
Stewart, C. C., 14
Strohecker, H. F., 63
Suda, I., 183
Swann, M. M., 192, 193
Sweeney, B. M., 194, 195, 196
Swensson, Å., 142
Szymanski, J. S., 2, 16, 19, 45, 63, 73, 74

T

Taylor, B. J. R., 179
Taylor, L. R., 13, 71
Tembrook, G., 96
Thorpe, W. H., 73, 158, 200
Thurston, J. P., 43
Tinbergen, N., 103
Tjønneland, A., 67, 91
Tretzel, E., 94
Tsang, Y., 148

U

Uvarov, P. B., 72, 172

V

Vachon, M., 59

van der Pol, B., 23, 187, 188, 189
Visscher, M. B., 141, 150
Volterra, V., 23, 32
von Frisch, K., 128, 132
von Stein-Beling, I., 120

W

Wahl, O., 128
Walhfart, G., 148
Walls, G. L., 74, 75, 76, 78
Waloff, N., 56
Walsh, B. M., 31
Watson, J. S., 11
Webb, H. M., 82, 83, 91, 109, 110, 111,
    112, 113, 115, 116, 117, 160, 162,
    177, 178
Weber, N. A., 186
Wells, G. P., 166, 167, 168, 169, 200
Welsh, J. H., 3, 7, 48, 74, 108, 149
Wheeler, J. F. G., 63, 82, 186
Whitehouse, H. L. K., 76, 96, 200
Wigglesworth, V. B., 172
Wilander, O., 148
Williams, C. B., 41, 58, 72, 91
Williams, E., 63, 74
Williams, G., 13
Wislocki, G., 149
Wolf, E., 97, 143, 144
Wolfe, U. K., 7, 49
Woods, L. P., 13, 63
Wynne-Edwards, V. C., 91

Y

Young, J. Z., 30

Z

Zeuthen, E., 192, 193

Subject Index

A

Acanthozostera gemmata, 89
Accipiters, 103, 106
Acrididae (see also under species), 20, 41,
    61, 67, 171, 174
Actinia equina, 45, 82
Actinozoa, 29, 45, 82
Adesmia, 60
adrenal, 148, 150, 155
Aedes aegypti, 70, 175
A. africanus, 69–70
A. cantans, 69
A. simpsoni, 69
A. variegatus, 44
Agriotes obscurus, 66
Agroeca brunnea, 94
A. proxima, 94
Agrolimax reticulatus, 46
aktograph, 13–21
algae, 181
'all or nothing' law, 29, 191
Alopex lagopus, 96
Amaurobius, 121
A. ferox, 57, 131, 179
A. similis, 57
Ambloplites rupestris, 73
Ameiurus melas, 73
A. nebulosus, 74
Amoeba, 26, 193
A. proteus, 193
amphibians (see also under species), 74–5
Amphitrite ornata, 89
ampullae of Lorenzini, 180
Anax imperator, 99
Anchistioides antiguensis, 82
Androctonus australis, 59
Anolis frenatus, 75
Anseres, 103, 106
Anthia venator, 132
Anthrenus verbasci, 100
antigen, 25
ant, 41, 63, 64, 79, 129–31
Apodemus flavicollis, 79

A. sylvaticus, 79
Arachnida (see also under species), 52,
    57–61
Arctosa perita, 134
Arenicola (see lug-worms)
A. ecaudata, 169
A. marina, 88, 166–9
Armadillidium vulgare, 55–6, 58
auditory aktograph, 14
Avena, 135

B

Badger, 7, 119
Baetis rhodeni, 67
Basiliscus basiliscus, 75
bat, 93, 105–6, 151–3, 179
bean, 135–7, 181, 193
bear, 77
bed-bug, 62
bee, 115, 116, 126–9, 187
beetle, 17, 20, 41, 60, 63, 64, 66, 67,
    173–5, 179, 186
birds (see also under species), 34–7, 75–6,
    101–7, 119, 120, 137–9, 150
Blaniulus guttulatus, 52, 176
Blatta orientalis, 3
blowfly, 2, 173
Bombyx mori, 101
Boophilus microplus, 72
brain, 150, 191–2
Branchipus serratus, 47
breeding cycle, 85–91, 101–7
bristle-tail, 39
budgerigar, 101
buffalo, 40–1, 77, 92
Bufo americanus, 74
B. fowleri, 74
B. marinus, 70
Buthus occitanus, 59
butterfly, 39, 174

C

Calliactis parasitica, 29

Callinectes sapidus, 84, 110
Calliphora, 2
Cambarellus shufeldti, 16
Cambaroides japonicus, 186
Cambarus bartoni, 108
C. pellucidus, 119
C. virilis, 84, 95, 113
Camnula pellucida, 174
capercailzie, 93
Caprimulgus europaeus, 91
Carabidae, 39, 63, 66
Carabus nemoralis, 63
Carassius auratus, 73, 96
C. vulgaris, 183
Carcinus maenas, 84
Carpocapsa pomonella, 173
Cassiopea, 28
cat, 119
cattle, 15, 119
Cavernularia obesa, 158
cells, periodicity in, 25–7, 192–8
centipede, 41, 51–6, 59, 60
Centrechinus setosus, 86
Ceratocephale osawai, 89
Ceriagrion tenellum, 100
Chaetopleura apiculata, 89
Chaetopterus variopedatus, 169
Chaoborus crystallinus, 69
Charadriiformes, 103, 106
Chironomidae, 65, 68–9, 120, 126, 189
Chironomus dorsalis, 68
Chloris chloris, 155
Chlorizagrotis auxiliaris, 173
chromatophore, 72, 74, 84–5, 108 et seq,
    132, 159–61, 178
cilia, 27
Cimex lectularius, 62, 175
civet, 76
Clethrionomys glareolus, 79
Clibanarius misanthropus, 82
Clunio marinus, 120
Cnemidophorus sexlineatus, 75, 163
cockroach, 3, 4, 7, 39, 61, 63, 99, 131,
    169–71, 176, 178, 179, 187, 190
codling moth, 173
Coelenterata (see also under species), 45
Coelotes atropos, 94
C. inermis, 94
Coenagrion mercuriale, 100
Colorado beetle, 66
communities, periodicities in, 32–3

contractile vacuole, 25–7, 189
controlled temperature cycles, 21
Convoluta roscoffensis, 45, 81, 86
Coraciiformes, 103, 106
Corethra plumicornis, 161
Corvus corone, 186
crane-fly, 68
crayfish (see also under species), 2, 15,
    179
Crassostrea virginica, 85
cricket, 20, 39, 67, 158, 187, 194
crow, 102, 186
Crustacea (see also under species), 49,
    108 et seq.
ctenophore, 27
Culex fatigans, 44
Culicoides impunctatus, 70
Cyprinus carpis, 73

D

Dacus tryoni, 125
Daphnia magna, 49–50
D. pulex, 47–8
Dectus verrucivorus, 67
deer, 102
desert, 41, 57–9, 76–7
diapause, 38, 91, 97–101, 120, 172
Dicaelus purpuratus, 63
Dictynidae, 61
Didinium nasutum, 32
Dipodymys, 76
Diptera (see flies), 187
Dirofilaria immitis, 43
Discophrya, 26
DNA, 198
dog, 107, 150
dogfish, 30
Drosophila, 6, 7, 135, 159, 194
D. melanogaster, 71, 121, 126, 174, 190
D. obscura, 70–1
D. pseudo-obscura, 70–1, 115, 120, 121–5
D. subobscura, 70–1
Dysderidae, 61

E

Earthworm, 2, 45–6
Ecdyonurus torrentis, 67
Echinoid larva, 48
eclipse, solar, 128, 186–7
Elasmobranch, 180
electrocorticogram, 183

elephant, 40, 77
emigration, 33–7
Enchelyopus cimbrus, 89
eosinophil rhythm, 141–2, 146–7
Ephestia (=*Anagasta*) *kühniella*, 121, 179
Eptesicus fuscus, 179
Euglena gracilis, 42, 180, 193
Eunice fucata, 89, 90
E. viridis, 89
Eupomotis gibbus, 73
Euscelis plebyus, 95
Euscorpius germanus, 59
eye, 71, 74, 76–8

F

Ferret, 102
fiddler crab (see *Uca*), 7, 72, 84–5, 109–
   16, 159–62, 177, 178
Filistata insidiatrix, 72
fire-fly, 67
fish, 20, 21, 73–4, 96, 180, 183
Flagellates, 51
fly (see *Drosophila*), 2, 14, 40, 44, 173, 186
Forficula auricularia, 94
Formica fusca, 129
F. rufa, 66
Fourier analysis, 22
fox, 96
frog, 30, 74
Fulmarus glacialis, 76

G

Galleria melonella, 173
gecko, 75
Geiger–Müller counter, 11
gene, 24
Geomyda amulata, 75
Geotrupes stercorarius, 186
Gerris rufoscutellatus, 41
Glaucomys, 77
Glossina, 40
Glossiphonia stagnalis, 45
glycogen rhythm, 148
goatsucker, 76, 92
Gonyaulax polyedra, 42, 194–8
Graafian follicles, 15
Grallae, 103, 106
greenfinch, 155
grasshopper (see also under species), 20,
   41, 61, 67, 171, 174
ground squirrel, 151–3, 155, 162

grunion, 89, 90
Gryllus campestris, 158, 164
guinea-pig, 156

H

Haematopota crassicornis, 70
H. pluvialis, 70
hamster, 140, 151–3, 156, 162
heart, 188, 191
Hemigrapsus nudus, 95
H. oregonensis, 95
Hemilepistus reaumuri, 55–6, 59
hen, 139
Heptagenia lateralis, 67
Herodiones, 103, 106
heron, 76
herring, 47
hibernation, 152–3, 162
hippopotamus, 40
honeybee, 115, 116, 126–9, 187
horse, 78
horse-fly, 40, 44
Huro salmoides, 73
Hyla arborea, 74, 186
Hymenoptera (see also under species), **13**
hypothalamus, 102, 105, 147, 150, 155

I

Ichthyometer, 20–1
Ilyanassa obsoleta, 82, 177
independence of rhythms, 159–61
insects (see also under species), 52–73
infra-red observation of rats, 11
inter-neural facilitation, 28
irruptions, 33–7
Ixodes ricinus, 72

J

Jerboa, 76–7
Junco hyemalis, 96, 102

K

Kangaroo rat, 76–7
kidney, 152, 154
klinokinesis, 31–2

L

Lacerta agilis, 75, 178
L. muralis, 75, 178
Lasius niger, 129–30
leech, 45

lemming, 33–7
lemur, 40
Leodoce fucata, 88
Lepidoptera (see also under species), 187
Lepomis pallidus, 73
Leptinotarsa decemlineata, 66
Leptohylemyia coarctata, 68
Leuresthes tenuis, 89, 90
Ligia baudiniana, 132
L. oceanica, 53
lion, 77, 78
Littorina, 45
L. littorea, 83
L. neritoides, 89
L. rudis, 82
lizard, 41, 75, 163, 165, 178
Loa loa, 44
Locusta migratoria, 61–2, 121
Lumbricus terrestris (see earthworm), 45–6
lug-worm (see *Arenicola*), 88, 166–9, 200
Lysidice oele, 89
lynx, 34
Lycosa amentata, 94
L. pullata, 94
L. tarsalis, 94

M

Mabuya mabuya, 75
malarial parasite, 42–3
mammalian activity recorder, 13
man, 77, 79–80, 92, 107, 141, 146, 147, 153–5
may-fly, 67
maze recorder, 14
medusa, 45
melanophore—see chromatophore
Melanoplus atlantis, 174
M. differentialis, 61
M. mexicanus, 174
Melolontha melolontha, 67
Melopsittacus undulatus, 101
menstruation, 92
Messor semirufus, 64
metachronal rhythm, 27
Metatetranychus ulmi, 99
Metriocnemus, 68
micro-aktograph, 17–20
microclimate, 76
microfilaria, 43–5
Microtus, 79
M. agrestis, 11

migration, 105
millipede (see also under species), 7, 17, 40, 51–6, 60, 94, 165, 176, 179
Miniopterus, 92
M. australis, 106
mite, 41, 99, 175
mitosis, 192, 193, 197, 198
mole, 78–9
Mollusca, 46
mongoose, 60
monkey, 43, 119, 150
mosquito (see also under species), 11, 12, 68–70, 175
moth (see also under species), 16, 63, 71, 173
mouse (see also under species), 7, 78–9, 97, 140, 141, 145, 155, 164
Mus wagneri, 97, 143
Musca domestica, 64
Myotis bicifugus, 179
Myrmecocystus mexicanus, 63
Myrmica laevinodis, 129
M. rubida, 130
Mysicola infundibulum, 169
Mytilus, 86
M. californianus, 82–3
M. edulis, 82–3
M. variabilis, 86

N

Navigation, 76, 137–9, 182
Nembutal, 151
Neomys fodiens, 78
Neptunus pelagicus, 86
Nereis diversicolor, 45, 82, 169
N. japonica, 89
nerve-net, 28–9
nervous conduction, 28–31
neuro-muscular facilitation, 29
nightjar, 76, 92
Noctuid moth, 63–4, 71

O

Odontosyllis enopla, 88, 89
O. hyalina, 89
O. phosphorea, 89
Oniscus asellus, 52–6, 58
Ophistreptus, 52, 165, 176
opossum, 77
Orchestia, 186
Orconectes clypeatus, 160

organisms, periodicity in, 31–2
Oribatid mite, 13
Ostrea edulis, 88, 89
O. virginica, 113
oviposition rhythms, 68
owl, 34, 76
Oxidus gracilis, 52, 176
Oxydesmus platycercus, 52, 176
oyster, 85, 86, 88–9, 113

P

Pachycephala pectoralis, 106
palolo, 87–8
pancreas, 147–8
Pandinus imperator, 60
Paramoecium, 25, 31–3, 42, 48
P. aurelia, 33
P. caudatum, 32
Passer domesticus, 96
Passeres, 103, 106
pectines, 59–60
Pedetes, 7
Pegomyia betae, 65
penguin, 107
Perca flavescens, 73
Periplaneta americana, 3, 4, 99, 131, 169–71, 176, 178, 179, 182
P. australasiae, 176
Peritrich ciliate, 25–7
Peromyscus leucopus, 140, 143–5
Phaseolus multiflorus, 135–7, 181, 193
Philoscia muscorum, 55–6, 58
Photinus pyralis, 67
Physa, 27
Pieris, 52
pitfall trap, 13
pituitary, 74, 102, 105, 139, 147 et seq.
plankton, 41, 46–51, 73
plant rhythm, 135–7
Plasmodium cathemerium, 42–3
P. relictum, 42
Platycercus venustus, 101
Platynereis dumerilii, 88–90
P. megalops, 89
Plusia gamma, 64
Poephila gouldiae, 102
Polychrosis botrana, 101
Popillia japonica, 173
Porcellio scaber, 52–6, 58
Porosagrotis orthogonia, 173
potato, 113, 117

Povilla adusta, 91
Prodenia lituria, 173
Proteus vulgaris, 184
Protofucellia syuitimorii, 186
Pseudosmittia arenaria, 126
Pteropus geddici, 105
Pterostichus vulgaris, 66
Ptinus tectus, 179
pupal emergence, 6, 7, 65, 120–6
Putonius vulgaris, 102
Pyrrhosoma nymphula, 65

Q

Q_{10}, 177 et seq, 195

R

Rabbit, 39, 79
rangemeter, 15
rat, 7, 11, 14, 60, 93, 140, 141–56, 164, 179
Rattus, 93
R. norvegica, 11
refection, 78–9
refractory period, 28
relaxation oscillation, 23, 24–5, 187–9
reptile (see also under species), 74
RNA, 184, 197
robin, 104
Romalea microptera, 171

S

Sabella pavonia, 169
S. spallanzani, 169
Saccharomyces exiguus, 33
salamander, 113
Saturniidae, 61
scent, 39
Schistocerca gregaria, 62, 64
Schizophora, 71
Schizophyllum sabulosum, 94
Sciurus, 78
scolopendra, 17
Scolopendra clavipes, 59
Scopaema stercoraria, 65
scorpion, 7, 17, 39–41, 59–60
Scorpio maurus, 59
sea-anemone, 29, 45, 82, 83
sea-urchin, 86
seasonal rhythm, 94
Serinus canarius, 42
sheep, 15, 119

shrew (see also under species), 60, 78
silver-fish, 39
Simulium, 40
sinus gland, 108
sloth, 40
slug, 46, 179
snail, 41, 46, 117
snake, 75
snow-shoe rabbit, 33–7
snowy owl, 34
Sorex, 79
S. araneus, 78
S. minutus, 78
Spaniotoma minima, 68
Spanistoma, 186
sparrow, 96
Sphaerodactylus lineolatus, 75,
spider, 7, 39, 41, 61, 72, 94, 134–5, 179
Spirorbis borealis, 89
Spodiopsar cineraceus, 186
squirrel, 14, 77–8, 151–3, 155, 162
'staircase' effect, 29
starling, 102, 134, 138, 186
statistical analysis, 22–3
Stegocephalia, 74
Sterna macrura, 76
S. fuscata, 107
Sternus vulgaris, 102
stick-insect, 39, 61
stomach peristalsis, 28
Strombidium occulatum, 25
Strongylocentrotus lividus, 86
Strumeta tryoni, 95
Sturnia violacea, 186
sub-oesophageal ganglion, 99, 170
suction-trap, 12–13, 72
supra-oesophageal ganglion, 108
Sylvia atricapella, 138
S. borin, 138
synapse, 28
synchronisation of rhythms, 161–6

T

Tabanidae, 40, 44
Taeniorhynchus africanus, 69
Talitrus saltator, 85, 133
Talpa europaea, 79
Tanacetum vulgare, 68
tapetum, 39, 77–8
Telea polyphemus, 74
temperature, fluctuating, 172–7
    independence, 177–85

template theory, 25
Tenebrio molitor, 64, 174
terminology, 2–9
Termes lucifugus, 130
Tetranychus althacae, 175
Tetrahymena pyriformis, 192
Tettigonia cantans, 67
T. viridissima, 67
Thecadactylus rapicaudus, 75
theories of rhythm causation, 9–10
thyroid, 149, 150
tick, 72
tidal rhythm, 45, 81 et seq.
Tipula paludosa, 68
Tipulinae, 68
tissues and organs, 28–31
toad, 30, 74
Toxoptera graminum, 173
Tribolium confusum, 175
Trichoptera, 67, 91
Triturus, 74
T. viridescens, 109
Troglodytes troglodytes, 76, 96
tropics, 105–7
turtle, 75

U

Uca (see fiddler crab), 83, 109–12
U. minex, 85
U. pugilator, 85, 109, 111
U. pugnax, 84, 109, 110, 116, 159–62, 177, 178
U. speciosa, 111
Urosalpinx cinereus, 83

V

Varying hare, 33–7
Veliger larva, 27
Venus mercenaria, 85, 113
vertebrate (see also under species), 73–80, 105–7
vole, 11, 33–7, 78–9, 97, 102
Vulpes vulpes, 96

W

Water-beetle, 41
water-relations of terrestrial arthropods, 51–61
water-skater, 41
whip-scorpion, 61
whitebait, 90

wind, 56, 70, 76

woodlouse (see also under species), 51–6, 60, 72

wren, 76, 96, 200–1

Wuchereria bancrofti, 43–5

Z

Zelotes latreillei, 94

Z. pratensis, 94

Zonotrichia albicollis, 96

Z. leucophrys, 96